Introduction to Minicomputers and Microcomputers

Addison-Wesley Publishing Company
Reading, Massachusetts • Menlo Park, California
London • Amsterdam • Don Mills, Ontario • Sydney

M. E. Sloan
Michigan Technological University

Introduction to Minicomputers and Microcomputers

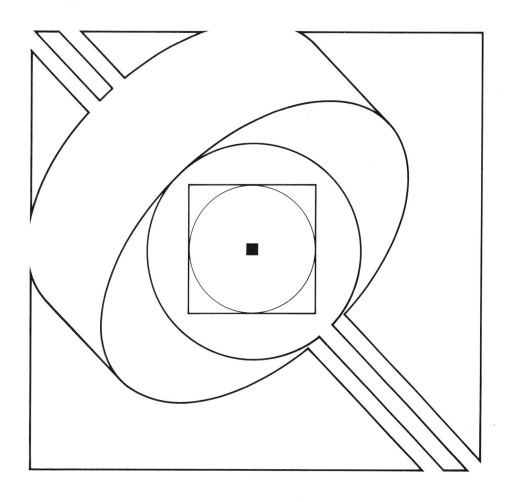

This book is in the
Addison-Wesley Series in Computer Science.

Consulting editor
Michael A. Harrison

Library of Congress Cataloging in Publication Data

Sloan, M. E.
    Introduction to minicomputers and microcomputers.

    Includes bibliographical references.
    1. Minicomputers. 2. Microcomputers. I. Title.
QA76.5.S558   001.6′4′04   78-74693
ISBN 0-201-07279-3

ISBN 0-201-07279-3
BCDEFGHIJ-MA-8987654321

Preface

Introduction to Minicomputers and Microcomputers is intended as an introduction to small computers. Its primary audience is college freshmen and sophomores in both two- and four-year schools. No background is assumed either in programming or in electrical theory or physics, although many students may be familiar with at least one high-level language. The purpose of the book is to develop sufficient skills and understanding that students who complete the course will be able to work with small computers to solve problems. A large number of students whose primary interests are in science, engineering, technology, and increasingly in other areas such as social science need and have time for only one course in small computers. Thus, although the book is intended to serve both as a first course for computer science and engineering students and as a general course for other students, developing a general conceptual background in computer science and engineering as a preparation for future work is secondary. Concepts are introduced in as natural and concrete a way as possible, with greater abstraction left for the advanced courses that will be taken by those students who intend to become computer professionals.

The book has 13 chapters. Their order reflects the author's experience in teaching an introductory course as well as comments from many others teaching such a course at a wide variety of schools. In particular, the author strongly believes that students should get "hands-on" experience as soon and as often as possible. Requiring students to program in machine language removes some of the mystery from a computer; hence machine language is covered early so that students can gain experience at this level. On the other hand, some schools may prefer instead to move directly to assembly language. For this reason, machine and assembly language are covered together; thus, if working in machine language is inappropriate for a particular course, the instructor can assign assembly language programs from the start. System software is also covered early in the text so that students will be able to take advantage of editors and debugging routines early in the course.

Once the student knows enough about programming to write simple programs, he or she can study programming in more detail. A series of chapters cover important topics in programming for small computers and provide practical examples. Near the end of the text the student is introduced to high-level languages as implemented on small computers and to interfacing.

Choosing a computer as the reference machine for a book such as this is always difficult. A hypothetical computer serves no one well and requires the instructor to expend effort in designing a simulator if students are to write and check programs. Furthermore, a hypothetical computer always seems more abstract than a real computer. And, since it is easier to learn about a complex topic from a concrete example than from an abstraction, it seems clear that beginning students should see a real machine. But which one? A basic theme of the text is that minicomputers and microcomputers differ in degree rather than in kind, and that it is becoming increasingly difficult to distinguish between them. Hence it is natural to treat the two together so that students can see this. By choosing the most popular minicomputer, the PDP-11, and the two most popular microcomputers, the Intel 8080/8085 and the Motorola 6800, we have a good chance of giving examples for the computers most students reading the text will have in their laboratories. The first programs are shown in detail for all three computers to minimize confusion while the student is learning one language. In later parts of the book some programs may be illustrated for one computer, some for another. In this way students learn to follow amply commented programs for more than one computer—a useful skill, since most students will encounter several small computers in their work.

Each chapter contains a number of features to aid learning. An introduction overviews the main ideas of the chapter to help students organize and plan their reading. Similarly, each chapter ends with a summary and with a list of key terms from the chapter. There is also a list of study questions that go beyond mere recognition of terms. Where appropriate there is a set of problems or programs, each keyed to the section that should be studied before starting the problem.

Chapter 1, *Introduction*, sets forth the theme of the book. It outlines computer organization, shows the overriding similarities among mini- and microcomputers, and examines software and hardware. Chapter 2, *Representation of Information*, presents standard material on representation that the student must master before starting to program. Emphasis is on information that is most useful in programming, not on general conversion. Chapter 3, *Flowcharts*, discusses program types and preparation for programming. Most instructors, even though they recognize the limitations of flowcharts, believe students should have some experience in preparing them.

Chapters 4 and 5 are parallel chapters on elementary programming. Chapter 4, *Elementary Programming for the PDP-11*, should be followed if the class is using a PDP-11 or a similar minicomputer. Alternatively, Chapter 5, *Elementary Programming for Microcomputers*, should be followed if the class is using a microcomputer; the specific examples shown are written for the 8080/8085 and the M6800, but discussions of some other microcomputers are included. Each chapter stands by itself; each contains programs for all the problems flowcharted in Chapter 3. Basic machine and assembly language is presented and instructions for each computer are introduced. Each chapter ends with a short section on how to run machine language programs.

Chapter 6, *System Software*, shows the principles and operation of basic system software, including editors, assemblers, loaders, and debugging routines. Concrete examples, including representative instructions, are shown for several small computers. This chapter should be supplemented by manuals for the system students are using.

The next five chapters present more advanced programming. Chapter 7, *Addressing Modes*, discusses this topic in detail, ending with a full description of all addressing modes for the PDP-11. (Modes for microcomputers were discussed in Chapter 5.) Chapter 8, *Subroutines, Coroutines, and Macros*, shows how to write and link subprograms. Chapter 9, *Arithmetic and Logical Operations*, includes binary and decimal arithmetic and the use of logical operations. Chapter 10, *Input-Output Programming*, illustrates the complexities of this important topic. Chapter 11, *Data Structures*, introduces some of the more common structures used for mini- and microcomputer programs. Inclusion of this topic is controversial, since many instructors rightfully think that students should study this in a separate course. However, since many students just do not have time to fit a course on data structures into their schedules, an overview of the topic is included in the text, to be covered or skipped at the option of the instructor.

Chapter 12, *High-Level Languages*, outlines the features of three common high-level languages—BASIC, FORTRAN, and PL/I—and discusses their implementation on small computers. While some instructors think that students need only machine and assembly language programming, high-level languages for small computers are improving and are becoming increasingly important. Hence students should have some familiarity with them. In fact, many students may already be familiar with one of these languages. Few, however, will know all three, so a brief discussion of their relative strengths and weaknesses can be useful. Then, by writing the same program in assembly language and in one or more high-level languages, students can see for themselves the differences in efficiencies of writing and execution.

Chapter 13, *Interfacing*, highlights the major hardware problems in system design. It introduces common integrated circuits, emphasizing their conceptual design rather than details of currently popular chips. It also describes conversion from analog to digital and back, and explains common bus standards. This chapter is intended to give the terminal student enough information that he or she will know how to begin a design or at least to discuss it with others. It also serves as an introduction to the usual next course on microcomputers for students who are specializing in computer science and engineering.

Trying to ensure that computer programs are free from errors is a tricky task. I wish to thank Alan Bessey and Ken Snyder, who ran all programs to verify their correctness and who helped proofread the manuscript. Thanks are also due the typists who spent so much time on various versions of the manuscript—Ruth Tepsa, Carol Frantti, and especially Phyllis Brumm. Finally I wish to acknowledge my appreciation to my family—Betsy, Graham, and Norman—for their patience during the time I was writing this book.

Houghton, Michigan   M.E.S.
November 1979

Contents

③ Flowcharts

④ Elementary Programming for the PDP-11

⑤ Elementary Programming for Microcomputers

⑥ System Software

⑦ Addressing Modes

⑧ Subroutines, Coroutines, and Macros

⑨ Arithmetic and Logical Operations

⑩ Input/Output Programming

11 Data Structures

12 High-Level Languages

⒔ **Interfacing Small Computers**

1

Introduction

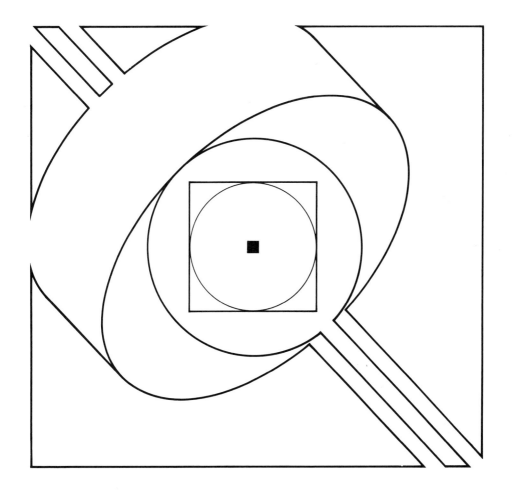

This chapter has two purposes—to acquaint you with the general organization of computers and to give you an overview of the information that will be presented in greater detail in later chapters. Don't worry if you don't understand everything in this chapter, because the rest of the book expands on its ideas. Instead, you should regard this chapter as primarily a road map for the route ahead.

As a first step, we will look at the organization of a simple computer. Minicomputers, microcomputers, and large computers share the same basic organizational principles. Although the details of organization can vary from computer to computer, once we understand the basic concepts we will be ready to look at some specific examples of computers.

The rest of the chapter is divided into three main parts—software, hardware, and systems. **Software** consists of the programs and routines that direct the computer's operation and process information. **Hardware** denotes the physical equipment and devices from which the computer and the external devices attached to the computer are constructed. A **system** combines software with hardware. Careful consideration of hardware, software, and the intended applications of the computer is essential to designing a successful computer system.

1.1   *A Simple Computer*

Computers are devices that are designed to process information, whether that be related to payrolls, fuel consumption, population growth rate, or the status of components in a spaceship. Each item of information, however complex, can be represented by some combination of components known as bits. A **bit** is a 0 or a 1. Bits are organized into a **word**—a group of bits that the computer treats as a single unit of information. The number of bits in a word varies. Small computers may use words of four or eight bits; large computers may use words of 32, 64, or more bits.

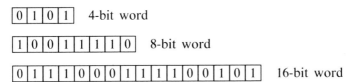

The basic organization of a small computer is shown in Fig. 1.1. This computer is not exactly like any of the real computers that we will study later. There are, in fact, exceptions to almost every principle of computer organization. Yet it is helpful to see a diagram of a simple computer before studying an actual computer. Then we can more readily recognize novel features when we encounter them.

As we see from Fig. 1.1, a typical small computer consists of four main units connected by links called buses. A **bus** is a communications link that

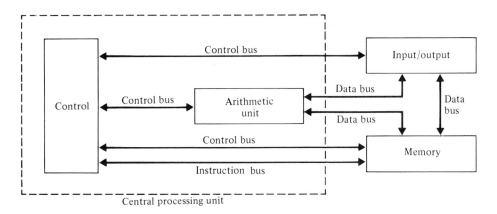

Fig. 1.1
Organization of a small computer.

carries information between units of the computer. We can think of a bus as a number of parallel wires that can transfer all the bits of information in one computer word simultaneously.

Computers deal with three types of information. Most problems that we wish to solve on a computer start with **data**, such as the sales figures from a store or the location and velocity of radar targets. Then, we need **instructions** to tell the computer what to do with the data, that is, how to solve the problems. Each instruction is a command to the computer to perform one or more operations chosen from a language available on that computer. Instructions and data are similar in that the computer receives both from the user. The third type of information, consisting of **control signals**, originates inside the computer. Control signals include timing signals (signals that determine the time of events) and signals that cause the computer hardware to carry out operations.

The three kinds of buses shown in Fig. 1.1 correspond to these three types of information. **Control buses** transfer control signals between the control unit and other parts of the computer. **Data buses** transfer data between units. The **instruction bus** transfers instructions from the computer memory to the control unit. On many computers one bus serves as both data bus and instruction bus.

Again referring to Fig. 1.1, we see that the four main units of the computer are the control unit, the arithmetic unit, the input/output unit, and the memory. The **control unit** interprets and executes instructions in the proper sequence and generates control and timing signals for the other computer units. The **arithmetic unit** performs arithmetic and logical operations. The combination of the control unit and the arithmetic unit is called the **central processing unit (CPU)** of the computer. The **memory** stores instructions and data for later recall. The **input/output unit** is the interface between the computer and the external world. It is connected to one or more **peripheral devices** that convert information from such forms as holes on paper tape or punches on a card to the electrical signals used by the computer. **Device controllers** may be associated with the input/output unit to control the peripheral devices.

1.1.1 *Minicomputers*

Minicomputers, as the name implies, are small computers. Their word lengths and their memory sizes are indeed small compared with those of large, general-purpose computers. Beyond this, however, it is difficult to define a minicomputer precisely. At one time minicomputers were defined very simply in terms of their word lengths and costs. But computer technology changes so rapidly that such definitions quickly become obsolete. Minicomputers are constantly evolving in the direction of larger size and more capability, just as large digital computers are. What is called a minicomputer today might have been considered a medium-scale computer ten years ago and possibly even a large computer twenty years ago. To be practical about it, in this book we will consider a minicomputer to be any digital computer that is currently described by its manufacturer as a minicomputer.

Although minicomputers are less standardized than large computers, they tend to be similar in their word lengths, the types of arithmetic operations they can perform, their memory size, their software features, and other characteristics that we will encounter later in the book. The typical minicomputer has a word length of 12 to 18 bits, most commonly 16 bits; some minicomputers, however, have 32-bit word lengths. Memory size is measured in thousands of words, or **kilowords**. (One kiloword, abbreviated as K word, is actually equivalent to 1024 words.) The typical minicomputer has a memory of 4K to 64K words, though much larger memories can be found. It is a general-purpose computer; that is, it is likely to be used by its owner for a wide range of activities rather than to be dedicated to a single application. Its operation is considered fast; it can perform single operations in about one **microsecond** (one-millionth of a second). It usually has one or more external devices for input and output. Programs can be written for it in simple versions of a few problem-oriented languages. These **high-level languages** allow users to direct the computer's operation by writing a series of statements that look more like English than the 1's and 0's into which they must be converted. Alternatively, the programs may also be written in assembly language, using statements that correspond directly to the bit patterns of 1's and 0's. Finally, we should note that minicomputers may require greater knowledge and sophistication from their users than do larger computers.

At the upper end of the scale of cost/size/capabilities, minicomputers are bounded by the so-called **midicomputer**. Midicomputers are manufactured by large computer manufacturers such as IBM and Control Data Corporation as well as by small-computer specialists such as Hewlett-Packard Corporation and Digital Equipment Corporation. One important distinction between minicomputers and midicomputers is that midicomputers generally have far more extensive software support. As a result, often they can run several programs at the same time, responding as needed to some programs, while running others in the background. Another difference is that midicomputers cost more, typically as much as $100,000. And midicomputers are physically more imposing; whereas mini- and microcomputers are often desktop devices, midicomputers are relatively large, free-standing machines. Their word size is typically 16 to 64 bits, their memory size may be 256K or more, and they have much more sophisticated error detection features. Nevertheless, the distinction between minicomputers and midicomputers is not sharp; the differences are matters of degree rather than kind.

1.1.2 *Microcomputers*

At the lower end of the scale, minicomputers are bounded by microcomputers. A **microcomputer** is a small computer that is usually implemented with large-scale integrated circuits. **Large-scale integration (LSI)** refers to semiconductor circuits that have the equivalent of 1000 or more individual circuits on each individual semiconductor chip. Such circuits are a relatively recent development resulting from advances in semiconductor technology. A microcomputer usually has a word length of 4, 8, or 16 bits. A **microprocessor** is the central processing unit of a microcomputer and is usually a single large-scale integrated circuit.

Although LSI circuits are characteristic of microcomputers, their presence or absence does not in itself enable us to distinguish between minicomputers and microcomputers. Many minicomputers today are constructed from one or more LSI circuits. Thus there is not much difference between a 16-bit microcomputer and a 16-bit minicomputer constructed from LSI circuits. If the computer is an improved version of a minicomputer that has existed for a few years, then it is ordinarily called a minicomputer. A new 16-bit computer constructed from LSI chips is more likely to be called a microcomputer.

We can partially distinguish between minicomputers and microcomputers according to the amount of software support and peripheral equipment available. The line here is gray, much like the line between minicomputers and midicomputers. However, both minicomputers and microcomputers are following the pattern of development of larger computers. In this pattern a computer proceeds from a simple, basic version, consisting of little more than hardware, to an advanced version with extensive software and a wide range of peripherals and memory. Since minicomputers have existed for many years, they naturally lead microcomputers in development.

Another hazy distinction between minicomputers and microcomputers is that microcomputers are more likely to be used as components of electronic systems, while minicomputers are more likely to be used as general-purpose computers. Microprocessors have replaced conventional digital logic in a wide variety of systems and have led to the development of such new systems as pocket calculators and point-of-sale terminals. If fact, the low price of microprocessors and their ability to substitute for conventional logic has lifted the sales volume of microprocessors far above that of minicomputers. However, this distinction also is not clear-cut. As microcomputers develop more advanced software and programming systems, they will compete increasingly with minicomputers as small general-purpose computers. The low price of microcomputers mean that many individuals can more readily afford them for use as personal computers. Hobbyists, working alone or in clubs, have helped to develop software that makes microcomputers even more attractive and more useful to individuals.

Mini- and microcomputers must not be confused with **programmable calculators**, which constitute another part of the fast-growing computer systems field. Calculators are intended for solving complex equations with direct contact between the user and the calculator. By comparison with all the devices discussed thus far, they are quite slow, since relatively little computing speed is needed to keep up with the demands of a single user. They have limited main memory. They often contain microprocessors. They are usually designed with a built-in display or printer and a keyboard so that peripheral equipment is not needed. Their keyboards have convenient keys that allow untrained users to learn to solve problems quickly; their languages are implemented as hardware rather than software. Thus calculators are less versatile and powerful than small computers and less demanding of their users.

Table 1.1 summarizes the distinguishing features of mini-, micro-, and midicomputers and of programmable calculators.

Table 1.1

Comparison of typical characteristics of programmable calculator, microcomputer, minicomputer, and midicomputer

Characteristic	Programmable calculator	Micro-computer	Mini-computer	Midi-computer
Typical number of bits per word	32–64	4–16	12–32	16–64
Function	Dedicated	Dedicated or general purpose	General purpose	Dedicated or general purpose
Speed	Very slow	Slow to fast	Fast	Fast
Required user understanding of machine	Very limited	Extensive	Fair to substantial	Limited
Typical high-level language	BASIC implemented in hardware	PL/M PASCAL	BASIC FORTRAN ALGOL	ALGOL BASIC FORTRAN COBOL
Typical programming methods	Manually from keyboard	Assembly language	Assembly or high-level language	High-level language
Typical applications	Calculations	Device control Accounting Replacement of digital logic	Problem solving Process control Device control	Solving large problems Systems control
Cost	Low	Very low to low	Low to medium	Medium to high

The terms minicomputer and microcomputer together cover a wide range of small computers. In this book we will use the term **small computers** when our discussion concerns both mini- and microcomputers. When discussing a specific machine, we will, as stated earlier, class that computer as a minicomputer or a microcomputer in accordance with the manufacturer's definition. In any case, throughout most of the book we will be dealing with the similarities between minicomputers and microcomputers, because their similarities far exceed their differences. However, when the differences are important, we will comment on them.

1.2   Software

Software consists of (a) the programs that a computer user writes to process information and (b) the routines that manage the computer's operation. We will first discuss representations of information. Then we will discuss user programs and the languages in which they can be written. For both we must realize that the hardware operates on **binary numbers**—numbers that are represented by the binary digits 0 and 1. Thus all data and instructions, whether for user programs or for computer management, must be expressed as patterns of 0's and 1's. Finally we will look briefly at the structures for data and control in minicomputers and microprocessors.

1.2.1   Representation of Information

Chapter 2 discusses representation of numbers and other kinds of information. Most computers represent numbers in **binary**, or base 2, because it is much easier to build devices that have two states (e.g., ON and OFF) than ones that have ten. The main problem of representation occurs in the handling of negative numbers. Nearly all minicomputers and microcomputers represent negative numbers in the same way, by **complementing** the positive number (that is, changing 0's to 1's and 1's to 0's) and adding 1. This representation, called **2's complement**, simplifies arithmetic calculations.

Although numbers are represented in base 2, we often find it simpler to cluster the binary numbers in groups of three or four and write them as **octal** (base 8) or **hexadecimal** (base 16) numbers, respectively. Since octal and hexadecimal numbers are easier for us to read and write, many computer manufacturers show instructions in octal or hexadecimal rather than binary.

Besides representing integers in 2's complement form, we must also be able to represent **floating-point** numbers, that is, numbers expressed in scientific notation, such as 3.2×10^7, and nonnumeric characters such as letters and punctuation symbols. Nonnumeric characters are represented by any of several codes that assign a binary number to each lower-case and upper-case letter and to each special symbol.

Some microprocessors, especially those intended for calculators, represent numbers in **binary-coded decimal (BCD)** form rather than as binary numbers. In

BCD, each decimal digit is represented by four binary bits. BCD requires more binary bits to represent a large decimal number, but calculations are simplified.

1.2.2 *Languages*

Computer languages allow us to direct the computer's operations. **High-level** languages, such as FORTRAN or PL/I, use instructions that look something like the English words and arithmetic expressions we use to describe the operations of solving a problem. For example, the FORTRAN statements

```
Y = A + B + C
```

and

```
GO TO 21
```

are easy to read even if we do not know FORTRAN. The meaning of other FORTRAN statements like

```
WRITE (1, 20)
```

and

```
IF (Y − X) 10, 11, 18
```

is not obvious, but it looks as if we could understand them with a little training.

A program called a **translator** is needed to convert instructions given in a high-level language to the patterns of 0's and 1's that direct the computer's operations. Although versions of high-level languages are available for most minicomputers and some microcomputers, they may be less satisfactory than versions of these languages for large computers. Because of their smaller configurations, minicomputers and microcomputers may not have enough memory to contain both a complex software translator and a large user program. Hence compromises are usually made, resulting in a simplified version of the high-level language that lacks many desirable features of the standard version used on larger computers. In addition, minicomputer manufacturers have not tried to coordinate their adaptations of high-level languages, which means that FORTRAN implementations on one minicomputer differ substantially from FORTRAN implementations for another minicomputer. Nonetheless, there is a strong trend toward increased use of high-level languages on both minicomputers and microcomputers.

Programs for minicomputers and microprocessors are often written in **assembly language**. Assembly language depends on the specific hardware configuration and so is different for each computer. Instructions in assembly language correspond directly to the **machine language** instructions that direct the basic operations of the computer, but are represented as abbreviations instead of as binary numbers. The abbreviations are usually three or four letters, such as STO for store or SUB for subtract. Hence they are much easier to remember and to use than the numbers, although they are usually not as easy as the commands of high-level languages. Assembly language instructions are also less powerful than those of high-level languages; one high-level instruction may be equivalent to ten or more assembly language instructions. The advantage of user programs written in assembly language is that they can be converted to machine language by a special translator called an **assembler**, which requires less space in memory than the translators needed for high-level languages.

In addition to machine and assembly language, some minicomputers and microcomputers operate at an even more basic language level known as **microprogramming**. In microprogramming, a smaller computer inside the main computer executes the control functions for the instruction set of the main computer. Microprogramming uses **microinstructions**, which require only a small part of a computer word.

1.2.3   *Software Systems*

Besides user programs designed to accomplish specific tasks, software includes various routines that simplify use of the computer. **Loaders** load programs into the computer. **Editors** simplify the task of preparing and changing a program. **Debug** routines help to detect errors. **Simulators** allow the testing of a model of a complete system. **Operating systems** control the use of other software.

The quality of software strongly influences the amount of time spent by programmers using the computer. Hence the variety and power of the software systems available for a computer is a major factor in selecting a computer, especially one that will require much user programming. For small computers that will be used only as components in large hardware systems, software characteristics are less important, since little user programming will be done. In such cases, the price of the computer may be much more important than programming ease.

Despite the importance of evaluating differences in software, people purchasing computers often spend most of their time looking at differences in the hardware. This is unfortunate, because the major cost for most computer systems, especially those used primarily for general-purpose computing, is software. If the available software is limited, programmers must spend time developing the programs and routines they need. Their time may represent a far greater expense than the hardware cost. Even for small computers that are intended for system components to be used with fixed programs, the cost of program development may exceed the cost of the central processor. To individuals purchasing personal computers, the cost of developing software may not seem important; however, the time they must spend in developing systems software may be time taken from enjoying use of the computer.

1.3 *Hardware*

As we saw in Fig. 1.1, the four main parts of the computer are the control unit, the arithmetic unit, the memory, and the input/output unit. In this section, we will briefly discuss each of these components to provide a background for the software chapters. The text later gives more detail on each component.

1.3.1 *Memory*

The memory is the area of the computer in which data and instructions are stored. In most minicomputers, both data and instructions may be stored in any area of memory. Microcomputers, however, often have two different types of memory, one for programs and the other for data.

Random-access memory (RAM) can be both read, to retrieve information, and written into, to store information. The name **random** access means that any word in RAM may be reached or accessed in the same amount of time. To understand this better, consider an array of postal boxes as they might be seen by a postal worker, shown in Fig. 1.2(a). The postal worker can access each box in the same amount of time. In contrast to this, consider the string of mailboxes on a rural route (Fig. 1.2b). Here, the letter carrier cannot access each box in the same amount of time; since they are arranged in sequence, the boxes at the start of the route may be reached in a few minutes, whereas those at the end may take several hours. This type of access, called **sequential access**, is also seen in tape recorders.

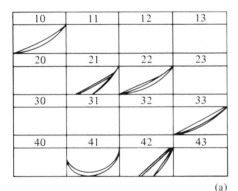

(a)

Fig. 1.2
Memory access. (a) Random access of postal boxes. (b) Sequential access of mailboxes.

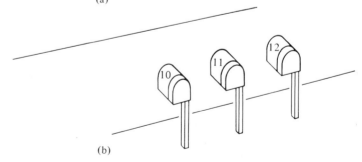

(b)

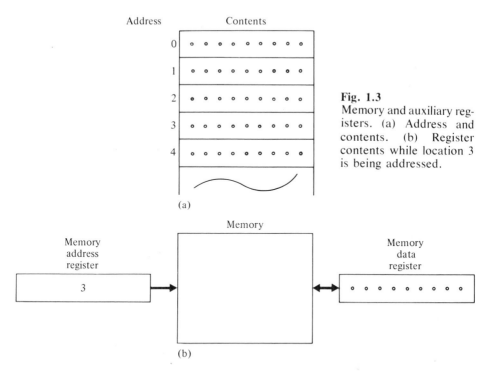

Fig. 1.3
Memory and auxiliary registers. (a) Address and contents. (b) Register contents while location 3 is being addressed.

We note, in passing, that each box in Fig. 1.2 has an **address**, such as 10 or 22, that shows its location. Each box also has **contents**—the information stored in it—such as a letter or a magazine. In a computer memory, if a box is empty, we say its contents are 0. The notions of address and contents are basic to discussions of memory. We will encounter them repeatedly.

RAM is used to store data and results and can be reused repeatedly for new data. It is also called **read/write memory** to emphasize that it has both functions. By contrast, **read-only memory (ROM)** provides permanent or semipermanent storage only; its contents can be read but cannot be rewritten during normal computer operation. ROM is usually used for permanent storage of instructions.

Our discussion so far has concerned only the **main memory** of the computer. In addition, many computers, both large computers and the more powerful small computers, have secondary memory. **Secondary memory** may consist of magnetic tapes, disks, and the like and is characterized by slower access but higher capacity than main memory. It holds backup information that is not needed immediately. Some computers have sophisticated schemes to switch blocks of information between main memory and secondary memory in such a way that the information needed by the computer is nearly always stored in main memory.

Storage of information in memory requires two auxiliary devices, usually called the **memory address register (MAR)** and the **memory data register (MDR)**. (A **register** is a device that can hold several bits. It can be read or written into relatively quickly.) Figure 1.3 shows the organization of memory and the two registers. In Fig. 1.3(a) the array of memory is shown. Addresses begin at 0 and continue to the highest memory location. Each memory location has contents, which we will think of as data.

Figure 1.3(b) shows the situation when memory location 3 is being addressed. To write a word in memory, the control unit sends the address of the desired location in memory to the memory address register. Thus, in the figure, 3 is sent to the MAR. At the same time, the control unit sends the word to be written into memory to the memory data register. Then the contents of the memory data register are stored in the location whose address is given by the contents of the memory address register. In this case the contents of the MDR become the contents of location 3, and the previous contents of that location are lost. Reading a word is done similarly. The address of the desired location is placed in the memory address register. Then the contents of that memory location are sent to the memory data register, from which they can be sent to any other register.

1.3.2 *Arithmetic Unit*

The arithmetic unit consists of one or more registers and circuits for arithmetic and logic operations. At least one register of the arithmetic unit is called an **accumulator**, because it accumulates or holds the results of arithmetic and logical operations. Other registers may also have special purposes, which we will consider later. Logic circuits in the arithmetic unit usually permit shifting the contents of a register one or more cells to the right or left, clearing the register (setting it contents to 0), and complementing each bit or all bits of the register, that is, interchanging 0's and 1's. The arithmetic unit nearly always contains an **adder**, a device that can add the contents of some other register or memory location to the contents of the accumulator and store the results in the accumulator. It may perform other arithmetic operations as well; with an adder and a shifter all arithmetic operations can be performed.

1.3.3 *Control Unit*

The control unit includes logic and timing circuits that control the operation of the computer. A basic unit has one or more clocks that provide the basic timing of operation. It contains decoders, which decode the instruction to be executed and activate the circuits to execute the instruction. It has an **instruction register (IR)**, which holds the current instruction. It also has a **program counter (PC)**, which holds the address of the next instruction to be executed. A program is stored in consecutive locations in memory. Instructions are usually executed in sequence, although occasionally jumps must be made to instructions elsewhere in the program. Thus most of the time the program counter can be advanced to the address of the next instruction by incrementing it (adding 1); a correction can then be made if a jump is necessary.

The execution of instructions requires two phases—**fetch** and **execute**. The actions that occur during these two phases are as follows.

Fetch

- The address of the current instruction is sent from the program counter to the memory address register.
- The current instruction is read into the memory data register and then sent to the instruction register of the CPU.
- The program counter is incremented to hold the address of the (presumed) next instruction.

Execute

- The instruction is decoded.
- Control signals to perform the operations of the instruction are sent to the appropriate registers, memory, or input/output devices.

1.3.4   *Input/Output Unit*

The input/output unit controls the transfers of information between a computer and its peripheral devices. There is more variety in input/output systems than in any other part of the computer. In fact, one computer we will study has no input/output unit.

In the chapter on input/output programming, we will study two main features of input/output systems: the organization of input/output systems and the control of information transfer. Later we will examine many common peripheral devices for minicomputers and microprocessors. Input/output systems can be organized with a device controller for each device or with one device controller for several devices. Information transfer can be strictly controlled by the user's program or external devices can be allowed to interrupt the computer and initiate information transfer. The interrupts can be done with or without a variety of complex priority schemes. The combination of all these possibilities results in input/output systems that vary considerably in their designs.

1.4   *Systems*

The topic of input/output leads naturally into discussion of the minicomputer and microprocessor system—the organization of a central processing unit, control unit, memory, and input/output devices into an efficient combination. Here we will discuss briefly some considerations necessary to the design and implementation of a successful system.

One aspect of system development is the computer's architecture—the structure of the hardware and software of the basic computer. The architecture of minicomputers has improved rapidly throughout their decade or so of existence. Microcomputers are following the same pattern of development, even more rapidly. The first minicomputers had one accumulator and crude instructions. Current minicomputers and microcomputers are comparatively sophisticated, with several registers and complex and flexible instructions. Minicomputer engineers have not only borrowed ideas from the architecture of large computers but have introduced new ones to fit their own special needs and limitations. Later in the text we will learn to evaluate and compare architectures, a topic that is especially important since computer manufacturers stress architecture in their advertisements.

Another aspect of systems is the applications for which the computer is needed. Minicomputers and microprocessors are used in a wide variety of applications. Many minicomputers are used as general-purpose computers to process the same kinds of information as large computers. Others are used as special-purpose computers to process a limited range of programs; these often use special operating systems that optimize performance for their particular programs. A growing use of minimum versions of minicomputers and of microprocessors is as components in large hardware systems. In these systems, the computers usually have their programs stored in ROM and repeatedly execute one or a few types of programs. Small computers are also used in **real-time** systems, in which they control one or more devices in direct response to signals from the devices.

A major consideration in systems is the **interface** between the computer and the input/output devices connected to the computer. The interface must handle any differences in voltage levels between the computer and the peripheral device. It must insure that the signals transferred are coded in a way that both the computer and the peripheral device can use.

1.5 *Minicomputer and Microprocessor Examples*

Our approach throughout this text will be to present each idea in its general form and then, wherever feasible, to illustrate the idea by showing its application to a specific minicomputer or microprocessor. Rather than trying to tie the text to just one computer, we have chosen several for our illustrations. One benefit of this approach is that it sometimes allows showing two quite different applications of one idea. The five computers that we have chosen are representative of a wide range of the most popular small computers. In this section, we will briefly describe these five computers. Later we will discuss them in more detail.

1.5.1 *PDP-11*

The PDP-11, made by Digital Equipment Corporation (DEC) is currently the most popular minicomputer. It comes in several versions. Its features include:

- 8 or 16 registers

- 16-bit words divided into two 8-bit bytes that can be individually addressed and manipulated (some models have 32-bit words)
- A single bus called a Unibus for operations with both memory and input/output devices.
- A processor status register that keeps track of four types of conditions
- Use of 2's complement arithmetic
- Acceptance of programs written in machine and assembly language, BASIC, FORTRAN, and special DEC languages

1.5.2   *PDP-8*

The PDP-8, also made by DEC, was one of the first minicomputers. It is widely available and has an especially simple design. Its features include:

- One accumulator
- 12-bit words
- Separate buses for memory and input/output
- Use of 2's complement arithmetic
- Acceptance of programs written in machine and assembly language, FORTRAN, BASIC, and the DEC language FOCAL

1.5.3   *8080/8085*

The Intel 8080/8085 microcomputer system is a family of microcomputers that share the same machine and assembly language. It is architecturally similar to the Zilog Z-80, which we will also discuss. Its features include:

- Seven user-accessible registers, including one accumulator
- 8-bit words with 16-bit addresses
- Five flags to show CPU status
- Use of 2's complement and BCD arithmetic
- Acceptance of programs written in machine and assembly language, BASIC, PASCAL, and PL/M—a subset of PL/I

1.5.4   *M6800*

The Motorola 6800 is a microcomputer system that resembles the 8080/8085 in many respects. Nonetheless it differs in some architectural features. It includes:

- Two accumulators and two specialized registers
- 8-bit words with 16-bit addresses
- Six flags to show CPU status

- Use of 2's complement and BCD arithmetic
- Acceptance of programs written in machine and assembly language, BASIC, PASCAL, and MPL—another subset of PL/I

1.5.5 *4040*

The Intel 4040 is an improved version of one of the early 4-bit microcomputers. Its features include:

- 24 registers
- 4-bit words with 12-bit addresses
- Use of 2's complement and BCD arithmetic
- Acceptance of programs written in machine and assembly language

1.S *Summary*

This chapter briefly summarizes the ideas that we will encounter throughout the book. It is intended as an overview of the book and provides enough background for the early chapters. We are concerned with hardware—the physical equipment that makes up a computer system, software—the programs and routines that direct the computer's operation, and systems—the combination of the two.

A computer consists of four main units linked by buses. The control unit controls the operation of the computer. The arithmetic unit performs arithmetic and logical operations. Together these units are called the central processing unit (CPU). The memory stores instructions and data. The input/output unit connects the computer to peripheral devices.

Minicomputers are small computers with word lengths usually ranging from 12 to 32 bits. Microcomputers are small computers that are implemented by large-scale integrated circuits and that have word lengths ranging from 4 to 16 bits. The distinction between minicomputers and microcomputers is not precise; similarly, the dividing line between minicomputers and larger computers is not precise. Microprocessors are CPUs constructed from one or a few integrated circuits.

Software is the term describing the programs that the computer user writes and the routines already in the computer to control its operation and simplify use. Programs may be written in languages varying from high-level languages, which are easiest to use, to machine language, whose instructions are strings of 1's and 0's. Languages for minicomputers and microprocessors are not yet as powerful and flexible as those for larger computers, but they are improving rapidly.

The most important aspect of hardware, in terms of understanding the chapters on software, is the operation of memory. The memory of a computer operates in association with two registers. The memory address register holds the address of the location in memory that is currently being read or written into. The memory data register holds the contents of that location (for a read operation) or the word to be transferred to that location (for a write operation).

In this introductory chapter, we have met a large number of ideas. To help you recall these ideas, a list of key terms is given below. Since these will be explained in more detail in later chapters, it is not necessary to try to master them now; however, you should check that you have a nodding acquaintance with the terms before proceeding.

Key Terms

accumulator
address
arithmetic unit
assembler
assembly language
BCD
binary-coded decimal
binary number
bit
bus
central processing unit (CPU)
complementing
contents
control bus
control signals
control unit
CPU
data
data bus
debug routine
device controller
editor
execute
fetch
floating-point
hardware
hexadecimal
high-level language
input/output unit
instruction
instruction bus
instruction register (IR)

interface
kiloword (K)
large-scale integration
loader
machine language
main memory
memory
memory address register (MAR)
memory data register (MDR)
microcomputer
microinstruction
microprocessor
microprogramming
microsecond
midicomputer
minicomputer
octal
peripheral device
program counter (PC)
programmable calculator
random-access memory (RAM)
read-only memory (ROM)
read/write memory
real-time
register
secondary memory
sequential access
software
simulator
translator
2's complement
word

1.R *References*

Descriptions of small computer operation can be found in Korn (1973, 1977) Soucek (1972), Weitzman (1974), and Eckhouse (1975). Many minicomputer and microprocessor manuals also contain good basic discussions of the operation of small computers. Abrams and Stein (1973) discuss the interrelations of software and hardware. You should also read the manuals for your computer, both for general information and for the features and operations of your system.

1.Q *Questions*

1.1 Examine the small computer available to you. How many registers does it have? How much memory? What is its word length? What languages does it have? What kind of arithmetic does it use? What other important characteristics can you describe?

1.2 What are the four main units of a computer? What purposes do they have?

1.3 What kinds of buses can a computer have? What purposes do they have?

1.4 What is the basic unit of information in a computer?

1.5 How is memory size measured?

1.6 Compare minicomputers and microcomputers.

1.7 For what types of applications would you prefer a minicomputer? A microcomputer? A programmable calculator?

1.8 How are numbers represented on small computers?

1.9 Describe the languages used on small computers.

1.10 What do translators do?

1.11 How do software systems simplify using a computer?

1.12 Distinguish between random access and sequential access memory.

1.13 Distinguish between memory and contents.

1.14 Explain how the MAR and MDR are used in writing into a memory location.

1.15 Explain the fetch and execute phases of instruction execution.

1.16 Compare the number of registers, word size, arithmetic, and languages of the five computers we will be using in our examples.

2 Representation of Information

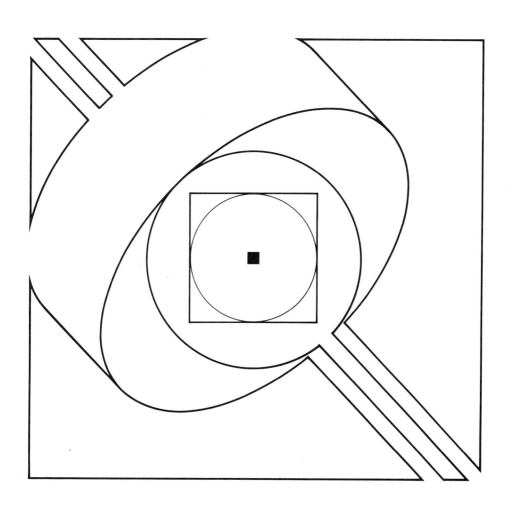

2.1 *Introduction*

Before we can begin to use a minicomputer or microcomputer, we must agree on the ways in which we will represent the information that goes into it. We must represent all numbers, letters, and punctuation with only the symbols 0 and 1. For this reason we naturally think of using binary numbers for basic number representation. Beyond this, we will need to adopt conventions for negative numbers. Also, we will find that reading, writing, and recalling binary numbers is both tedious and error provoking. Hence we will at times find it convenient to arrange binary numbers into groups of three or four bits each and convert them to another form. If we are dealing primarily with numbers that have a large range of magnitudes, such as in scientific calculations, we will want to use floating-point numbers. If we are doing business calculations, we will want to have a number representation that converts simply to and from decimal. Finally, for text with letters and punctuation, we will need some means of coding such characters. We will use either of two standard codes for character representation. This chapter discusses the means of representing information that are most commonly used on minicomputers and microcomputers.

2.2 *Binary Numbers*

All the computers that we will consider calculate with binary numbers instead of decimal numbers. The advantage of binary numbers is that it is much easier to design logic that has two states, such as ON and OFF or 0 and 1, instead of ten states. You may be familiar with the binary number system. Here, we will quickly review aspects of it that we will need for working with minicomputers and microcomputers.

The binary number system is a positional number system much like the decimal number system. Each position of the number carries a weight. In the decimal system the weight is a power of 10; in the binary number system the weight is a power of 2. The weights of a binary number are increasing positive (and zero) powers of 2 to the left of the **binary point** (the binary equivalent of the decimal point) and increasing negative powers of 2 to the right of the binary point.

$$2^7 \ 2^6 \ 2^5 \ 2^4 \ 2^3 \ 2^2 \ 2^1 \ 2^0. \ 2^{-1} \ 2^{-2} \ 2^{-3} \ 2^{-4}$$

By the correct choice of either 0 or 1 for each position, it is possible to represent any number uniquely. Table 2.1 shows the binary equivalents of selected decimal numbers.

As we saw earlier, each binary digit (0 or 1) is called a bit. The leftmost nonzero bit of any binary number is the **most significant bit**, abbreviated **MSB**. For example, in the binary integer 110101, the most significant bit is the 1 at the beginning; it has a weight of 2^5 or 32. Similarly, the rightmost bit (whether 0 or 1) is the **least significant bit** or **LSB**. For 110101 the least significant bit is the 1 at the end; it has a weight of 2^0 or 1.

Table 2.1
Binary equivalents of selected decimal numbers

Decimal	Binary	Power of 2
0	0	—
1	1	0
2	10	1
3	11	—
4	100	2
5	101	—
6	110	—
7	111	—
8	1000	3
9	1001	—
10	1010	—
16	10 000	4
32	100 000	5
64	1 000 000	6
128	10 000 000	7
256	100 000 000	8
512	1 000 000 000	9
1024	10 000 000 000	10
2048	100 000 000 000	11
4096	1 000 000 000 000	12
8192	10 000 000 000 000	13
16384	100 000 000 000 000	14
32768	1 000 000 000 000 000	15
65536	10 000 000 000 000 000	16

In a somewhat different sense we can refer to the LSB and MSB of a computer word. Suppose the bits of a word are numbered from right to left, starting with bit 0. (Many computer manufacturers do this; others number from left to right.) Then for a 16-bit word the MSB is bit 15; the LSB is bit 0.

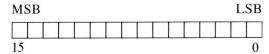

MSB .... LSB

15 0

Similarly, for an 8-bit word the MSB is bit 7; the LSB is bit 0.

MSB .... LSB

7 0

Note that the MSB of a computer word is a particular bit determined by the length of the word. Unlike the usual MSB of a binary integer, it may be either 0 or 1. When we refer to the MSB of a binary integer, we mean the 1 of the largest weight occurring in the integer. We make this distinction because binary integers are sometimes written with leading 0's inserted to fill out a desired number of places. Thus 110101 will sometimes be written 00110101. The MSB is still the leftmost 1—that is, we ignore higher positions having only 0's.

Because of the simple weighting system used in positional number systems, converting a binary number to its decimal equivalent is easy. We simply add the weights of the nonzero positions of the binary number—the positions in which the number has 1's. To see how this works, consider Example 2.1. (In this and following examples, note that we show the base or **radix** of a number as a subscript when needed for clarity.)

Example 2.1:   Converting a binary number to decimal

Task: Convert 1101101.0101_2 to decimal.

Procedure: Add the weights of the nonzero positions.

$1101101.0101_2 = 1 \times 2^6 + 1 \times 2^5 + 1 \times 2^3 + 1 \times 2^2 + 1 \times 2^0 + 1 \times 2^{-2} + 1 \times 2^{-1}$
$= 64 + 32 + 8 + 4 + 0.25 + 0.0625 = 108.3125_{10}$

Much of the time when we are working with small computers, we will be concerned with integers only. Consider the conversion of a typical 8-bit binary integer.

Example 2.2:   Converting a binary integer to decimal

Task: Convert 11011001_2 to decimal.

Procedure: Add the weights of the nonzero positions.

$11011001_2 = 1 \times 2^7 + 1 \times 2^6 + 1 \times 2^4 + 1 \times 2^3 + 1 \times 2^0$
$= 128 + 64 + 16 + 8 + 1 = 217_{10}$

Converting a decimal number to binary is a little more difficult because we must treat the integer and fractional parts of the number separately. We convert the integer part of a decimal number to binary by repeatedly dividing the decimal number by 2 until the quotient is 0. Then we write the remainders of the division in reverse order. That is, the first remainder is the LSB (rightmost bit); the last is the MSB (leftmost bit).

Example 2.3:   Converting a decimal integer to binary

Task: Convert 157_{10} to binary.

Procedure: First, divide 157 by 2 repeatedly until the quotient is 0.

$157/2 = 78 +$ remainder of 1   LSB
$78/2 = 39 +$ remainder of 0
$39/2 = 19 +$ remainder of 1
$19/2 = 9 +$ remainder of 1
$9/2 = 4 +$ remainder of 1
$4/2 = 2 +$ remainder of 0
$2/2 = 1 +$ remainder of 0
$1/2 = 0 +$ remainder of 1   MSB

Then arrange the remainders in reverse order—first at right, last at left.

$157_{10} = 10011101_2$

To remember that the first remainder is the least significant bit, think of the first division as showing whether the decimal integer is even or odd. If it is even, the first remainder will be 0; hence there are no 1's; hence the LSB is 0. If instead the decimal integer is odd, the first remainder will be 1; hence there is one 1, and the LSB is 1. Similarly, we can think of the last remainder as showing the highest power of 2 contained in the decimal integer. Thus the last remainder is the most significant bit.

To convert a decimal fraction to binary, we invert this approach; that is, we repeatedly *multiply* the decimal fraction by 2 until the product to the right of the point is 0. We note carries across the decimal point into the 1's position, but at each multiplication we multiply only the previously obtained decimal fraction, not the integers carried to the 1's position. When only a 0 remains to the right of the point, we form the equivalent binary fraction by writing down the carries in the order they were obtained.

Example 2.4:   Converting a decimal fraction to binary

Task: Convert 0.671875_{10} to binary.

Procedure: First, multiply the decimal fraction repeatedly by 2. Watch carries across the decimal point; they are underlined.

$0.671875 \times 2 = \underline{1}.343750$ MSB
$0.343751 \times 2 = \underline{0}.68750$
$0.6875 \times 2 \quad = \underline{1}.3750$
$0.375 \times 2 \quad = \underline{0}.750$
$0.75 \times 2 \quad = \underline{1}.50$
$0.50 \times 2 \quad = \underline{1}.0$ LSB

Then write the carries from left to right in the order they occurred.

$0.671875_{10} = 0.101011_2$

As the example shows, the first carry is the MSB; it shows whether the decimal fraction is less than 0.5 (MSB of 0) or equal to or greater than 0.5 (MSB of 1). The last carry is the LSB.

Not all decimal-to-binary conversions are as neat as this. Some decimal fractions do not convert exactly to binary, just as some fractions, such as 1/3, do not convert exactly to decimal. Try, for example, converting 0.1_{10} to binary. Thus, instead of persisting in our multiplications until only a 0 appears to the right of the point (it may never do so!) we may have to end the conversion process after we have as many binary places as we desire.

To convert a decimal number with both integer and fractional parts to decimal, we can use both procedures (Examples 2.3 and 2.4) and combine the resulting binary integer and fraction. Alternatively, we may scale numbers so that we are working only with integers or with fractions. Another alternative is to use floating-point numbers, which are expressed as binary fractions times a binary power; this is explained in a later section.

As we saw in Chapter 1, computers have special formats for working with binary information. Bits are grouped into **words**, which correspond to the number of bits the computer can handle at one time in its registers or memory. Typical microcomputer word lengths are 4, 8, 12, or 16 bits, and typical minicomputer word lengths are 12, 16, or 32 bits. Note that word lengths are usually multiples of 4 bits and often of 8 bits. As we will see in Section 2.7, one reason for this is that letters and punctuation marks can be represented with 8 bits. Word lengths that are not multiples of 4 or 8 bits are occasionally seen. For example, some minicomputers use 18-bit words; the extra two bits provide information to detect errors.

Sometimes people disagree on the word length of a particular computer. For example, many microcomputers have both 8-bit and 16-bit registers, use 16-bit addresses, and have 8-bit, 16-bit, and 24-bit instructions. What is their word length? Some people will say they have 16-bit words because of their 16-bit addresses and 16-bit registers. Usually, however, such microcomputers can transfer only 8 bits of data at a time between memory and any register; therefore, we will consider them to have 8-bit words. That is, we will consider word length to be the number of bits a computer can transfer at one time—the width of its data bus.

Word length determines the number of different numbers that one word can represent. Words of 4 bits can represent 2^4 or 16 different numbers. Words of 8 bits can represent 2^8 or 256 numbers. Words of 16 bits can represent 2^{16} or 65,536 numbers. The words of small computers are often too short to store numbers with the precision needed for scientific computations. Thus, most small computers provide for storage of a single number in two or three words so that the desired precision can be obtained. Calculations that use two words for one number are called **double-precision** calculations.

Many small computers can also deal with units smaller than a word called **bytes**. A byte is generally understood to be 8 bits, although it can be 6 bits as on the PDP-8. Most recently designed 16-bit minicomputers have words organized as two 8-bit bytes. Most microcomputers, since they have 8-bit words, naturally deal in 8-bit bytes. The capability of handling bytes is helpful in storing characters and in dealing with small numbers.

2.3 Negative Numbers

Until now we have dealt with **unsigned** numbers—numbers that we can assume to be positive. We naturally would like to calculate with both positive and negative numbers, that is, to deal with **signed** numbers. Thus we need a way to represent negative numbers. We cannot use the symbols + and − to show sign because our computers have only 0's and 1's. One solution is to assign one symbol, say 0, for + and the other symbol, 1, for −. We can then use one bit of a computer word for the **sign bit** (the leftmost bit) and the remaining bits for the magnitude. With a computer word of four bits, for example, we could represent

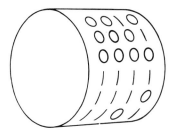

Fig. 2.1
Four-bit binary numbers arranged on a circular band.

$+6_{10}$ as 0110 and -6_{10} as 1110. This solution, called **sign-and-magnitude** representation, is only occasionally used on small computers because addition and other arithmetic operations are more costly to implement in sign-and-magnitude.

The representation of negative numbers usually used in minicomputers is **2's complement**. To understand 2's complement, picture all four-bit binary integers arranged in order on a circular band, somewhat resembling a car odometer, as shown in Fig. 2.1. We will say that 0000 is 0. If we start at 0000 and go forward three numbers, we arrive at 0011, which we can consider $+3$. If we start at 0000 and go backward three numbers, we end at 1101, which we can consider -3. Since the band is circular, we could also reach 1101 by starting at 0000 and going forward 13 numbers; we would then consider the number as $+13$. Obviously, then, if we are to have unique representations for positive and negative numbers, we should agree on which numbers are positive and which negative. In 2's complement, the convention is that numbers whose sign bits are 0 are positive (or zero) and numbers whose sign bits are 1 are negative. For the four-bit numbers shown in Fig. 2.1, the largest positive number is $0111 = +7$. The most negative number is $1000 = -8$.

More generally, in 2's complement representation with an n-bit word, we use one bit for sign and the other $n - 1$ bits for the magnitude. We can then represent numbers ranging from -2^{n-1} to $+2^{n-1} - 1$. Suppose we have 8-bit words. Reserving one bit—the leftmost—for sign, we have seven bits for magnitude. The most negative number we can represent is -2^7 or -128. The most positive is $+2^7 - 1$ or $+127$. We can always represent one more negative number than positive in this system. Why? (Think of representing zero.)

To convert from decimal to binary in 2's complement, we write positive numbers with a 0 for the sign followed by their usual binary representation using $n - 1$ bits. In other words, we insert leading 0's to fill out the number of bits. For example, the 2's complement representation of $+21$ in an 8-bit word would be 00010101.

The procedure for finding the 2's complement representation of a negative decimal number is more complicated:

1. Write the binary equivalent of the positive number, adding as many leading 0's as needed to make an n-bit word.

2. *Complement* the number by changing each 1 to 0 and each 0 to 1.
3. Add 1.

Example 2.5: Forming the 2's complement of a negative decimal integer

Task: Represent -21_{10} in 8-bit 2's complement.
Procedure:

1. Write the binary equivalent of $+21$ in 8 bits, yielding 00010101.

2. Form the logical complement by complementing each bit of the number (changing 1's to 0's and 0's to 1's). The logical complement of 00010101 is 11101010.

3. Add 1.

   $11101010 + 1 = 11101011$

Thus -21_{10} in 2's complement is 11101011_2.

We use a similar procedure to form the 2's complement of a negative binary number. In brief, the procedure for forming the 2's complement of any number is:

1. Write the n-bit number. (Add leading 0's to positive numbers; add leading 1's to negative numbers.)

2. Complement each bit of the number.

3. Add 1.

Using this procedure, find the 2's complement of 11101011. You should get 00010101, showing that the 2's complement of a negative number is a positive number with the same magnitude—its positive counterpart. For any given number of bits, however, there is one 2's complement number that has no positive counterpart. What is it?

2.4 Binary Arithmetic

2.4.1 Binary addition

We will find binary arithmetic much simpler than decimal arithmetic because there is far less to remember. The tables are just 2×2 instead of 10×10. The addition table is

+	0	1
0	0	1
1	1	10

In adding $1 + 1$, the table shows a sum of 10, which we know is the same as 2 in decimal. Alternatively, we can say the sum is 0 and the carry is 1. Then we can add numbers with several bits in the same way we would add decimal numbers with several digits. We begin at the right with the LSB and add one position at a time, passing carries to the next position. We note that $1 + 1 + 1 = 11$, corresponding to a sum of 1 and a carry of 1.

Example 2.6:   Binary addition

Task: Find the sum of 1101011 and 1001011.
Procedure: Beginning at the right, add one position at a time, passing carries to the next position.

```
  1101011
+ 1001011
 10110110
```

<h3 style="text-align:right">2.4.2   2's Complement Addition</h3>

The main reason that 2's complement is so popular in small computers is that addition in 2's complement can be done very easily. The rules for addition in 2's complement are:

1. Add the two numbers.
2. Observe carries into and out of the sign bit.
3. If there are no carries or two carries involving the sign bit, the sum is correct. If there is just one carry involving the sign bit, the sum is incorrect because of **overflow;** that is, the sum is too large to be represented correctly.

Example 2.7:   Addition in 2's complement

a) *Addition of two positive numbers*

$+3$	sign bit ⌐ 0011	
$+4$	0100	
$+7$	0111	No sign bit carries; the sum is correct.
$+5$	0101	
$+4$	0100	
	1001	Carry into the sign bit but not out of the sign bit; overflow.

b) *Addition of two negative numbers*

−3		(1)101
−2		(1)110
−5	Carry out (1)1011	Carries into and out of the sign bit; sum, 1011, is correct.

−4		1100
−6		1010
	Carry out 10110	Carry out of but not into the sign bit; overflow.

c) *Addition of one positive and one negative number*

−3		1101
+7		0111
+4	Carry out 10100	Carries into and out of the sign bit; sum, 0100, is correct.

+2		0010
−6		1010
−4		1100	No sign bit carries; sum is correct.

We can observe some common features from these examples. First, overflow occurs only when we are adding two positive or two negative numbers. Second, we ignore carries out of the sign bit in evaluating the sum; that is, the sum is limited to the same number of bits as the numbers to be added. Most small computers have a special one-bit register, usually called a **carry register** or **flag**, that holds carries out of the sign bit so that they can be inspected for overflow. However, the carry register does not hold part of the sum. Third, carries into but not out of the sign bit accompany overflow of two positive numbers; carries out of but not into the sign bit accompany overflow from addition of two negative numbers. You should convince yourself of the reasons for these observations. (See Problems 2.11 and 2.12.)

2.4.3 *Subtraction*

Subtraction for small computers is often done by forming the 2's complement of the minuend and adding. Thus the usual add operation is used; a special subtraction operation is not needed.

Example 2.8: Subtraction by complementing and adding

Task: Subtract 2 from 7 in 4-bit 2's complement.
Procedure: Write the subtrahend and the minuend in binary.

(+7)	Subtrahend	0111
−(+2)	Minuend	−0010

Form the 2's complement of the minuend, yielding 1110. Now add; the sum will be the desired difference.

(+7)	Addend	0111
+(−2)	Augend	+1110
	Sum	10101

Carries into and out of the sign bit; sum is correct.

The difference is 0101 or +5.

Many microcomputers have a distinct subtract operation. They subtract using the basic laws of binary subtraction:

$0 - 0 = 0$
$1 - 0 = 1$
$1 - 1 = 0$
$0 - 1 = 1$ with a borrow of 1

Computers that subtract in this way use a carry flag (a bit or register) to keep track of borrows beyond the sign bit. In some cases, such as when the magnitude of a positive minuend exceeds the magnitude of a positive subtrahend, it is necessary to borrow. You should be able to develop rules for binary subtraction in 2's complement similar to the rules for addition in the last section.

2.4.4 *Binary Multiplication*

Binary multiplication is most simply done in computers by converting both numbers to positive numbers, ignoring the sign bit, multiplying by one bit of the multiplier at a time, and adding after each multiplication step. As in decimal multiplication, each partial product is shifted to the left to line up with each bit of the multiplier. The correct sign for the product can be added after multiplication is completed. The product must be positive if the multiplier and multiplicand are both positive or both negative. The product must be negative if the multiplier and multiplicand have opposite signs. The product may require twice as many bits as the multiplier or multiplicand.

The binary multiplication table is:

·	0	1
0	0	0
1	0	1

As we can see, binary multiplication is particularly simple because there are only two cases. Thus if the multiplier bit is 1, the multiplicand is copied as the partial product. If the multiplier bit is 0, the partial product is also 0.

Example 2.9: Multiplication

Task: Multiply +6 by −5 in 4-bit 2's complement, yielding an 8-bit product.
Procedure: Ignoring sign, write the binary equivalents of the multiplier and the multiplicand; then find each partial product, adding as you go along.

(+6)	Multiplicand	110
×(+5)	Multiplier magnitude	101
		110 First partial product
		000 Second partial product
		0110 Sum of first two partial products
		110 Third partial product
		11110 Product of magnitudes

Determine the correct sign for the product and convert to 2's complement if the sign should be negative:

$11100010_2 = -30_{10}$.

The steps taken in this multiplication example differ slightly from the way that we would do the multiplication by hand. We would probably write down each partial product first and then add all the partial products after we had finished the last multiplication. However, computers are usually built to add just two numbers at a time. Hence computers add each partial product as it is formed.

We can summarize the procedure for binary multiplication as follows.

1. Multiply magnitudes of multiplicand and multiplier, starting with the right-most bit of the multiplier. For each bit of the multiplier
   a) if the multiplier bit is 1, add the multiplicand to the product; otherwise add nothing;
   b) shift left one position to the next bit of the multiplier.
2. Calculate the sign of the product (+ × + = +; + × − = −; − × + = −; − × − = +). If the sign should be negative, form the 2's complement of the product.

2.4.5 *Binary Division*

Binary division may be done by hand in a manner much like decimal division. As in binary multiplication, it is easier to work with magnitudes and to handle the sign separately.

Example 2.10: Division

Task: Divide $+35$ by -5.

Procedure: Ignoring sign, write the binary equivalents of the divisor and dividend, and obtain a quotient as in decimal division.

$$
\begin{array}{r}
111. \\
\hline
\end{array}
\qquad \text{Quotient of magnitudes}
$$

$$
+5\,\overline{\,)\,+35} \qquad\qquad 101\,\overline{\,)\,100011.0} \qquad \text{Magnitudes of divisor and dividend}
$$

$$
\begin{array}{r}
-101 \\
\hline
111 \\
-101 \\
\hline
101 \\
-101 \\
\hline
000
\end{array}
$$

Determine the correct sign for the quotient and adjust by forming the 2's complement if the quotient should be negative:

$$1001_2 = -7_{10}.$$

On computers binary division is usually done by procedures called restoring or nonrestoring division. These are discussed in the references.

On small computers, both multiplication and division may be done either with hardware or with software. Some minicomputers have built-in hardware for multiplication and division so that the user does not need to deal with the individual steps needed for these procedures. Instead he or she can program directly with multiplication and division commands. This feature is called hard-wired multiplication or division. In a later chapter we will look at the problem of programming multiplication and division if such commands are not available.

2.5 *Octal and Hexadecimal Numbers*

Although computers use binary numbers for their calculations, we will often find it more convenient to use another number system for entering numbers into computers. Most of us find it difficult to remember and use a string of 16 bits. However, it is easy to group the binary numbers into groups of three or four bits to convert the groups to **octal** (base 8) or **hexadecimal** (base 16), respectively. We can more readily remember the six octal or four hexadecimal numbers that are equivalent to 16 binary numbers. Thus, for ease of operation, most small computers include some provision for octal or hexadecimal inputs. Bit switches are usually grouped or color coded so that it is easy to enter binary numbers in groups corresponding to octal or hexadecimal numbers.

In the octal number system (base 8) the digits 0, 1, 2, 3, 4, 5, 6, 7 have the same values as in the decimal system. The numbers 8_{10} and 9_{10} are represented by 10_8 and 11_8 respectively. The octal number system, like the decimal and binary systems, is a positional number system. Hence 100_8 is equivalent to 64_{10} (8_{10}^2). What is 1000_8?

The hexadecimal system (base 16) represents the digits 0 through 9 in the same way as the decimal system. For the six additional symbols required to represent the decimal numbers 10 through 15, the letters A through F are used. Thus we count in hexadecimal as 0, 1, 2, 3, 4, 5, 6, 7, 8, 9, A, B, C, D, E, F, 10, 11,. . . . We need to practice with hexadecimal numbers before we can instantly recognize C as 12_{10} or F as 15_{10}. Again, the hexadecimal system is a positional system. Hence 100_{16} is equivalent to 256_{10} (16_{10}^2). What is 1000_{16}?

Table 2.2 shows the correspondence of the first 16 numbers in decimal, binary, octal, and hexadecimal.

Table 2.2
Decimal, binary, octal, and hexadecimal
numbers

Decimal	Binary	Octal	Hexadecimal
0	0	0	0
1	1	1	1
2	10	2	2
3	11	3	3
4	100	4	4
5	101	5	5
6	110	6	6
7	111	7	7
8	1000	10	8
9	1001	11	9
10	1010	12	A
11	1011	13	B
12	1100	14	C
13	1101	15	D
14	1110	16	E
15	1111	17	F

The main advantage that octal and hexadecimal numbers have over decimal numbers is that they can be easily converted to and from binary numbers. We convert a binary integer to octal or hexadecimal by arranging the binary number in groups of three or four respectively, starting from the right or the binary point. We then replace each group by its octal or hexadecimal equivalent.

Example 2.11: Binary–octal conversion

Task: Convert 1011000111101111_2 to octal.
Procedure: First arrange the bits in groups of three, starting from the right. Then replace each group by its octal equivalent.

1	011	000	111	101	111
↓	↓	↓	↓	↓	↓
1	3	0	7	5	7

$1011000111101111_2 = 130757_8$

Example 2.12: Binary–hexadecimal conversion

Task: Convert 1011000111101111_2 to hexadecimal.
Procedure: First arrange the bits in groups of four, starting from the right. Then change each group to its hexadecimal equivalent.

1011	0001	1110	1111
↓	↓	↓	↓
B	1	E	F

$1011000111101111_2 = B1EF_{16}$

The procedure for converting a binary fraction to octal or hexadecimal is similar. The main point to remember is that the grouping of bits always begins at the binary point. Thus a binary fraction is divided into groups of three bits for octal or four for hexadecimal starting from the *left*.

Conversion from octal or hexadecimal to binary is just as easy. We simply replace each octal or hexadecimal digit with the corresponding group of three or four bits. We may need to add leading 0's (that is, 0's at the left) to fill out each group to three or four bits.

Example 2.13: Octal–binary conversion

Task: Convert 164352_8 to binary.
Procedure: Replace each octal digit with the corresponding three-digit binary number.

1	6	4	3	5	2
↓	↓	↓	↓	↓	↓
001	110	100	011	101	010

$164352_8 = 1110100011101010_2$

Example 2.14:   Hexadecimal–binary conversion

Task: Convert $AC27_{16}$ to binary.
Procedure: Replace each hexadecimal digit with the corresponding four-digit binary number.

A	C	2	7
↓	↓	↓	↓
1010	1100	0010	0111

$AC27_{16} = 1010110000100111_2$

You may be wondering whether it is possible to convert between octal or hexadecimal and decimal. In this text we prefer to use binary as an intermediate base instead of converting directly. Thus to convert from decimal to hexadecimal we will first convert from decimal to binary, then from binary to hexadecimal. Similarly, when converting from octal to decimal, we will first change octal to binary, then binary to decimal. More direct methods are possible, however, and you may prefer to develop and use them.

The main advantage of hexadecimal representation for small computers is that it neatly fits word lengths that are multiples of four bits. We can represent a 16-bit number with exactly four hexadecimal digits. The same 16-bit number requires six octal digits, one of which can only be 0 or 1. Thus hexadecimal numbers are more compact. They are, however, less easy to convert than octal numbers, because the mixture of numerals and letters in hexadecimal can be troublesome.

Most of the minicomputers we will study use octal representation. We will consistently use octal when we discuss the PDP-11 or the PDP-8. Microcomputers, by contrast, more commonly use hexadecimal representation. However, it is not standard. You may see computer systems based on the Intel 8080/8085 microprocessor that use either octal or hexadecimal. But we will generally deal in hexadecimal when discussing microcomputers.

In working with small computers, we will usually use octal or hexadecimal numbers only as a shorthand convenience for binary numbers. We will not do arithmetic calculations in octal or hexadecimal. The calculations in binary are simpler, so we prefer to convert from octal or hexadecimal to binary, calculate in binary, and then convert back. Nonetheless, we can make up addition and multiplication tables for these two number systems for use in checking binary results (see Problems 2.17 and 2.20). We can also define representation of negative numbers as 8's complement and 16's complement (see Problems 2.21 and 2.22).

2.6   *Floating-Point Numbers*

The numbers we have used so far have all been **fixed-point** numbers. That is, the binary point has been fixed in one place, usually at the far right of the number. This restriction limits the range of numbers we can use. We could solve this problem by scaling the numbers by powers of 2 and keeping track of the scale factor during multiplication or similar procedures. However, we would like to be able to deal with a wide range of numbers without bothering to remember scale factors. Floating-point numbers let us do just that.

Floating-point numbers require two numbers to represent any desired number X. One number is a k-bit signed binary fraction Y, called a **mantissa**. The second is an m-bit signed binary integer Z used as an **exponent** of 2. X can then be represented as

$$X = Y \times 2^Z.$$

Thus, in an 8-bit word, we can use, say, five bits for the mantissa and three for the exponent. We can then represent some of the following numbers.

$$+101.1 \;\; = +.1011 \times 2^{+11}$$
$$-1.011 \;\; = -.1011 \times 2^{+01}$$
$$-.00011 = -.1100 \times 2^{-11}$$

Floating-point representation is not unique; that is, it permits us to write the same number in more than one form. We can represent the number $+0.001$ as $+.1 \times 2^{-10}$ or as $+.01 \times 2^{-01}$ or as $+.001 \times 2^{+00}$, etc. The first floating-point form, in which the most significant bit of the magnitude of the mantissa is 1, is called the **normalized** form and is the one usually used. Alternatively, we say that a number is normalized if its exponent is as small as possible and the magnitude of the mantissa is greater than or equal to $1/2$.

The mantissa is usually represented in sign-and-magnitude instead of 2's complement. This representation, although it makes addition more difficult, makes multiplication simpler. The exponent may be given in either sign-and-magnitude or 2's complement. Sometimes the exponent is added to a constant C so that all exponents are represented as positive numbers. For example, we can represent exponents ranging from -64 to $+63$ as positive numbers ranging from 0 to 127 by adding the constant 64 to all exponents.

Because minicomputer words are so short, floating-point numbers often take two or three words. (Microcomputers less commonly deal with floating-point numbers, possibly because four or more words would be needed for much accuracy.) Several floating-point formats for small computers are shown in Fig. 2.2. Each portion of a computer word that is dedicated to a specific use, such as a mantissa, is called a **field**. The bits of a computer word are numbered from 0 to n, where n is the word length. The numbers are shown below the bits. Some computer manufacturers number from right to left; others number from left to right.

Other variations of binary floating-point are possible. Some computer manufacturers, Data General and Interdata for example, have a hexadecimal floating-point representation in which numbers are represented as

$$X = Y \times 16^Z.$$

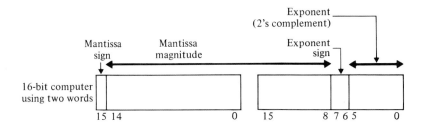

Exponent
(2's complement)

Mantissa sign   Mantissa magnitude   Exponent sign   Exponent sign

16-bit computer using two words

15 14   0   15   8 7 6 5   0

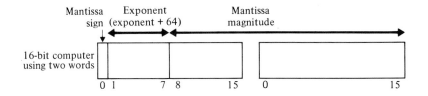

Mantissa sign   Exponent (exponent + 64)   Mantissa magnitude

16-bit computer using two words

0 1   7 8   15   0   15

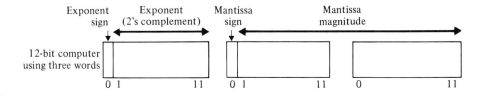

Exponent sign   Exponent (2's complement)   Mantissa sign   Mantissa magnitude

12-bit computer using three words

0 1   11   0 1   11   0   11

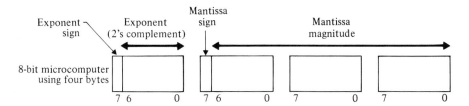

Exponent sign   Exponent (2's complement)   Mantissa sign   Mantissa magnitude

8-bit microcomputer using four bytes

7 6   0   7 6   0   7   0   7   0

Fig. 2.2
Possible floating-point formats for small computers.

Here Y is a binary fraction and Z is a binary integer. A normalized mantissa will have at least the magnitude 1/16. That is, at least one of the four most significant bits of the mantissa will be 1.

Although minicomputers may use binary floating-point for their calculations, many also allow input and output in decimal floating-point format. The floating-point format usually looks like FORTRAN format, with which you may be familiar. The number $0.365_{10} \times 10^3$ will be written as 0.365E+03. We will discuss this in more detail in the chapter on FORTRAN.

The main advantage of floating-point format is the large range of numbers that can be handled easily. If the exponent has m bits, the range of numbers that can be handled is nearly -2^{2m-1} to $2^{2m-1} - 1$. This range exceeds 10^{76} for $m = 8$. Thus scaling can be avoided for all but the most exotic scientific calculations.

The disadvantages of floating-point format are longer computing time, more costly hardware, and reduced precision per bit. Floating-point requires space for the exponent that does not contribute any precision to the result.

Procedures for calculating with floating-point numbers may be found in the references.

2.7   BCD Numbers

Some computers, especially business-oriented ones, store numbers in **binary-coded decimal (BCD)** form. BCD codes each digit in a multidigit decimal number as the four-bit binary number equivalent to that digit. It thus takes 16 bits to represent a four-digit decimal number in BCD. For example, 9736 is coded as 1001011100110110. Although the numbers 10 through 15 could also be coded as four-digit binary numbers, this is not done in BCD. In fact, the binary numbers corresponding to 10 through 15 are not used at all. Thus BCD code is inefficient, because 6/16 of the available binary numbers are not used. A 16-bit minicomputer word can store an unsigned binary number of $2^{16} - 1$ or 65,535, whereas the largest unsigned BCD number it can store is $10^4 - 1$ or 9999. Thus 55,535 of 65,536 possible combinations are not used.

However, conversion from binary to BCD is much simpler than conversion from binary to decimal. The bits wasted in coding in BCD are traded for faster conversion time. Hence BCD can be useful in business applications where both input and output are decimal numbers and only a small amount of calculations will be done on the numbers. BCD codes are also used for keyboard inputs and for displays.

Arithmetic can be done directly in BCD but corrections are required. For example, BCD addition requires corrections both to generate carries and to correct sums greater than 9. The addition of 8 and 7 should result in 15. However the binary addition of 8 and 7, that is,

```
  8          1000
 +7          0111
 ──          ────
 15          1111
```

results in 1111, the binary equivalent of 15, which, as we have noted, is not used in BCD. To get 1 0101, the BCD representation of 15, we simply add 0110, the binary equivalent of 6, that is,

```
  8          1000
 +7          0111
 ──          ────
 15          1111
            +0110
          ────────
        1    0101.
```

The addition of 6 automatically corrects the addition to give the desired BCD result whenever the sum exceeds 9. We can think of the added 6 as taking the sum past the unused positions from 10_{10} through 15_{10}. The 6 may be added by a hardware circuit or by software. Most microprocessors provide software commands to correct BCD operations. We will illustrate this later.

2.8 *Representation of Nonnumeric Information*

Not all the information that we will use with a computer is numeric. We also must be able to represent such characters as letters and punctuation. Since the computer is limited to 0's and 1's for their representation also, we must agree on combinations of 0's and 1's for these characters. Two standard 8-bit codes—ASCII (American Standard Code for Information Interchange) and EBCDIC (Extended Binary Coded Decimal Interchange Code)—are usually used. Both codes can represent both upper- and lower-case letters, numerals, and a wide variety of punctuation. EBCDIC is mainly found on IBM computers; ASCII is found on most other computers. Hence we will use ASCII. Table 2.3 shows the representations of some symbols in both ASCII and EBCDIC.

There is a pattern to the choice of codes for letter characters. Look at the ASCII codes. They begin

A	1100	0001_2	$C1_{16}$
B	1100	0010_2	$C2_{16}$
C	1100	0011_2	$C3_{16}$

and run through

| Z | 1101 | 1010_2 | DA_{16} |

If we can remember the code for A, we can generate the code for any other letter by adding its position in the alphabet beyond A to the code for A. For example, in the alphabet the letter N is thirteen positions beyond A. Thus by adding 1101_2 to $1100\ 0001_2$, the code for A, we obtain $1100\ 1110_2$, the code for N.

Alternatively we can think of $1100\ 0000_2$ (C_{16}) as the base of the alphabet. To get the code for any letter, we add its position in the alphabet to the base. Because N is the fourteenth letter of the alphabet, we add 1110_2 to $1100\ 0000_2$ to obtain the code for N, 1100 1110.

Similarly, the codes for decimal digits also have a pattern. They begin

0	1011	0000_2	$B0_{16}$
1	1011	0001_2	$B1_{16}$
2	1011	0010_2	$B2_{16}$

How would you generate the code for any decimal digit?

Table 2.3
ASCII and EBCDIC representations of selected symbols

Character	ASCII representation	EBCDIC representation		Character	ASCII representation	EBCDIC representation
A	1100 0001	1100 0001		Blank	0000 0000	0100 0000
B	1100 0010	1100 0010		Period,		
C	1100 0011	1100 0011		decimal point	1010 1110	0100 1011
D	1100 0100	1100 0100	<	Less than	1011 1100	0100 1100
E	1100 0101	1100 0101	(	Left		
F	1100 0110	1100 0110		parenthesis	1010 1000	0100 1101
G	1100 0111	1100 0111	+	Plus sign	1010 1011	0100 1110
H	1100 1000	1100 1000	&	Ampersand	1010 0110	0101 0000
I	1100 1001	1100 1001	$	Dollar sign	1010 0100	0101 1011
J	1100 1010	1101 0001	*	Asterisk	1010 1010	0101 1100
K	1100 1011	1101 0010	)	Right		
L	1100 1100	1101 0011		parenthesis	1010 1001	0101 1101
M	1100 1101	1101 0100	;	Semicolon	1011 1011	0101 1110
N	1100 1110	1101 0101	–	Minus,		
O	1100 1111	1101 0110		hyphen	1010 1101	0110 0000
P	1101 0000	1101 0111	/	Slash, division	1010 1111	0110 0001
Q	1101 0001	1101 1000	,	Comma	1010 1101	0110 1011
R	1101 0010	1101 1001	%	Percent	1010 0101	0110 1100
S	1101 0011	1110 0010	>	Greater than	1011 1110	0110 1110
T	1101 0100	1110 0011	?	Question		
U	1101 0101	1110 0100		mark	1011 1111	0110 1111
V	1101 0110	1110 0101	:	Colon	1011 1010	0111 1010
W	1101 0111	1110 0110	#	Number sign	1010 0011	0111 1011
X	1101 1000	1110 0111	@	At sign	1100 0000	0111 1100
Y	1101 1001	1110 1000	'	Prime,		
Z	1101 1010	1110 1001		apostrophe	1010 0111	0111 1101
0	1011 0000	1111 0000	=	Equal sign	1011 1101	0111 1110
1	1011 0001	1111 0001	"	Quotation mark	1010 0010	0111 1111
2	1011 0010	1111 0010				
3	1011 0011	1111 0011				
4	1011 0100	1111 0100				
5	1011 0101	1111 0101				
6	1011 0110	1111 0110				
7	1011 0111	1111 0111				
8	1011 1000	1111 1000				
9	1011 1001	1111 1001				

You may occasionally see 6-bit and 7-bit ASCII codes as well as variations of the 8-bit code shown here. Sometimes the eighth bit (the MSB) is used as a parity bit. **Parity** is the evenness or oddness of the number of 1's in a word. Adding a parity bit can help us detect errors.

Suppose the eighth bit is an **even parity** bit. Then it will be selected so that the total number of 1's in the word is even—0, 2, 4, 6, or 8. For example, the 7-bit ASCII code for A is 100 0001. As this code has an even number of 1's, the parity bit chosen is 0. The resulting code for A is 01000001, which has two 1's and hence even parity. (What would be the code for B?) Now suppose a single error is made; that is, one bit is accidentally changed from 0 to 1 or from 1 to 0. The resulting word will have an odd number of 1's—**odd parity**. We can thus easily determine whether a single error has occurred by checking parity. Can we spot two errors that occur in the same word?

Because both ASCII and EBCDIC use 8 bits to encode a character, two characters can be stored or **packed** in a typical 16-bit minicomputer word. Similarly, one character can be stored in an 8-bit microcomputer word and three characters can be packed in a 24-bit word. Three characters can also be packed in two 12-bit words of a PDP-8, but the programming needed for this is more complicated.

2.S *Summary*

Binary numbers are used for most computer calculations. Decimal numbers can be converted to binary by successively dividing the integer part by 2 and listing the remainders in reverse order. Decimal fractions can be converted to binary by successively multiplying the fraction by 2 and writing down carries into the 1's position. Binary numbers can be converted to decimal by adding the weights of the nonzero positions.

Negative numbers are represented either as sign-and-magnitude or as 2's complement. Sign-and-magnitude representation expresses the magnitude of the number in binary, prefixed by 0 for + and 1 for −. The 2's complement representation is the same for positive numbers but expresses negative numbers as the complement of the positive number + 1. Addition of 2's complement numbers is correct if there are either no carries or two carries involving the sign bit.

Binary subtraction is usually done by complementing and adding the minuend. Binary multiplication and binary division are performed much like decimal operations except that they are simpler. Both multiplication and division may be done with hardware (on more advanced machines) or with software.

Octal and hexadecimal numbers are a convenient shorthand notation for binary numbers. Conversion between binary and octal or hexadecimal is a simple grouping process.

Floating-point numbers require separate representations for mantissa and exponent. Floating-point numbers usually require use of two or three computer words. They allow simple expression of a wide range of numbers and are convenient for multiplication and division.

BCD numbers use four bits to express any decimal digit. Although BCD representation wastes space, it is convenient for business calculations and for displays. BCD arithmetic requires corrections to binary arithmetic.

Nonnumeric information is usually represented on minicomputers in one of two codes, ASCII or EBCDIC. Both can represent upper- and lower-case letters, numerals, and a wide variety of punctuation.

Key Terms

ASCII	least significant bit
BCD	LSB
binary-coded decimal	mantissa
binary point	most significant bit
bit	MSB
byte	normalized
carry register	octal
double-precision	odd parity
EBCDIC	packing
even parity	parity
exponent	sign-and-magnitude
field	signed numbers
fixed point	2's complement
flag	unsigned numbers
floating-point	word
hexadecimal	

2.R   References

The material discussed in this chapter is standard and is discussed in many introductory computer books. Booth and Chien (1974) provide a good overview of most aspects of information representation. Korn (1973), Gruenberger and Babcock (1973), and Soucek (1972) discuss their application to minicomputers. Barna and Porat (1976), Hilburn and Julich (1976), Osborne (1976), Peatman (1977), Klingman (1977), and Korn (1977) discuss their application to microcomputers. McCluskey (1965) has excellent discussions of computer arithmetic. Gear (1974) and Stone (1972) discuss number representation in the context of computer organization. The user's manual for your minicomputer or microprocessor will explain what representations your computer uses.

2.Q   Questions

2.1 Why do computers use binary numbers?

2.2 How are binary numbers converted to decimal?

2.3 How are decimal numbers converted to binary?

2.4 Explain two ways to represent negative binary numbers.

2.5 How many unsigned binary integers can be represented by a word of n bits? What is the largest magnitude that can be represented?

2.6 How many binary integers can be represented in 2's complement by a word of *n* bits? What is the largest magnitude that can be represented?

2.7 Why are binary calculations simple?

2.8 Why do small computers use 2's complement?

2.9 State the procedure for 2's complement addition.

2.10 Why do we use octal or hexadecimal numbers?

2.11 What are the advantages and disadvantages of octal and hexadecimal numbers?

2.12 What are the advantages and disadvantages of floating-point numbers?

2.13 What are the advantages and disadvantages of BCD numbers?

2.14 How is a decimal number converted to BCD?

2.15 What is the purpose of a parity bit?

2.P *Problems*

Section 2.1

2.1 Convert the following numbers from binary to decimal.
a) 11101011   b) .1101   c) 101101010   d) .01101

2.2 Convert the following numbers from binary to decimal.
a) 10101101   b) 10111101   c) .10101   d) .00111

2.3 Convert the following numbers from decimal to binary.
a) 179   b) 236   c) 154   d) 1019   e) 561

2.4 Convert the following numbers from decimal to binary.
a) 0.5625   b) 0.78175   c) .09375   d) .265625

2.5 How many different numbers can be represented in fixed-point by the following?
a) an 18-bit word   b) two 16-bit words   c) two 12-bit words
d) three 12-bit words

Section 2.2

2.6 Express the following decimal integers in 8-bit 2's complement.
a) -71 b) $+29$ c) -53 d) -117 e) -89

2.7 Express the following decimal integers in 6-bit 2's complement.
a) -27 b) -18 c) -5 d) $+13$ e) -21

2.8 What is the range of numbers that can be represented in 2's complement fixed-point by the following?
a) an 8-bit word   b) a 12-bit word   c) a 16-bit word
d) two 12-bit words   e) an 18-bit word

2.9 Add the following pairs of decimal integers in 6-bit 2's complement.
   a) +28 and −17   b) +15 and +19   c) −31 and +14
   d) −32 and +3   e) −11 and −25

2.10 Add the following pairs of decimal integers in 8-bit 2's complement.
   a) +76 and −120   b) −65 and −89   c) +43 and +96
   d) −121 and −5   e) −101 and +97

2.11 Prove that overflow will occur in 2's complement addition only when the numbers being added are either both positive or both negative.

2.12 a) Prove that overflow from 2's complement addition of two positive integers is shown by a carry into but not out of the sign bit.
   b) Prove that overflow from 2's complement addition of two negative integers is shown by a carry out of but not into the sign bit.

Section 2.3

2.13 Perform the following subtractions in 6-bit 2's complement by complementing the minuend and adding.
   a) +26 − (−4)   b) −13 − (+7)   c) −19 − (+15)
   d) +29 − (−17)

2.14 Multiply the following pairs of decimal integers in binary. Express the product in 12-bit 2's complement.
   a) +7 and −13   b) −14 and +29   c) −31 and −15
   d) +26 and +14

2.15 Divide the following decimal integers in binary.
   a) +63 divided by −7   b) +108 divided by +9
   c) −132 divided by −11   d) +36 divided by +6

Section 2.4

2.16 Convert the following binary numbers into both octal and hexadecimal.
   a) 110101010111110   b) 1011100011110101   c) 1011110010010111
   d) 1010111010110001

2.17 Convert the following octal numbers to binary.
   a) 167342   b) 054613   c) 32617   d) 14521

2.18 Convert the following hexadecimal numbers to binary.
   a) ABC6   b) 9ED4   c) 76FA   d) 3FB5

2.19 Construct octal addition and multiplication tables.

2.20 Construct hexadecimal addition and multiplication tables.

2.21 a) Define 8's complement representation for negative octal numbers.
   b) State rules for addition in 8's complement.

2.22 a) Define 16's complement representation for negative hexadecimal numbers.
   b) State rules for addition in 16's complement.

Section 2.5

2.23 Express the following numbers in the first 16-bit minicomputer floating-point representation shown in Fig. 2.2.

a) 147.5   b) −0.0069   c) −1.55 × 10⁻⁴   d) 276 × 10²

2.24 Express the following numbers in the 12-bit minicomputer floating-point format of Fig. 2.2.

a) −4.67 × 10⁵   b) +125 × 10⁻⁷   c) −9.43 × 10⁻¹²
d) +6.45 × 10¹⁰

Section 2.6

2.25 Code the following decimal integers into BCD.

a) 2694   b) 7839   c) 1546   d) 42,739

Section 2.7

2.26 Show the resulting binary number from packing the ASCII equivalents of the following pairs of characters into 16-bit words.

a) IF   b) 6.   c) 2A   d) EZ

3

Flowcharts

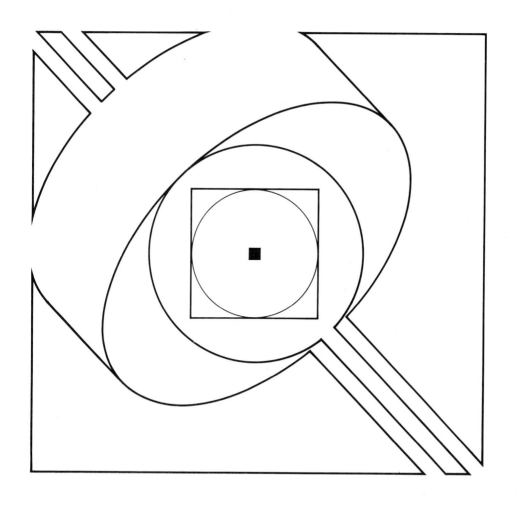

3.1 *Introduction*

In order to use a computer, we must learn how to program it. This requires that we first learn how to organize our problems for computer solution. Perhaps the best way to do this is to use **flowcharts**—graphical layouts of our problem-solving methods. Flowcharts are complex enough to be the subject of an entire book. Yet we will find that we can describe some typical problems with simple flowcharts that use only four symbols and follow a few rules. In this chapter, then, we will look at typical problems and how they can be flowcharted, and we will learn about flowchart symbols and procedures.

We may think of a flowchart as showing the structure of a program, much as an outline shows the structure of a term paper. Your English teachers have probably advised you to construct a careful outline before beginning to write. Although you may have preferred to ignore this advice, without an outline you may have had trouble organizing your paper. You may have written some ideas twice while omitting other important ideas. Your logic may have been unclear. Flowcharts, like outlines, are intended to help us organize our thoughts before we start to write.

3.2 *Programming Steps*

For the next several chapters we will be concerned with programming—writing a series of instructions that direct the computer to solve a problem. Programming, as we will do it, proceeds in four steps:

1. *Writing* a clear statement of the problem to be solved. As a student, you will frequently have this description handed to you readymade, but as a scientist or engineer, you will have to write your own problem statements.

2. *Planning* a course of action for the computer to use in solving the problem. Here is where flowcharts are helpful, since they show, step by step, the operations the computer must perform.

3. *Coding* the program. Using the flowchart as a guide, we translate each operation and datum into a form the computer can read. Beginning programmers often mistakenly consider this step to be the only important one. Actually, if the first two steps are done thoughtfully, this step may be almost mechanical.

4. *Debugging* the program—correcting the errors. It is virtually certain that our program will not work exactly as we hoped when we actually run it. Therefore, all but the most trivial programs will require careful analysis to detect and correct bugs.

3.3 *Flowchart Symbols*

Often we want the computer to calculate a value, such as a sum. For example, suppose we wish the computer to calculate the sum $S = A + B + C$. We can represent this on a flowchart with a rectangle.

$$\boxed{S \leftarrow A + B + C}$$

A **rectangle** shows an action or actions to be taken. The arrow $\leftarrow$ means "assign a value to." (More precisely, it means "replace the value on the left by the value on the right.") This rectangle directs the computer to calculate the sum of A, B, and C and to assign the value of the sum to S.

   You will note that we prefer to use an assignment arrow instead of the more familiar equals sign. This is because using the equals sign will often prove awkward. The statement

$$S = A + B + C$$

can be interpreted two ways:

1. S now has the value of the sum of A, B, and C.
2. Assign to S the value of the sum of A, B, and C.

In using a computer, it is the latter meaning we most often intend. Suppose we wish to change the contents of the location corresponding to S by adding D to S. The notation

$$S = S + D,$$

looks like nonsense, whereas our choice,

$$S \leftarrow S + D,$$

looks more reasonable.

   To show entry to and exit from an action we add lines to the rectangle. The lines may have arrows to show the direction of flow. These arrows differ from the assignment arrows within rectangles.

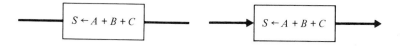

On a horizontal flowchart action usually flows from left to right. Therefore, arrows are really needed only for right-to-left flow; they are optional for left-to-right flow. Similarly, on a vertical flowchart action usually flows from top to bottom. Thus arrows are needed to show upward flow but can be omitted for downward flow. In this book, however, we will use arrows for all flows.

   If we wish to separate our calculation of the sum into three parts, we can represent the steps by three rectangles.

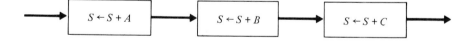

The arrows show the order in which the calculations are to be done. First, A will be added to S, then B, and then C.

The three separate additions will give us the correct value of S only if S is 0 before the numbers are added. This value cannot be taken for granted—it must be specified at the start. So, to make sure that S is initially 0, we begin the flowchart by setting S equal to 0. We call this step **initialization**.

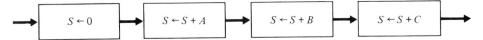

Now the computer will calculate the desired sum every time the flowchart is used. If we had not initialized S as 0, the computer would add the new values of A, B, and C to the previous final value of S every time the program was run. Initialization is essential in all computer work, and we must learn to initialize our values at the start of every program.

Of course, we may choose to flowchart this calculation with only two rectangles—the choice depends on how much detail we wish to show.

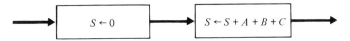

A rectangle may show several actions which will be performed in the order listed.

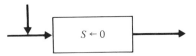

Each rectangle can have only one entrance and one exit. If it can be approached by two paths we merge the two arrows outside, rather than showing two arrows entering the rectangle.

All simple flowcharts must have a beginning and an end. We use an **oval** to show the terminals of a flowchart.

Start

End

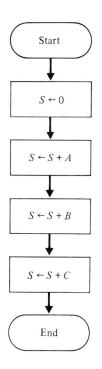

Fig. 3.1
Flowchart for addition of three numbers, $S = A + B + C$.

3.4 *Straight-Line Flowcharts*

With rectangles and ovals, we can construct a complete flowchart for the calculation of $S = A + B + C$ as shown in Fig. 3.1. This calculation requires only a **straight-line flowchart** because its action moves in one path from beginning to end without branching or looping. Straight-line flowcharts are the easiest to do. They do not require the computer to compare quantities or to repeatedly perform a calculation. To write more complicated flowcharts, we need a symbol from which there can be two or more exits.

3.5 *Branching*

A **diamond** symbol is used when the computer must make a decision to follow one of two or more paths. The decisions involved are usually based on comparisons. Suppose that we wish to take one action if A is positive or zero and another action if A is negative. We represent this comparison and branching with a diamond that is usually entered at the top.

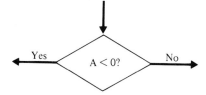

The symbol < means "less than"; the question inside the diamond asks whether *A* is less than zero. If *A* is positive or zero, action follows the right-hand path; if *A* is negative, action follows the left-hand path.

The diamond can also be used for three-way comparisons. Suppose that we wish to take one of three paths, depending on whether *A* is greater than, equal to, or less than zero. The diamond below shows this decision.

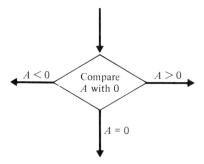

The left branch is followed if *A* is less than zero; the bottom branch, if *A* equals zero; and the right branch if *A* is greater than zero ($A > 0$).

Because comparisons are needed so often in flowcharts, we sometimes use a colon to show comparison. The statement *A:B* means "compare *A* with *B*." The diamond

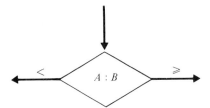

shows action proceeding to the left if *A* is less than *B* and to the right if *A* is greater than or equal to *B*.

A diamond must show exit paths for all possible outcomes of a comparison. The flowchart segment below is not correct because there is no path for $A = B$.

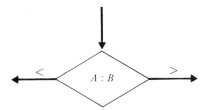

A flowchart with one or more comparisons but no loops (see Section 3.6) is called a **branching flowchart**. Suppose that we wished to add the absolute

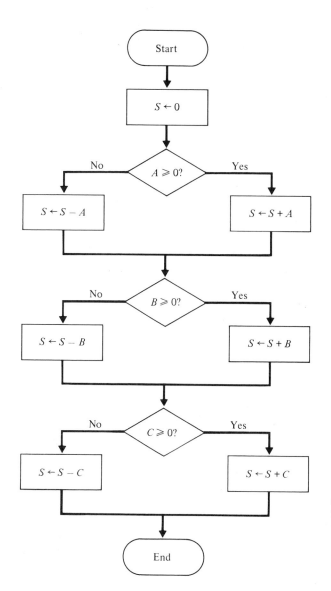

Fig. 3.2
Flowchart for addition of absolute values of three numbers, $S = A + B + C$.

values of A, B, and C, $S = |A| + |B| + |C|$. The absolute value of A, written $|A|$, is the value of the number without regard to sign. Thus it equals A if A is positive or zero and equals $-A$ if A is negative. For example, the absolute value of $+6$ is 6; the absolute value of -6 is $-(-6)$. (Absolute value is also called magnitude.) To add absolute values on the computer, we must determine in each case whether the number is negative. If it is, we subtract it from S. If the number is positive or zero, we add it to S. This procedure is flowcharted in Fig. 3.2.

Another way to calculate $S = |A| + |B| + |C|$ is to determine in each case whether the number is negative, to complement it by the methods of Chapter 2 if it is, and to add the resulting positive number to S. You should try to flowchart this procedure (Problem 3.1).

3.6 *Loops*

Many flowcharts require repeated calculations. For example, suppose we wish to add 100 numbers. We would not like to construct a flowchart showing 100 separate additions. Instead we repeat one basic addition step 100 times. We vary the number to be added to the sum S by arranging the numbers in sequence and adding the first, the second, the third, and so forth. In conventional mathematical notation the numbers would be denoted $x_1, x_2, x_3, ..., x_{100}$. Computers, however, are not equipped to handle subscripted numbers, so parentheses are used instead. We call the numbers $X(1)$, $X(2)$, and so on, up to $X(100)$. More formally we call this structure an **array** (Fig. 3.3). The Ith number of the array is $X(I)$. We refer to I as an **index**; it shows the position of the number in the array.

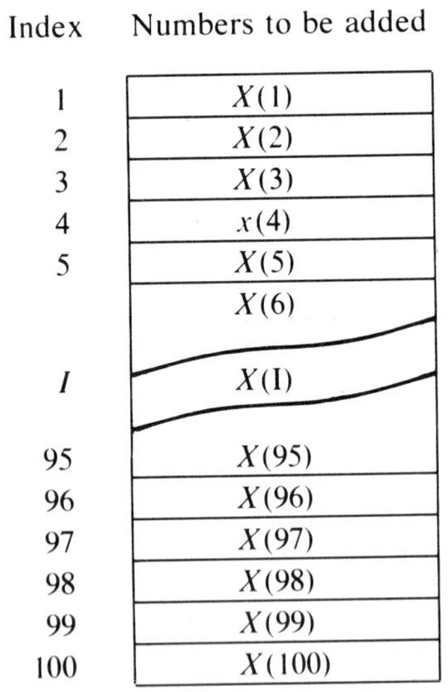

Index   Numbers to be added

Index	Numbers to be added
1	$X(1)$
2	$X(2)$
3	$X(3)$
4	$x(4)$
5	$X(5)$
	$X(6)$
I	$X(I)$
95	$X(95)$
96	$X(96)$
97	$X(97)$
98	$X(98)$
99	$X(99)$
100	$X(100)$

Fig. 3.3
An array of 100 numbers.

Figure 3.4 shows one correct flowchart for the addition of 100 numbers,

$$S = \sum_{I=1}^{100} X(I)$$

(the Greek letter sigma, Σ, means sum). The statement $S \leftarrow S + X(I)$ is the basic addition operation that will be repeated 100 times. After each addition, we increment (increase) I by 1. In other words, we tell the computer to move to the

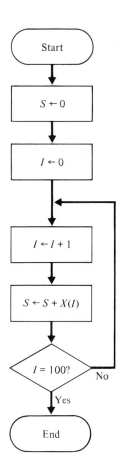

Fig. 3.4
Flowchart for addition of 100 numbers, $S = \sum\limits_{I=1}^{100} X(I)$.

next number in the array. The addition is complete when the 100th number has been added. We check this by inspecting I to see whether it is 100; if it is, the addition is finished; if not, we go back, increment I, and repeat the addition. We call this procedure a **loop**. We must be careful to leave the loop immediately after the addition of $X(100)$. If the flowchart is not properly constructed, we may stop adding after the 99th number or we may try to add 101 numbers.

Variations in the procedure shown are possible. We can save one step by initializing I as 1 and putting the $I \leftarrow I + 1$ step into the return branch of the loop. Or we can compare I with 101 before we add. More important, because there is nothing magic about the number 100, we can use the same basic flowchart for the addition of N numbers by simply comparing I with N instead of with 100.

3.7 *Subroutines*

Large programs are best divided into smaller parts called subroutines. A **subroutine** is a subprogram that performs a given set of actions whenever it is

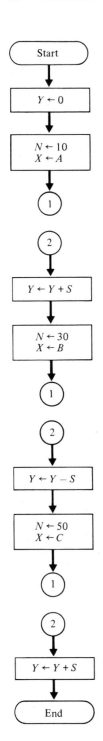

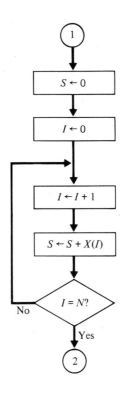

Fig. 3.5
Flowchart with subroutine for calculating

$$Y = \sum_{I=1}^{10} A(I) - \sum_{I=1}^{30} B(I) + \sum_{I=1}^{50} C(I).$$

Fig. 3.6
Flowchart symbols. (a) Terminal. (b) Action. (c) Decision. (d) Connection.

needed by the main program. We say that the main program **calls** the subroutine to perform a calculation. Once the subroutine is prepared, we don't need to code the calculation over and over, every time it is needed. By flowcharting and coding a calculation only once we not only save effort but also reduce the number of errors and simplify debugging.

Suppose we wish to calculate

$$Y = \sum_{I=1}^{10} A(I) - \sum_{I=1}^{30} B(I) + \sum_{I=1}^{50} C(I).$$

The easiest way to do this is to make a subroutine from our previous program for the calculation of the sum of 100 numbers. We will use the subroutine three times in its general form for adding N numbers. Each time we call the subroutine we will give the value of N and the name of the array to be added, such as $A(I)$. Figure 3.5 shows a flowchart for this calculation. The subroutine is on the right. The **circle** connectors guide us through the flowchart. Each time we reach a circle marked 1 in the main program, we jump to the beginning of the subroutine. When we reach the circle marked 2 at the end of the subroutine, we return to the corresponding 2 in the main program. (For now we will ignore the problem of selecting the correct return point in the main program.) We will discuss subroutines in more detail in a later chapter.

Figure 3.6 summarizes the four flowchart symbols used in this book—the oval for terminals, the rectangle for action, the diamond for decision, and the circle for connection. You will find that other symbols are used in flowcharts elsewhere. For example, several different symbols are used for input and output to show the medium used (punched card, paper tape, etc.) However, the four symbols shown here are enough to show the logic of any program.

3.8 *Flowchart Levels*

Flowcharts can be written at several levels of detail. These include, in order of increasing detail:

- The conceptual level—an overview showing the "big picture."
- The algorithmic level—a graph of the algorithms (an algorithm is a procedure that ends).
- The instruction level—a display of the instructions.

The choice of level for a flowchart depends on many factors. One is the complexity of the problem. When first thinking about solving a difficult problem we may decide to write a flowchart at the conceptual level. Each box on the flowchart may represent a series of operations. Later, as we understand the problem better, we can write a more detailed flowchart showing the algorithms to solve each part of the problem. We may then be able to code from the algorithmic flowchart without writing a more detailed one. On the other hand, when solving a simple problem, we may write just one flowchart at either the algorithmic or instruction level.

Another factor in choosing the level for a flowchart is our experience as programmers. Beginning programmers often prefer to show all the detail. They may write flowcharts that show every instruction written in the computer's code. Their flowcharts may in fact be nothing more than boxes around instruction codes. It is best to avoid flowcharts that are so detailed and that are necessarily specialized for a particular computer. Flowcharts, as we use them, are *planning* aids. As such, they are intended to show the logic, not the instructions, of a program.

Yet another consideration in choosing the level of a flowchart is its intended audience. Sometimes, as in this book, flowcharts communicate information to people who are unfamiliar with the program. Such flowcharts should be carefully written so that they communicate clearly. Other flowcharts may be read only by their authors. Even then, however, they should be clearly written to aid their authors in testing and debugging programs. Well-made flowcharts can also serve as quick reviews of programs that have not been used recently.

3.9 *Flowchart Guidelines*

Careful use of flowcharts will help you in both programming and debugging. Because flowcharts are personal devices, you will develop your own style as you write them. Yet because flowcharts are intended to communicate, they should not become so personal that someone else can't understand them without talking with you. While you should feel free to use either English or mathematical statements, you should not invent your own symbols. A few other general guidelines can help you avoid common pitfalls.

1. Choose your variables carefully. Avoid the single letter O, which can easily be confused with the numeral 0. Avoid variables that have special meanings for the computer you will use. (You will find these identified in your user's manual.)

2. Begin all paths in your flowchart at a single origin and end them at specific points. (Although you can have only one beginning, you may have more than one end; for example, you could have special ends for errors.) Avoid careless dangling ends.

3. Label all branches of a decision. Be sure that the branches include all possible outcomes, including those the computer identifies as errors.

4. Don't let two branches of a decision go to the same place. Combine two such branches into one, or eliminate the decision.

3.10 *Flowcharts—The Ongoing Debate*

Before leaving flowcharts to discuss coding programs, we should take note that not everyone agrees on the desirability of flowcharts. Some studies of both experienced and student programmers seem to indicate that flowcharts are not especially helpful—that they are no more useful in explaining a program than are comments, and that they may not help people to prepare programs more rapidly or accurately. Because of these studies, some computer scientists argue that flowcharts are a waste of time. Others point out that flowcharts are often written after rather than before the programs and hence are of no great value.

Obviously, we take a different view. We have found flowcharts helpful both in developing and in explaining our own programs. We have also found them invaluable in explaining many students' programs. Therefore we strongly recommend their use.

Even among those of us who advocate using flowcharts, however, there is considerable disagreement on the best way to prepare them. Some computer scientists like detailed flowcharts; others prefer an overview. Some argue that there is one best flowchart for any problem; others are more flexible. We recommend that you develop your own style. Naturally, if you are a student, you will want to follow your instructor's ideas.

3.S *Summary*

Flowcharting is the second of four steps taken in programming. The first is writing a problem statement. The third is coding the program—translating the program into instructions that can be read by the computer. The fourth is debugging—finding and correcting errors.

A flowchart pictures the steps a computer should take to solve a problem. We use four symbols—rectangles for action, diamonds for decisions, ovals for end points, and circles for connections.

Straight-line flowcharts are used for programs that proceed directly from start to finish. Branching flowcharts are needed when decisions or comparisons must be made. Loops show repeated actions. Subroutines are designed for calculations that may be needed to be performed the same way at several points in a program.

Constructing a good flowchart requires considering the complexity of the problem and the nature of the audience. A flowchart should communicate the logic of a program.

Key Terms

algorithm	circle	oval
array	coding	rectangle
arrow	debugging	straight-line flowchart
assignment	diamond	subroutine
branching	flowchart	
branching flowchart	index	
bug	initialization	
call	loop	

3.R References

Gruenberger and Babcock (1973) has a clear and lively discussion of flowcharting as applied to small computers. Schriber (1969) and Bycer (1975) are texts devoted to flowcharts.

3.Q Questions

3.1 What are the four steps in programming?

3.2 Why are flowcharts useful?

3.3 Why do we use an assignment arrow instead of an equals sign?

3.4 Which of the four flowchart symbols must every flowchart have?

3.5 Why is initialization important?

3.6 What is the advantage of arranging data in an array?

3.7 When and why do we use subroutines?

3.8 How do we decide how much detail to include in a flowchart?

3.P Problems

Section 3.5

3.1 Construct a flowchart to calculate $S = |A| + |B| + |C|$ by testing each number to see whether it is negative and, if so, complementing it before adding it to the sum.

3.2 The flowcharts for addition in the text have assumed that we can add arbitrarily large numbers. A 16-bit computer cannot represent numbers with magnitude larger than $2^{15} - 1$ in one word. Construct a flowchart that checks the sum after each of N numbers is added, to insure that its magnitude does not exceed $2^{15} - 1$; if it does, the flowchart should show an ERROR condition.

3.3 Construct a flowchart to verify that incoming data have values either between 100 and 200 or greater than 400. Any data with other values should result in showing an ERROR condition.

Section 3.6

3.4 Construct a flowchart for adding 100 numbers by initializing the counter as 1 and incrementing in the return branch.

3.5 Construct a flowchart for calculating the sum of the absolute values of N numbers.

3.6 Construct a flowchart to sort the numbers in three locations—A, B, and C—so that the largest number is in A, the next largest in B, and the smallest in *C*. Your flowchart should sort correctly regardless of the values in the three locations at the start.

3.7 Locations *A*, *B*, and *C* contain three integers representing the lengths of line segments. Construct a flowchart to determine whether the lengths could form a triangle; the lengths can form a triangle if and only if each length is less than the sum of the other two.

3.8 A simple method for calculating an approximate square root of an integer *N* involves repeatedly subtracting odd integers 1, 3, 5, ... from *N*. By counting the number of odd integers that can be subtracted before the difference becomes negative, we approximate the square root. For example, we approximate the square root of 25 as 5, because we can subtract 5 successive odd integers from 25 before the difference becomes negative; $25-1-3-5-7-9=0$. Flowchart this procedure.

Elementary Programming for the PDP-11

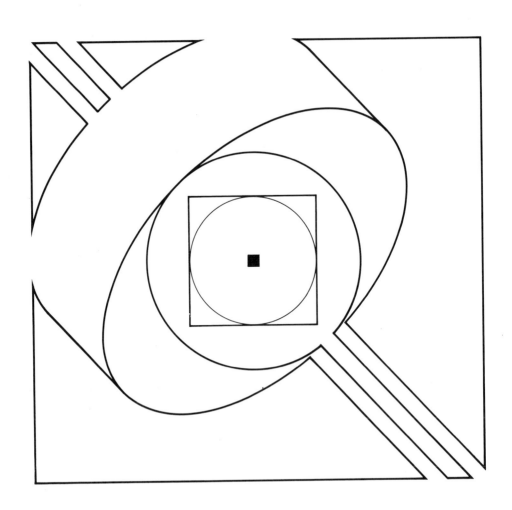

4.1 *Introduction*

We are now ready to learn to program a minicomputer, the PDP-11. If your main interest is microcomputers, you may wish to skip this chapter and go to Chapter 5, which presents the same concepts with reference to microcomputers.

In this chapter we will first look at the organization of the PDP-11 in more detail. Then we will look at the instructions of the PDP-11 and write programs for the problems of Chapter 3. The chapter ends with directions for loading and running machine language programs. When we have finished the chapter, we will still have much to learn about PDP-11 programming. However, we will know enough to write and run simple programs.

4.2 *Organization of the PDP-11*

As we noted in Chapter 1, the PDP-11 is a 16-bit minicomputer available in several versions. Its basic organization is shown in Fig. 4.1. Its CPU contains a processor status register (see below), an arithmetic unit, and 8 general-purpose registers, numbered 0 through 7. The CPU is connected to memory and peripheral devices by the Unibus, a 56-line bus.

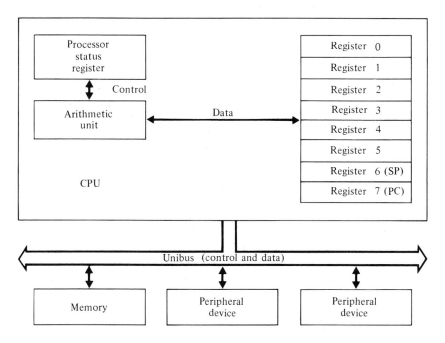

Fig. 4.1
Basic organization of the PDP-11.

Register 7 serves as the program counter (PC). Register 6 normally serves as the stack pointer (SP); we will explain stack operations in a later chapter. The other six registers, called R0 through R5, are identical and may be used interchangeably. In this general use of registers the architecture of the PDP-11 differs from the architecture of other small computers, on which most of the registers have specialized functions. We will find the availability of half a dozen identical registers to be convenient in programming.

The **processor status register** shows significant results of the previous operation in four **condition codes** or **flags**. These are one-bit registers that are **set** (to 1) or **cleared** (to 0) to show various conditions. The condition codes of the PDP-11 are typical of those of most minicomputers. They are:

- Z (Zero):
    1—last result was zero
    0—last result was not zero

- N (Negative):
    1—last result was negative
    0—last result was zero or positive

- C (Carry):
    1—last operation had a carry from bit 15
    0—last operation had no carry from bit 15

- V (oVerflow):
    1—last operation resulted in arithmetic overflow
    0—last operation did not result in overflow

Be careful how you interpret the Z bit. Note that Z is 1 when the last result was zero. (To avoid confusion, think of all flags in terms of "1=yes" and "0=no.") The N bit is just bit 15 (the sign bit) of the last result. The V bit is set whenever there is exactly one carry involving bit 15. We will see examples of the use of the V and C flags in a later chapter.

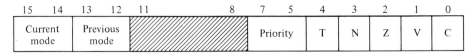

15 14	13 12	11 8	7 5	4	3	2	1	0
Current mode	Previous mode		Priority	T	N	Z	V	C

Fig. 4.2
PDP-11 processor status word.

These condition codes take up only four of the 16 bits of the program status register. We call the 16-bit contents of this register the **program status word**

(PSW). See Fig. 4.2. The four condition flags are bits 3–0 at the left. The purposes of the remaining bits are as follows.

Bits 15–12   Current and previous modes of memory management (not important)
Bits 11–8   Not used
Bits 7–5   Priority of the CPU, used for interrupts
Bit 4   Trap bit (T), used in debugging

We can address the memory of the PDP-11 in terms of its 16-bit words or its 8-bit bytes. Figure 4.3 illustrates these types of addresses in octal. As the figure shows, word addresses are always even; byte addresses may be even or odd. The word at each address N contains the byte at address N and the byte at address $N + 1$. Thus word 1000 consists of byte 1000 and byte 1001. Note that we are referring to a word or a byte simply by giving its address, much as we refer to a house by giving its address. It is important that we not confuse that address with the *contents* or *value* of the word or byte. We would not confuse the address of a house with its value!

	15 8 7 0
Word 1000	Byte 1001 | Byte 1000
Word 1002	Byte 1003 | Byte 1002
Word 1004	Byte 1005 | Byte 1004
Word 1006	Byte 1007 | Byte 1006
Word 1010	Byte 1011 | Byte 1010
(a)	(b)

Fig. 4.3
Memory addressing in the PDP-11 with (a) word addresses and (b) byte addresses in octal.

The memory of the PDP-11 consists of modules of 4K, or 4096_{10} bytes. (In computer jargon 1K is 1024_{10} or 2000_8.) The first 400_8 bytes are reserved for interrupt vectors. Hence we will not start our programs there.

Peripheral devices are assigned **device addresses** that resemble memory addresses. Depending on the maximum memory size of a particular PDP-11 model, the device addresses may range between 164000_8 and 177776_8 or between 764000_8 and 777776_8. The processor status register and the 8 general-purpose CPU registers also have device addresses.

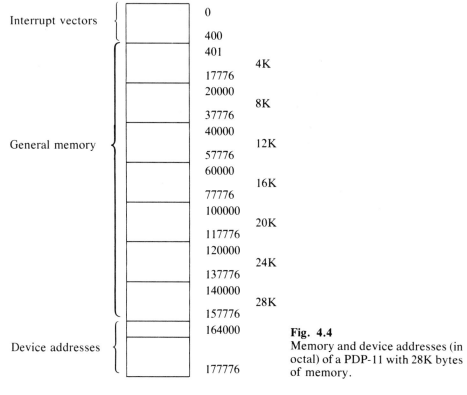

Interrupt vectors

	0
	400
	401
	4K
	17776
	20000
	8K
	37776
	40000
	12K
	57776
	60000
	16K
	77776
	100000
	20K
	117776
	120000
	24K
	137776
	140000
	28K
	157776
	164000
	177776

General memory

Device addresses

Fig. 4.4
Memory and device addresses (in octal) of a PDP-11 with 28K bytes of memory.

Figure 4.4 shows the memory and device addresses of a PDP-11 with a maximum of 28K bytes of memory.

4.3 *Instruction Formats*

Now that we know a little about the organization of the PDP-11, we are ready to learn about its instructions. In this section we will look at a few instructions in both their assembly language and machine language forms. In **assembly language** we can use symbolic addresses, such as %3 for register 3. We can also use **mnemonic** instructions, such as MOV or HALT. A wit once said that mnemonic comes from the Greek word for "hard to remember." However, we will usually find that mnemonic instructions—typically three- or four-letter abbreviations—are easier to remember than binary or octal numbers. In **machine language** we can use only binary or (for the PDP-11) octal addresses and instructions. As we indicated in Chapter 1, assembly language programs (they are also called **source** programs) are converted to machine language programs (**object** programs) by special programs called **assemblers**. But we can also perform the conversion ourselves (**hand assembly**), and in this chapter we will do that as we go along, to illustrate how the process works.

Instructions have two basic parts. The **operation code** (commonly called **op code**) names the action or operation that the computer will perform. For example, the mnemonic instruction MOV tells a PDP-11 to move data. Similarly, CLR tells it to clear something, and HALT tells it to halt or stop operating. The **operand** names the location or locations to be acted on. Thus the statement MOV %1, %2 tells the PDP-11 to move data from register 1 to register 2. (The % sign is the PDP-11 symbol for register.) Similarly, the instruction CLR %4 means "clear register 4." The HALT instruction does not need an operand; we can say that HALT means "halt the computer" or, in other words, that computer is an understood operand.

Each part of an instruction is represented inside the computer by a field of one or more bits. We can represent a general instruction as

Op code	Operand

The three instructions we have just discussed can be represented as

MOV	%1	%2

CLR	%4

HALT

Because the PDP-11 is a 16-bit machine, each instruction has 16 bits, numbered from bit 15 on the left to bit 0 on the right. (Other computers may have bits numbered in the reverse order.) A few instructions that we will not consider now require more than one word. Some machine language instructions in binary are as follows.

```
MOV %1, %2   | 0 | 0 0 1 | 0 0 0, 0 0 1 | 0 0 0, 0 1 0 |
              15 14    12 11              6 5            0

CLR %4       | 0 | 0 0 0, 1 0 1, 0 0 0 | 0 0 0, 1 0 0 |
              15 14                      6 5            0

HALT         | 0 | 0 0 0, 0 0 0, 0 0 0, 0 0 0, 0 0 0 |
              15 14                                    0
```

For the MOV instruction, bits 15 to 12 name the op code. For all instructions, bit 15 is 0 if the instruction is to operate on words and is 1 if the instruction is to operate on bytes. Thus bit 15 is a **word/byte bit**. We will look only at word instructions now. Bits 14 to 12 name the MOV command. The first operand field, consisting of bits 11 to 6, is used to name register 1, the **source** of the transfer. The second field, bits 5 to 0, is used to name register 2, the **destination** of the transfer. The rule followed is that all instructions with two operands name first the source of origin for the operation and then the destination. The first (leftmost) three bits of the source and destination fields are reserved for the **mode** or type of addressing, discussed in a later chapter. The last (rightmost) three bits of each field name the operand.

The op code field for CLR %4 takes bits 15 to 6. The last six bits, 5 to 0, are the operand field, with bits 5 to 3 reserved for the mode and bits 2 to 0 for the operand.

The HALT instruction uses all 16 bits for the op code field. Note that it is an all-0 instruction.

For convenience we may convert the binary machine language instructions into octal, which, as you will recall, we accomplish by grouping bits into sets of three, starting from the right. The lower tick marks on the preceding binary instructions show the octal groupings. MOV %1, %2 (0 001 000 001 000 010$_2$) converts to 010102$_8$; CLR %4 is 005004$_8$; HALT is 000000$_8$.

You may have noticed that operands are more complicated than op codes. Each of the instructions above had just one op code, but it had two, one, or no operands. Instructions with no operands usually assume the operand is known, either because the operation can have only one operand (halt the computer) or because we have just addressed a location and will continue using it until we name another operand. Microcomputers often adopt the second convention because they can use shorter instructions if the operand is named by a separate instruction. The shorter word lengths of microcomputers require greater cleverness in the design of instructions.

The CLR instruction, because it involves a single operand, has 9 bits available for naming the op code, aside from word/byte bit 15. With 9 bits, 2^9 = 512 instructions can be named, far more than any computer needs to use or than anyone wants to remember. By contrast, the double-operand MOV instruction has only three bits, other than the word/byte bit, in its op code field. With three bits, only 2^3 = 8, different instructions can be named. At the other extreme, a no-operand instruction, such as the HALT instruction, can theoretically be one of 2^{16} instructions. Thus we can see that the more space we use for the op code field, the fewer instructions we can distinguish. Minicomputers and microcomputers with fewer than 16 bits, such as the 12-bit PDP-8 or the 8-bit 8085 and M6800, must either settle for few instructions or use tricks such as multiple-word instructions.

4.4 *Some Programming Examples*

We still have much to learn about instruction types, addressing modes, and so forth, but we know enough now to write a few simple programs. Because writing programs is more interesting than learning more theory, this exercise will help to motivate our further study of subtleties.

Our first program will be for the addition of three numbers as flowcharted in Fig. 3.1. We will assume that numbers A, B, and C are initially stored in registers 0, 1, and 2, and that our answer S is to be stored in register 3. (We usually choose registers 0, 1, 2, 3, and 4 for storing operands, leaving registers 5, 6, and 7—the program counter—for special uses.) Besides the CLR and HALT instructions, we need an ADD instruction to sum the numbers. The instruction ADD X, Y adds the contents of location X to the contents of location Y and stores the sum in Y.

We write the assembly language instructions for the addition with comments marked off by semicolons. Each instruction below has three parts—an op code, operand(s), and comment.

Op code	Operand	Comment
CLR	%3	; CLEAR REGISTER 3
ADD	%0, %3	; ADD A
ADD	%1, %3	; ADD B
ADD	%2, %3	; ADD C, REGISTER 3 HOLDS SUM
HALT		; STOP

For the assembly language program to be complete, we need two more instructions. They are **pseudoinstructions,** or messages to the **assembler**—a program that translates assembly language instructions into binary. Pseudoinstructions are sometimes called **assembler directives** because they direct the assembler. An **origin pseudoinstruction** (.=) tells the assembler the origin of the program—the octal address for the first instruction. Thus .=500 means that the first instruction should be stored in octal memory location 500. An **end** pseudoinstruction (.END) tells the assembler that all instructions and data for the program have been given. (The origin and end pseudoinstructions may differ depending on the system used.)

The complete assembly language program and its machine language equivalent are shown in Table 4.1. To the assembly language instructions given above we have added only the two pseudoinstructions plus a comment at the beginning that describes the program, including the registers used. Note that comments can run as many lines as we wish, provided we start each line with a semicolon.

The form of the machine language program requires explanation. For each instruction, the memory address where it is to be stored is shown. The address of the first instruction, 500, is the location named by the .=500 pseudoinstruction of the corresponding assembly language program. The next instruction begins in octal location 502, the next in 504 and so on. Each instruction takes two bytes. Note that at each step the octal contents of the designated location

Table 4.1
Assembly and machine language programs for adding three numbers

Assembly language program

Op code	Operand	Comment
		; A PROGRAM TO ADD THREE
		; NUMBERS, A IN R0, B
		; IN R1, AND C IN R2 —
		; SUM WILL BE IN R3
.=	500	; BEGIN AT MEMORY ADDRESS 500
CLR	%3	; CLEAR REGISTER 3
ADD	%0, %3	; ADD A
ADD	%1, %3	; ADD B
ADD	%2, %3	; ADD C, REGISTER 3 HOLDS SUM
HALT		; STOP
.END		; END OF PROGRAM

Machine language program

Memory address	Contents	Comment
500	005003	Clear register 3
502	060003	Add A
504	060103	Add B
506	060203	Add C; sum is in register 3
510	000000	Halt

are shown. The contents of location 500, 005003, constitute the machine language equivalent of the CLR %3 instruction, obtained as in Section 4.3. In this simple program the octal contents are always instructions; in other programs they can also be data.

Comments in the machine language program show the correspondence of the machine and assembly language instructions. We show the assembly language comments in upper-case letters because they are an integral part of the assembly language program and are actually written that way as the program is prepared for input to the computer. The machine language comments, however, are simply aids to ourselves and will not be entered into the computer. The machine language program is basically a list of memory addresses and their contents.

Working with the % designations for registers can be awkward. Therefore, we may want to use a **direct assignment** pseudoinstruction to assign a symbolic name, or **label**, to a register. Once this is done, in the rest of the program we can refer to the register by that label. For example, the direct assignment pseudoinstruction

A = %0

Table 4.2
Second assembly language program for adding three numbers

Label	Op code	Operand	Comment
			; A PROGRAM TO ADD
			; THREE NUMBERS
	.=	500	; START AT 500
SUM	=	%3	; SUM IS REGISTER 3
A	=	%0	; A IS REGISTER 0
B	=	%1	; B IS REGISTER 1
C	=	%2	; C IS REGISTER 2
	CLR	SUM	; SET SUM TO 0
	ADD	A, SUM	; ADD A
	ADD	B, SUM	; ADD B
	ADD	C, SUM	; ADD C
	HALT		; STOP
	.END		; END OF PROGRAM

equates A to register 0 for use in our program. We will discuss the way in which labels may be chosen in a moment.

Table 4.2 shows the assembly language program for adding three numbers as it would look when rewritten using direct assignments. Note the label column that has been added on the left. The ADD instructions now have symbolic operands that correspond to those of the equation. Hence the instructions for the calculations are more natural and easier for us to read. Also, we have been able to shorten our first comment because the assignment statements help to explain the program. But this convenience has not been cost-free—the assembly language program is now longer, because we have added four direct assignment pseudoinstructions. In a complex or lengthy program, however, we usually prefer the convenience of symbolic addressing and are willing to pay the price of the few assignment statements. The machine language program is not shown in Table 4.2 because it is exactly the same as before. The assignment statements are only messages to the assembler; they are not translated into machine code.

The labels used in a program must meet several requirements. Each label must begin with a letter and can have no more than six characters, these being either letters or numbers. It cannot include punctuation marks or embedded spaces. For example, we may use as labels A, LOOP1, STOP, and NEG24, but we may not use 1, A ONE, or CONSTANT. Our labels should be as descriptive as possible to help make our programs clear. Naturally, however, we will not use as labels anything that the PDP-11 reserves for op codes or other special uses. We will not, for example, try to use HALT or MOV as a label. In an assignment statement, a label must be followed by an equals sign, as shown in Table 4.2. A label that applies to an instruction (Section 4.4.2) is followed by a colon.

We have now described all four elements that may be present in an assembly language statement—label, op code, operand, and comments. In the format we prefer, the elements are arranged in fields as shown in Table 4.2. Each instruction may use as few as one or as many as four fields. The label field is required for some instructions, such as assignments; it is optional for most instructions. The op code field is always used. The op code determines whether the operand field will be used. For example, HALT requires no operand while MOV requires two. Use of the comment field is always optional. Thus we can have instructions such as those below, either with or without comments:

```
      HALT
      MOV   %1, %2
SUM =       %3
```

As shown above, in writing instructions and other statements we prefer to align them in columns by fields, using spaces freely. We do this for clarity and for readability only. The computer will accept an assembly language program that is not aligned in columns. Moreover, we can insert spaces as we like, except within a label, op code, or operand. For example, we can write

```
MOV %1, %2
MOV %1,%2
```

Since we find it easier to read the first version, we prefer to insert a space or two between the operands. We must have a space between the op code and the operand. The computer will not accept

```
MOV%1, %2
```

4.4.2 *Addition of the Absolute Value of Three Numbers*

Our next example is an assembly language program to calculate the sum of the absolute values of three numbers, as flowcharted in Fig. 3.2. This program involves branching, since we test each number to see if whether it is negative and follow different paths on the basis of the outcome.

To determine whether a number is positive or negative, we use a compare instruction to compare each number with zero. If we store 0 in a location labeled ZERO, we can compare A with 0 by the instruction

```
CMP A, ZERO
```

The compare instruction directs the computer to subtract the contents of the destination, ZERO, from those of the source, A. When this operation has been completed, the condition codes in the processor status register are set or cleared, to indicate the result, as described in Section 4.2. However, the contents of the source and the destination are not changed. Because it has the advantage of affecting the condition flags without changing the operands, the compare instruction is used for most decisions.

To store 0 in the location named ZERO, we use the **word constant** pseudoinstruction

```
ZERO:   .WORD 0
```

ZERO is a label that names the memory location in which we will store 0. The op code .WORD shows that the octal constant named by the operand (here 0) should be stored in that memory location. Note the colon used after the label that applies to this and other instructions.

A similar **byte constant** pseudoinstruction stores the byte named by the operand into the location named by the label. For example, the pseudoinstruction

```
X:   .BYTE 15
```

stores the octal number 15 (decimal 13) into the byte of memory named X. If we are using only words, we can drop the .WORD part of the word instruction and simply write

```
Y:   240
```

to store 240_8 (160_{10}) in location Y. The constant is interpreted as a word constant unless it is specified as a byte constant. However, it is better to specify word or byte routinely.

Because we wish to treat negative numbers differently from positive numbers, we must use branch instructions. All computers are designed to accept certain instructions that will change the normal sequence of execution—instructions that transfer control to some instruction other than the one found next after the current instruction. These **transfer** instructions are usually called BRANCH, JUMP, or SKIP instructions. (The capitalized instruction names here represent instruction types—not op codes for the PDP-11.) BRANCH and JUMP instructions are alike in that they transfer control to whatever address is shown in the operand field. For example, the instruction (for some hypothetical computer)

BRANCH   LOOP

would transfer control to the location with the symbolic address LOOP. SKIP instructions do not require an address (or operand) because they simply direct the computer to skip one instruction.

JUMP, BRANCH, and SKIP instructions may be unconditional or conditional. **Unconditional** transfer instructions always transfer control to the address shown (or implied, in the case of SKIP). **Conditional** transfer instructions are more interesting; they direct the computer to test one or more condition flags and to take one of two or more actions depending on the flags. They have the general form

BRANCH   CONDITION   ADDRESS

An instruction in this form says:

- If CONDITION is true, transfer control to the location named ADDRESS.
- If CONDITION is false, proceed with the next instruction in sequence.

The PDP-11 has more than ten branch instructions. We choose the BMI instruction—<u>B</u>ranch if <u>MI</u>nus. It transfers control of the program to the location named by the operand if the result of the previous instruction is negative. Otherwise control proceeds in sequence. For our purpose we can use the following sequence of instructions:

```
      CMP A, ZERO
      BMI ANEG
      ADD A, S
      ⋮
ANEG: SUB A, S   (s-a)
```

If the result of the comparison is negative—that is, if A is negative—control transfers to the memory location named ANEG. (We name this location ANEG to avoid confusing it with A, the location where the value of A is stored.) The contents of the program counter are replaced by the address of location ANEG. The SUBtract instruction stored at ANEG causes the contents of A to be subtracted from the contents of S (that is, the source is subtracted from the destination). As we saw in Chapter 3, subtracting a negative number yields the same result as adding its magnitude.

If, instead, A is positive or zero, control proceeds in sequence to the ADD A, S instruction. Then, if we continued in sequence, we would reach the instruction labeled ANEG. To avoid this, after the ADD A, S instruction we write another branching instruction, a JUMP instruction, to take us to the next part of the program. On the PDP-11 the JUMP op code is JMP. Thus

```
JMP BNEXT
```

transfers control to location BNEXT, in which we store the next desired instruction. (Why can't we call this location B?)

Table 4.3 presents a program that calculates the absolute values of three numbers. Note that the data to be used are placed after the HALT instruction so that in processing the program the computer will not try to interpret data as an instruction. The .END instruction follows all instructions and data. Don't confuse HALT and .END. HALT tells the computer to stop; .END tells the assembler that all instructions and data for the program have been given.

4.4.3 *Addition of N Numbers*

Let us now work out a program to calculate the sum of N numbers, as flowcharted in Fig. 3.3 for N equal to 100. For the repeated summing of $X(I)$, we will use a **loop**. A loop, you will recall, is a program segment that is executed

Table 4.3
Assembly language program for adding the absolute values of three numbers

Label	Op code	Operand	Comment
			; CALCULATION OF SUM OF
			; ABSOLUTE VALUES OF A,
			; B, AND C
	.=	400	; START AT 400
S	=	%3	; SUM IS REGISTER 3
	CLR	S	; CLEAR SUM
	CMP	A, ZERO	; COMPARE A WITH ZERO
	BMI	ANEG	; GO TO ANEG IF A IS NEGATIVE
	ADD	A, S	; A IS POSITIVE, ADD A TO SUM
	JMP	BNEXT	; GO TO BNEXT
ANEG:	SUB	A, S	; A IS NEGATIVE, SUBTRACT A
			; FROM SUM
BNEXT:	CMP	B, ZERO	; COMPARE B WITH ZERO
	BMI	BNEG	; GO TO BNEG IF B IS NEGATIVE
	ADD	B, S	; B IS POSITIVE, ADD B TO SUM
	JMP	CNEXT	; GO TO CNEXT
BNEG:	SUB	B, S	; B IS NEGATIVE, SUBTRACT B FROM SUM
CNEXT:	CMP	C, ZERO	; COMPARE C WITH ZERO
	BMI	CNEG	; GO TO CNEG IF C IS NEGATIVE
	ADD	C, S	; C IS POSITIVE, ADD C TO SUM
	JMP	DONE	; GO TO DONE
CNEG:	SUB	C, S	; C IS NEGATIVE, SUBTRACT C FROM
			; SUM
DONE:	HALT		; HALT
ZERO:	.WORD	0	; ZERO = 0
A:	.WORD	146	; A = 146 OCTAL
B:	.WORD	136405	; B = −41373 OCTAL
C:	.WORD	221	; C = 221 OCTAL
	.END		; END OF INSTRUCTIONS AND DATA

repeatedly. We usually use a **counter** to keep track of the number of times we go around the loop. We can initialize the counter with the instruction

```
MOV N, COUNT
```

Each time we go through the loop we will decrement the counter after we have completed the basic calculation of the loop. The instruction

```
DEC COUNT
```

will DECrement the contents of the counter by 1. When the counter becomes 0, we want to leave the loop. The BGT instruction—Branch if Greater Than (zero)—is needed to accomplish this. The instruction

```
BGT LOOP
```

passes control to location LOOP if the result of the preceding instruction (DEC COUNT) is greater than 0. When the counter becomes 0, control will pass to the instruction following BGT LOOP; thus the computer will halt.

Instead of using a counter to determine when to leave the loop, we may test the value of some variable in the problem. Suppose we wish to keep adding numbers until the sum exceeds some number, which we call VALUE. We do not know how many numbers we will need to add before this occurs. We can continue the loop calculations so long as SUM is less than or equal to VALUE with the instructions

```
CMP VALUE, SUM
BGT LOOP
```

We initialize the **pointer**—a register that holds the address of the data we are interested in—by moving the starting address of the list of N numbers into it; then the pointer holds 200_8, the first address of the N numbers to be added. We will increment the pointer by 2 to point to each number in turn; that is, the pointer will hold 200_8, 202_8, 204_8..., the successive addresses of the N numbers. (Remember that all words have even addresses; only bytes have odd addresses. This is why the pointer must increment by 2 to point to the next number.)

We add the N numbers by using the ADD instruction with a new addressing mode. **Autoincrement addressing** uses a register as a pointer and then adds 2 to the contents of the register. Autoincrementing is denoted by (REG) +, where REG is the name of a register. The parentheses mean "contents of" and the plus sign means "increment." Since the plus sign is last, it means "increment afterwards." Thus the instruction operates on the contents of the location shown by the register and then increments the contents of the register.

The instruction

```
ADD (POINT)+, SUM
```

causes two actions:

- The contents of the memory location whose address is in POINT (register 2) are added to the sum in register 0.
- Then the contents of POINT are incremented by 2.

We can describe these actions more concisely by extending our notation for flowcharts. We can say that

```
ADD (POINT)+, SUM
```

has two effects:

SUM ← SUM + (POINT)
POINT ← POINT + 2

Again, the parentheses mean "contents of." Thus (POINT) means "contents of POINT." We now interpret the assignment arrow to show that the *value* on the right is transferred to the *location* on the left. Thus the statement

SUM ← SUM + (POINT)

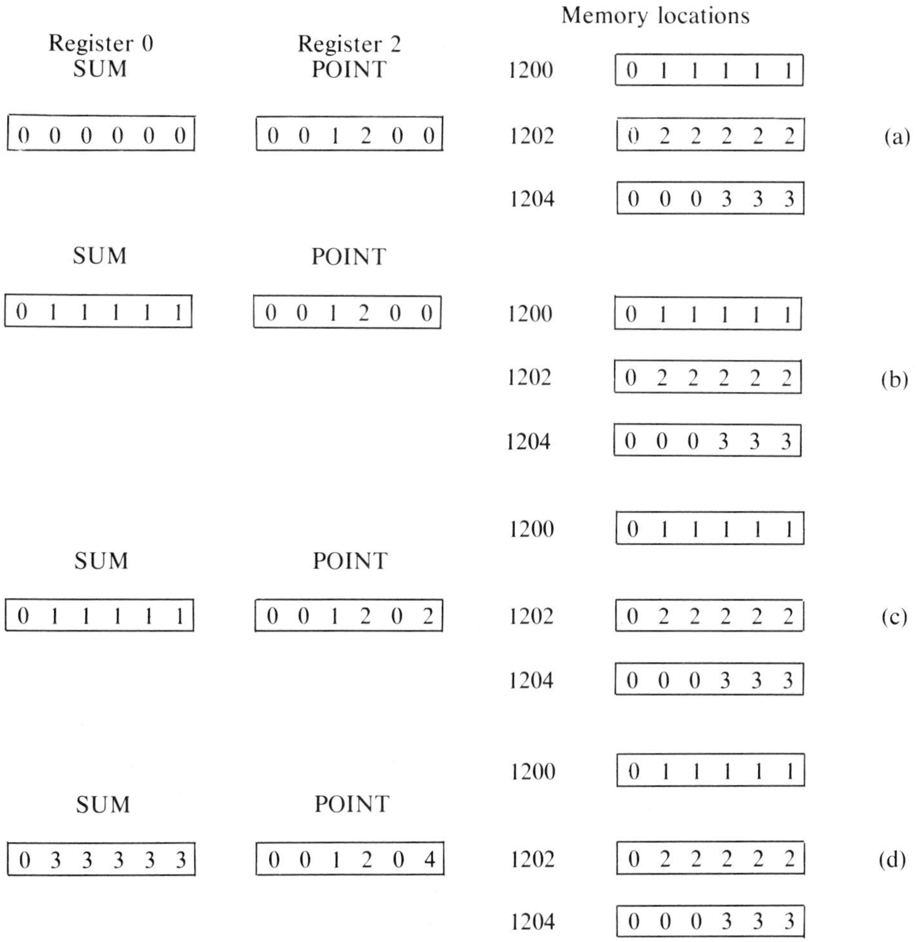

Memory locations

Register 0 SUM	Register 2 POINT		
0 0 0 0 0 0	0 0 1 2 0 0	1200	0 1 1 1 1 1
		1202	0 2 2 2 2 2 (a)
		1204	0 0 0 3 3 3

SUM	POINT		
0 1 1 1 1 1	0 0 1 2 0 0	1200	0 1 1 1 1 1
		1202	0 2 2 2 2 2 (b)
		1204	0 0 0 3 3 3

		1200	0 1 1 1 1 1
SUM	POINT		
0 1 1 1 1 1	0 0 1 2 0 2	1202	0 2 2 2 2 2 (c)
		1204	0 0 0 3 3 3

		1200	0 1 1 1 1 1
SUM	POINT		
0 3 3 3 3 3	0 0 1 2 0 4	1202	0 2 2 2 2 2 (d)
		1204	0 0 0 3 3 3

Fig. 4.5
Use of a pointer in addition. (a) POINT is set to first address. (b) Contents of location shown by POINT are added to SUM. (c) POINT is incremented to point to second address. (d) Second number is added and POINT is incremented.

means that the value of SUM plus the value of the contents of POINT—the value stored in the location whose address is in POINT—is transferred to SUM.

We can visualize this process as shown in Fig. 4.5. The contents of POINT, SUM and four memory locations are shown as six-digit octal numbers. In Fig. 4.5(a), POINT has been set to 1200_8 by the instruction

```
MOV STADR, POINT
```

Table 4.4
Program for adding N numbers

Label	Op code	Operand	Comment
			; ADDITION OF 100 NUMBERS
			; BEGINNING IN LOCATION
			; 1200 OCTAL
	.=	1200	
SUM	=	%0	; SUM IS REGISTER 0
COUNT	=	%1	; COUNTER IS REGISTER 1
POINT	=	%2	; POINTER IS REGISTER 2
	MOV	N, COUNT	; INITIALIZE COUNTER AT N
	MOV	STADR, POINT	; INITIALIZE POINTER WITH STARTING
			; ADDRESS
	CLR	SUM	; CLEAR SUM
LOOP:	ADD	(POINT)+, SUM	; ADD NUMBER TO SUM AND MOVE
			; POINTER TO NEXT ADDRESS
	DEC	COUNT	; DECREASE COUNTER BY 1
	BGT	LOOP	; GO TO LOOP IF COUNTER IS
			; GREATER THAN 0
	HALT		; STOP WHEN COUNTER IS 0
N:	.WORD	144	; N = 100 DECIMAL
STADR:	.WORD	1200	; STARTING ADDRESS IS 1200 OCTAL
	.END		

in which STADR is the label chosen for the starting address. The sum has been cleared by the instruction

```
CLR SUM
```

Figure 4.5(b) shows the contents of the registers and memory locations after the first action of the instruction

```
ADD (POINT)+, SUM
```

The computer adds to SUM the value 11111_8, the contents of memory location 1200_8 shown by the pointer. Figure 4.5(c) shows the result of completing the ADD operation in autoincrement mode; the pointer is incremented to show 1202_8, the second address. Figure 4.5(d) shows the results of the second complete execution of the ADD instruction; 022222_8 is added to SUM, and POINT is incremented to point to the third location. This process continues until the counter is 0. The complete program is shown in Table 4.4.

4.4.4 *A Subroutine for Adding N Numbers*

Our fourth example, which we will consider only briefly, uses a subroutine to calculate the sum of N numbers. We will assume that we are somewhere in the middle of a main program as shown in Table 4.5. We want a subroutine to calculate the sum of N numbers. We will assume that N is in register 1, which the subroutine will use as a counter. We will assume that the first address of the

Table 4.5
Main program with subroutine for adding N numbers

Label	Op code	Operand	Comment
			; PROGRAM SEGMENT
			; SHOWING USE OF SUBROUTINE
			; MAIN PROGRAM
	JSR	%5, ADDN	; TRANSFER CONTROL TO SUBROUTINE
			; ADDN
NEXT:			; INSTRUCTION TO FOLLOW SUBROUTINE
			; REST OF MAIN PROGRAM
ADDN:	SUM =	%0	; BEGIN SUBROUTINE–ASSIGN
			; REGISTERS
	COUNT =	%1	; N IS IN REGISTER 1 FROM MAIN
			; PROGRAM
	POINT =	%2	; FIRST ADDRESS IS IN REGISTER 2
			; FROM MAIN PROGRAM
	CLR	SUM	; CLEAR SUM
LOOP:	ADD	(POINT)+, SUM	; ADD NUMBER TO SUM AND MOVE
			; POINTER TO NEXT ADDRESS
	DEC	COUNT	; DECREASE COUNTER BY 1
	BGT	LOOP	; GO TO LOOP IF COUNTER IS
			; GREATER THAN 0
	RTS	%5	; RETURN FROM SUBROUTINE

N numbers is in register 2. The subroutine will calculate the sum in register 0. Fortunately, in this simple example we can spare three registers for the subroutine calculation. In more complex examples, as we will see later in the book, we must use other ways to **pass parameters** (exchange information) between the main program and the subroutine.

We **call** (transfer control to) the subroutine ADDN with the instruction

```
JSR %5, ADDN
```

The operands of JSR (<u>J</u>ump to <u>S</u>ub<u>R</u>outine) are a register and the name of the subroutine. The register holds the return address in the main program—the address of the next instruction after the JSR instruction. It is called a **subroutine linkage register** because it links the main program with the subroutine.

The subroutine ends with the instruction

```
RTS %5
```

RTS (<u>R</u>eturn from <u>S</u>ub<u>R</u>outine) transfer control back to the main program via the linkage register—the same register as in the JSR instruction. We will consistently use register 5 for subroutine linkage.

We may call subroutines as many times in a program as we like. Each time after the subroutine is executed, control returns to the instruction immediately following the JSR that called the subroutine.

4.5   *A Closer Look at PDP-11 Instructions*

Now that we have seen how to write several programs, we will stop to examine the instructions we have used so far and to consider other instructions. We want to be sure that we understand these instructions well enough to program with them in both machine and assembly language. Hence we will study both the mnemonic and the binary forms of the instructions.

4.5.1   *Double-Operand Instructions*

We have seen three main types of PDP-11 instructions—double-operand, single-operand, and branch instructions. Table 4.6 shows double-operand instructions. The operation code uses the leftmost four bits—bits 15 through 12. Bit 15, for some but not all double-operand instructions, is a **word/byte** bit. Where it is a word/byte bit, it is listed in the table as 0/1, meaning that a choice must be made between 0 for word and 1 for byte. Note that bit 15 is 0 for ADD and 1 for SUB, meaning that those operations may be performed only on words. For the time being, we will deal only with word instructions. Hence we will use bit 15 as 0 when there is a choice. Bits 11 through 6 are used to code the address of the source; bits 5 through 0 are used to code the address of the destination. In the table we have shown the op code bits in groups of three to simplify conversion to octal.

Table 4.6
PDP-11 double-operand instructions

Field use:	Op code		Source		Destination	
	15	12	11	6	5	0

Binary op code		Assembly code	Meaning
0/1	001	MOV	MOVe source to destination
0/1	010	CMP	CoMPare source to destination
0	110	ADD	ADD source to destination
1	110	SUB	SUBtract source from destination

4.5.2   *Single-Operand Instructions*

General single-operand instructions, shown in Table 4.7, use the leftmost 10 bits—15 through 6—for the operation code. For word instructions, the leftmost four bits are all 0. You may have noticed that the pattern of four 0's for bits 15 through 12 did not appear in the table of double-operand instructions. The four 0's pattern is reserved to show single-operand instructions on words. We call this saving of a bit pattern to define a class of instructions a **class code**. Small computers often employ class codes. Similarly, the bit pattern 1 000 in bits 15

Table 4.7
PDP-11 general single-operand instructions

Field use:	Op code	Destination
	15 6	5 0

Binary op code	Assembly code	Meaning
0/1 000 101 000	CLR	CLeaR destination
0/1 000 101 001	COM	COMplement destination (complement each bit of contents of destination)
0/1 000 101 010	INC	INCrement destination by 1
0/1 000 101 011	DEC	DECrement destination by 1
0/1 000 101 100	NEG	NEGate destination (replace contents of destination by 2's complement)

through 12 is the class code for single-operation instructions on bytes. The rightmost six bits—bits 5 through 0—are used to determine the address of the destination.

4.5.3 *Branch Instructions*

Branch instructions are shown in Table 4.8. We may consider branch instructions as a subclass of single-operand instructions in which the operand is a memory location determined by an offset. The **offset** is the difference between the branch destination and the address of the instruction after the branch instruction.

Suppose we know the address of a branch instruction and the address of the branch destination—the location to which we wish to branch. We must calculate the offset. We can write the relationship between these two addresses and the offset as an equation. Suppose we let

A = address of the branch instruction,
D = destination of the branch instruction,
O = offset in words.

Then to find the branch destination we write

$$D = A + 2 + 2 \times O.$$

We can justify this equation. $A + 2$ is the address of the instruction after the branch instruction because each instruction takes two bytes. Since O is the offset in words, to calculate the destination address in bytes we must add $2 \times O$. To calculate the offset, we manipulate the equation to obtain

$$O = \frac{D - (A + 2)}{2}.$$

Table 4.8
PDP-11 branch instructions

Field use:	Op code	Offset
	15 8	7 0

Binary op code	Assembly code	Meaning	Branch condition
0 000 000 1	BR	Branch (unconditionally)	Always
0 000 001 0	BNE	Branch if Not Equal (to zero)	$Z = 0$
0 000 001 1	BEQ	Branch if Equal (to zero)	$Z = 1$
0 000 010 0	BGE	Branch if Greater than or Equal (to zero)	$N = 0$ and $V = 0$ *or* $N = 1$ and $V = 1$
0 000 010 1	BLT	Branch if Less Than (zero)	$N = 0$ and $V = 1$ *or* $N = 1$ and $V = 0$
0 000 011 0	BGT	Branch if Greater Than (zero)	As for BGE except no branch if $Z = 1$
0 000 011 1	BLE	Branch if Less than or Equal (to zero)	As for BLT *or* $Z = 1$
1 000 000 0	BPL	Branch if PLus	$N = 0$
1 000 000 1	BMI	Branch if MInus	$N = 1$
1 000 010 0	BVC	Branch if oVerflow is Clear	$V = 0$
1 000 010 1	BVS	Branch if oVerflow is Set	$V = 1$
1 000 011 0	BCC	Branch if Carry is Clear	$C = 0$
1 000 011 1	BCS	Branch if Carry is Set	$C = 1$

Example 4.1: Calculation of branch destination

Task: Calculate the destination of a branch instruction stored at memory location 4244_8 with an offset of 013_8.

Procedure:

1. Calculate $A + 2$, the address of the next instruction.

   $$A + 2 = 4244_8 + 2_8 = 4246_8$$

   (Check this in binary if the octal addition isn't obvious to you.)

2. Double the offset.

   $$2 \times O = 2 \times 013_8 = 2 \times 00001011_2$$
   $$= 00010110_2 = 026_8$$

3. Add the results of 1 and 2.

   $$4246_8 + 026_8 = 100010100110_2 + 00010110_2$$
   $$= 100010111100_2$$
   $$= 4274_8$$

Example 4.2:   Calculation of offset

Task: We wish to branch from memory location 5702_8 to location 5644_8. Calculate the offset.

Procedure:

1. Add 2 to the address of the branch instruction.

   $5702_8 + 2_8 = 5704_8$

2. Subtract your result from the branch destination, expressing your answer in 8-bit 2's complement.

   $5644_8 - 5704_8 = 101\ 110\ 100\ 100_2 - 101\ 111\ 000\ 100_2$
   $$= 11\ 100\ 000_2$$
   $$= 340_8$$

3. Divide by 2 to convert bytes to words. Express the result in 8-bit 2's complement.

   $11\ 100\ 000_2 / 10_2 = 11\ 110\ 000_2$
   $$= 360_8$$

The offset is interpreted in 2's complement; thus the 8-bit offset allows branching $+127_{10}$ or -128_{10} words from the location of the instruction after the branch instruction. Equivalently, the offset allows branching $+177_8$ or -200_8 words.

The conditional branches test the state of one or more condition flags. The last column in Table 4.8 shows the state of these flags for conditional branches. (As before, we suggest you think in terms of "0=no" and "1=yes.") The bits can also be set or cleared by other instructions that we do not consider here.

In addition to the instructions just discussed, there are three other branch instructions for us to consider—the JMP instruction and two subroutine instructions, shown in Table 4.9. The JMP instruction is similar to the BR (unconditional branch) instruction but it allows more flexibility in naming the destination. Six bits are allocated for determining the destination, which can be calculated in the same way as the destinations of most other instructions. Similarly, the JSR (Jump to SubRoutine) instruction allows six bits for the destination and three bits for the subroutine linkage register. The RTS (ReTurn from Subroutine) instruction names the same subroutine linkage register.

The last instruction we need to know is the HALT instruction. Because its code is all 0's, this is the easiest instruction to remember.

4.5.4 *Source and Destination Codes*

We have examined the op codes for all of the PDP-11 instructions discussed so far, but we still need to examine the codes for naming sources and destinations. Basically, each source or destination is described by six bits. The first three bits

Table 4.9
PDP-11 jump and subroutine instructions

Field use	Binary op code	Assembly code	Meaning
Op code | Destination 15 6 5 0	0 000 000 001	JMP	JuMP to destination
Op code | Register | Destination 15 9 8 6 5 0	0 000 100	JSR	Jump to SubRoutine
Op code | Register 15 3 2 0	0 000 010 000	RTS	ReTurn from Subroutine

give the addressing mode; the last three are the octal number of the register. The PDP-11 has twelve addressing modes, which are described in detail in a later chapter. For now we will examine only the two modes used in the examples in this chapter—register addressing and autoincrementing.

Source or destination | Mode | Register number |
       3 bits   3 bits

    In **register addressing**, the register named is the address; the operand is the contents of the register. If we wish to add the contents of register 3 to register 4, we use register addressing for both registers. Register is commonly shortened to R; we will follow this convention. Thus R3 is the source, and R4 is the destination in which the sum will be stored. To form the machine language code for this instruction we place the ADD operation code, 0 110, in bits 15 through 12. The mode bits that signal register addressing are 000. Thus for bits 11 through 6, specifying the source, we write 000 for the mode and 011 for R3. Similarly, for bits 5 through 0, specifying the destination, we write 000 for the mode and 100 for R4. Combining these we have

0 110   000 011   000 100
(Op code   (Register   (Register
for ADD)   mode, R3)   mode, R4)

    The octal form of this instruction is 060304_8. The assembly language code for this instruction is ADD %3, %4.

    In **autoincrement** mode, the register points to the location of the desired operand. After the operand is used, the contents of the register are incremented by 2. The autoincrement code is 010. Thus if we wished to use R3 as a pointer

and add the contents of the location to which it points to register 4, we would
write

0 110	010 011	000 100
(Op code	(Autoincrement	(Register
for ADD)	mode, R3)	mode, R4)

The octal code is 062304_8. The assembly language code for this instruction is

ADD (%3)+, %4

4.5.5 *A Machine Language Program for Adding N Numbers*

Using the procedure just explained, let us write a machine language program to
add N numbers. We will assume that we start the program in location 1030_8. We
will also assume that register 2 holds the address of the first number and that
register 1 initially contains N—the number of numbers. Table 4.10 shows the
program. On the right, the assembly language program is shown for reference.

The first instruction, CLR %3, is easy to write. We write the octal code for
CLR, 0050, and continue with the code for register 3 in register mode, 03; thus
we write 005003.

The second instruction, ADD (%2)+, %3, requires writing the octal code
for ADD, 06, followed by the code for register 2 in autoincrement mode, 22,
followed by the code for register 3 in register mode, 03. The result is 062203.

The DEC %1 code consists of the code for DEC, 0053, and the code for
register 1 in register mode, 01; thus it is 005301.

Calculation of the BGT Loop code is more complicated. Having performed
the first addition and decremented the counter, we want to branch back from
1040, the memory location after the BGT Loop instruction, to 1032, the ADD

Table 4.10
Machine language program for adding N numbers

Memory address	Contents		Assembly language instruction	Comment
				; ADDITION OF N NUMBERS
				; SUM IS IN R3
				; R2 POINTS TO NUMBERS
				; R1 INITIALLY CONTAINS N
1030	005003		CLR %3	; CLEAR REGISTER 3 TO START
				; SUM
1032	062203	LOOP:	ADD (%2)+, %3	; ADD NUMBER POINTED TO BY
				; R2 AND INCREMENT R2
1034	005301		DEC %1	; DECREMENT COUNTER IN R1
1036	003375		BGT LOOP	; BRANCH TO LOOP IF COUNTER
				; GREATER THAN ZERO
1040	000000		HALT	; STOP

instruction. Thus we wish to branch back three words (or six bytes). We calculate the 8-bit 2's complement of 3 as 11111101_2 or 375_8. We write the octal code for BGT, 003, and then the offset, 375; the result is 003375.

Finally, for memory location 1040 we write the HALT code, 000000.

4.6 *Running Machine Language Programs*

Now that we can write machine language programs, we are ready to learn how to load them into the computer and to run them. We will look at two ways to enter machine language programs into the PDP-11. The hands-on experience of entering and running programs on a small computer console gives insight into computer organization and operation that can be gained no other way.

4.6.1 *Console with Bit Switches*

The first console we will consider uses bit switches for data entry and looks something like Fig. 4.6. The power switch has a lock with three positions. Besides the normal OFF and POWER positions, it has a LOCK position that locks the console switches with the power on. When the key is turned to the LOCK position, it may be withdrawn while the computer is operating. This allows the operator to leave the computer running, yet prevents anyone from tampering with the switches.

The console has two main displays. The **address register** displays the address of data just examined or deposited. During program execution it shows

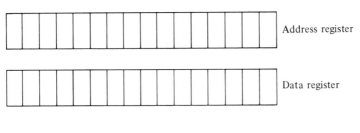

Fig. 4.6
PDP-11 console.

the next instruction address. The **data register** displays data just examined or deposited. During a HALT it displays the contents of register R0.

The console has a **switch register** with 16 bit switches for entering data with UP as 1 and DOWN as 0. It has six control switches. The switch marked LOAD ADRS (for "load address") transfers the contents of the switch register to the **bus address register** inside the CPU and simultaneously displays them in the *address register*. The EXAM ("examine") switch displays in the *data register* the contents of the location shown by the bus address register. The CONT ("continue") switch causes the CPU to continue operating from the point at which it had stopped. The ENABLE/HALT switch allows the CPU to operate normally when in the ENABLE position and stops it when in the HALT position. The START switch allows the CPU to restart if it had stopped and if the ENABLE/HALT switch is in the ENABLE position; it differs from the CONT switch in that it causes a system reset signal to occur. The DEP ("deposit") switch transfers the contents of the switch register into the location specified by the bus address.

To see how the switches work, let us go through the procedure of loading a program for this model. The steps are as follows.

1. Turn the POWER switch to the POWER position.
2. Converting the octal digits to binary, enter the first address on the switch register.
3. Depress the LOAD ADRS switch to transfer this address into the bus address register and display it on the address register.
4. Enter the instruction on the switch register.
5. Raise the DEP switch to transfer the instruction into the memory location specified by the bus address. The bus address, shown in the address register, will automatically increment by 2.
6. Continue steps 4 and 5 until all instructions and data are loaded into the computer. If any address is out of sequence, repeat steps 2 and 3 to reach the desired location.

Running the program is also easy. The steps are:

1. Check to see that the power switch is in the POWER position.
2. Enter the first address on the switch register.
3. Depress LOAD ADRS.
4. Put the ENABLE/HALT switch in the ENABLE position.
5. Depress START.

The computer will then run until it reaches a HALT command.

We can view the contents of any memory location either before or after running a program. To do this we enter the address on the switch register and depress the LOAD ADRS switch. We then depress the EXAM switch, and the contents of the memory location are displayed in the data register. At the same time the contents of the address register are incremented to show the next memory location. Repeated depressing of the EXAM switch thus lets us look at the contents of successive memory locations.

4.6.2 *Console with Decwriter*

We will look more quickly at running machine language programs on another PDP-11 system—one with a Decwriter for program entry. A Decwriter is a special DEC device that resembles a typewriter. On its keyboard we can enter instructions and data in octal instead of converting to binary.

The console panel will have the switches needed to start the PDP-11. Typically we will need to turn the power ON and to press switches marked CONTROL and BOOT. This will cause the PDP-11 to print the contents of R0, R4, R6, and R7 on the Decwriter. We can then type commands with single letters.

L—Load address
D—Deposit data and increment address by 2
E—Examine contents
S—Start program

Each command is followed by the appropriate octal address or data, if any, and (for all commands except E) ends with a keyed RETURN. We can see the use of these commands most easily by an example.

Example 4.3: Loading an octal program with a Decwriter

Task: Load, inspect, and run the program of Table 4.1.
Procedure: Assuming the PDP-11 system is ready, load the starting address, 500_8, by typing L 500. Then deposit the instructions by typing

D   5003
D   60003
D   60103
D   60203
D   0

Note that we can omit typing leading 0's. To examine the contents of all five memory locations, we type

L   500

and then type

E

five times. To run the program, we type

L   500
S

We now know enough about PDP-11 programming to write simple programs and to run them. In a later chapter we will learn more advanced methods
of programming, including more modes of addressing that will allow us to write
more powerful programs. We will also learn how to use the computer's system
software—editor, assembler, and debug routine—to let us run large programs
easily.

4.S *Summary*

The PDP-11 has eight 16-bit registers—a program counter, a stack pointer, and
six general-purpose registers. Its CPU is connected to memory and external
devices by a 56-line bus called a Unibus. The PDP-11 has a processor status
register with flags for zero, negative sign, carry, and overflow.

Instructions consist of operation codes and operands. The PDP-11 has
16-bit instructions that may be represented in binary, octal, or mnemonic
forms. Double-operand instructions operate on a source and a destination.
Single-operand instructions operate on a destination only. Some instructions,
such as HALT, have no operands.

Although special programs called assemblers are available to convert assembly language (source) programs to machine language (object) programs, we
should be aware of the process involved and so in this chapter we have hand
assembled our programs. When we write machine language programs, we must
give the address and contents of every memory location that the computer will
use. For documentation we may also list the mnemonic form of the operation
codes and give comments.

When we write assembly language programs, we do not need to specify
every memory location; the assembler will assign memory locations. We may
give a starting address. Besides the instructions that will be translated into
machine instructions, we write pseudoinstructions—messages to the assembler
such as .END for the end of the program. We use symbolic labels to mark
statements and to define operands.

We studied two modes of addressing. Register addressing means that the
register named is the address and its contents are the operand. Autoincrement
addressing means that the contents of the register named are the address of the
operand, and that after the operand is retrieved, the contents of the register are
incremented by 2.

Branch instructions give an offset and an operation code for an unconditional branch or for a branch conditional on the state of one or more condition
flags. The offset allows branching forward 127_{10} words or backward 128_{10}
words; the actual offset of the instruction is multiplied by 2 and added to the
address of the instruction following the branch instruction.

The subroutine call instruction, JSR, names the subroutine and a linkage
register in which the return address will be saved. The contents of that register
are saved on a stack that has register 6 as a stack pointer. The subroutine return

instruction, RTS, names the same linkage register. The return address is sent from that register to the program counter while the previous contents of the linkage register are restored from the stack.

To run machine language programs on the PDP-11, addresses and data may be entered on bit switches or on a Decwriter, depending on the model.

Key Terms

address	negative bit
assembler	object program
assembler directive	offset
assembly language	operand
autoincrement addressing	operation code (op code)
branching	origin
byte constant	overflow bit
call	pointer
carry bit	processor status register (PSR)
class code	program counter (PC)
conditional transfer	program status word (PSW)
condition code	pseudoinstruction
counter	register addressing
destination	sign bit
device address	source
direct assignment	source program
field	stack pointer (SP)
flag	status register
hand assembly	subroutine
label	trap bit
linkage register	unconditional transfer
loop	word/byte bit
machine language	word constant
mnemonic	zero bit
mode	

4.R *References*

Gear (1974), Stone and Sieworek (1975), Eckhouse (1975), Cooper (1977) and Hamacher, Vranesic, and Zaky (1978) treat PDP-11 programming and organization. Southern (1972) is a self-instructional workbook for the PDP-11 programming. Manuals for the PDP-11 or whatever computer you are using are invaluable in programming.

4.Q *Questions*

4.1 Discuss the organization of PDP-11 registers.

4.2 Explain the PDP-11 processor status register.

4.3 What are the basic parts of an instruction?

4.4 What is the difference between instructions and pseudoinstructions?

4.5 What are the four fields of an assembly language statement? Which are required and which are optional?

4.6 What instructions are used for making decisions?

4.7 What purposes do counters serve in loops?

4.8 What are the three main types of PDP-11 instructions?

4.9 What is the address of an operand with register addressing? What is the address of an operand with autoincrement addressing?

4.P Problems

Section 4.3

4.1 Identify the fields of the following double-operand instructions.
a) 01 04 02   b) 11 03 01   c) 06 04 02   d) 12 01 04

4.2 Identify the fields of the following single operand instructions.
a) 00 50 04   b) 10 51 03   c) 00 52 02   d) 10 53 01

Section 4.4

4.3 Modify the program of Section 4.4.1 so that it will add four numbers. Show both machine and assembly language forms.

4.4 State whether the following names are valid labels.
a) BEGIN   b) 1A   c) HALT   d) DOWN   e) HI-LO
f) PROGRAM   g) END   h) THREE

4.5 Write an assembly language program to test the three numbers stored in R0, R1, and R2 to determine how many are 0. The count should be made in R4.

Section 4.5

4.6 Calculate the destinations of branch instruction stored at memory location 3216_8 with the following offsets.
a) 024_8 b) 145_8 c) 210_8 d) 377

4.7 Calculate the memory offset needed to branch from memory location 4120_8 to the following locations.
a) 4200_8 b) 4000_8 c) 3776_8 d) 4126_8

4.8 State the addresses of the following operands. Use parentheses to denote "contents of," where necessary.
a) 03_8 b) 24_8 c) 00_8 d) 06_8

4.9 Write an assembly language program for Problem 3.1 (absolute values).

4.10 Write an assembly language program for Problem 3.2 (overflow).

4.11 Write an assembly language program for Problem 3.4 (loops).

4.12 Write an assembly language program for Problem 3.6 (sorting). Assume A, B, and C are in R0, R1, and R2 respectively.

Elementary
Programming
for Microcomputers

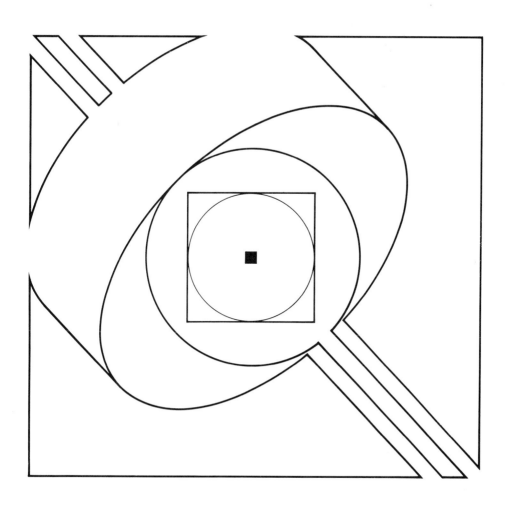

5.1 *Introduction*

We can now learn to program a microcomputer. In this chapter we will first look at the organization of two typical 8-bit microcomputers—the Intel 8080/8085 and the Motorola M6800. Then we will look at the instructions of these two processors and write programs for the examples of Chapter 3. Finally we will see how to run machine language programs on microcomputers. When we have finished, we will be able to write and run simple programs and will have gained a strong background for future work.

Many of the concepts discussed in this chapter were also discussed for the PDP-11 in Chapter 4. This chapter is intended to stand alone so that if you are interested only in microcomputers you may read this without having read Chapter 4. However, we will compare the microcomputers with the PDP-11 in case you are interested in both minicomputers and microcomputers.

5.2 *Organization*

Most 8-bit microcomputers are organized as shown in Fig. 5.1. They have four main parts. Each may occupy a separate semiconductor chip or, as on many newer microcomputers, most or all of the parts may be on a single chip. The parts are:

- A CPU for control and arithmetic functions.
- **ROM** (read-only memory) for permanent storage of programs and constant data.
- **RAM** (random-access memory) for temporary storage of data.
- **Interface** logic for connecting the computer with peripheral devices.

These four basic parts are interconnected by three buses:

- An 8-bit **data bus**.
- A 16-bit **address bus**.
- A **control bus** (with varying numbers of bits, depending on the computer).

With the 16-bit address bus, 2^{16} or 65,536 bytes of memory can be addressed. The 8-bit data bus can transfer just one of 2^8 or 256 patterns at one time. As we saw in Chapter 2, 8 bits of data can represent one nonnumeric character, two BCD digits, or a limited range of 2's complement numbers. This may be adequate for many applications, especially for control or nonnumeric applications. If it is not adequate multiple-precision arithmetic is needed. For this reason some 8-bit microcomputers provide instructions for 16-bit arithmetic.

The 8-bit data bus also carries instruction codes. Because we do not wish to be limited to instructions that are only 8 bits long, 8-bit microcomputers are designed to accept variable-length instructions. Typically they accept 8-bit,

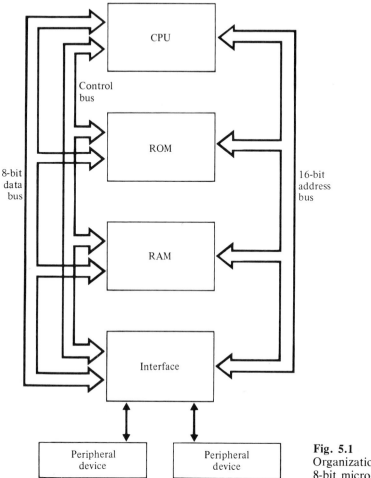

Fig. 5.1
Organization of a typical 8-bit microcomputer.

16-bit, and 24-bit instructions. The first 8 bits of an instruction include information on its length.

5.2.1 *Intel 8080/8085*

The Intel 8008 was one of the earliest 8-bit microcomputers. Intel has enhanced the 8008 by improving both hardware and software features, resulting in first the 8080, then the 8085, and more recently the 16-bit 8086. In this book we will sometimes discuss features that are common to both the 8080 and the 8085; when doing so we will sometimes say the 8080/8085 and other times just say the 8085. When our discussion applies only to the 8080 or only to the 8085, we will try to make that clear. Comparing the features of the 8085 with those of the 8080 will help illustrate the growth of microcomputer technology. Most of the hardware improvements will be considered later; basically, the 8085 requires fewer and simpler supporting circuits than does the 8080. Intel designed the improved software of the 8085 in such a way that programs written on the 8080 can be executed on the 8085. This feature is called **software compatibility**. In particular, because 8080 programs will run on the 8085 but the reverse may not be true, the software is said to be **upward compatible**. Similarly the instruction set of the 16-bit 8086 was designed as a superset of 8080 and 8085 instructions. Hence the 8086 can execute all 8080 and 8085 8-bit instructions as well as special 16-bit instructions.

The heart of the 8080/8085 is an 8-bit accumulator called register A. Memory addresses are made up of two bytes—16 bits. The 8085 may be interfaced with up to 256 input ports and 256 output ports as determined by an 8-bit address. Each input or output **port** has an 8-bit buffer register that stores external device information temporarily. Input/output instructions are separate from memory instructions; thus the 8080/8085 is unlike the PDP-11, in which the same instructions are used for input/output and for memory operations. We call this separation of input/output from memory **isolated input/output**. The 8085—but not the 8080—can, alternatively, have input/output devices connected to the memory control lines so that the devices respond in the same way as memory.

The registers of the 8085 are less versatile than those of the PDP-11. Seven 8-bit registers—A, B, C, D, E, H, and L—can be directly addressed by the programmer. All seven registers can be addressed individually; the last six can also be addressed as three 16-bit **register pairs**. As shown in Fig. 5.2, register pair H includes H and L; pair B includes B and C; and pair D includes D and E. Even register A is one half of a register pair called **PSW**, for **program status word**; the other half of PSW holds the five 8080/8085 condition codes that show the status of the CPU. Register pairs are named for their high-order bytes. Thus in register pair H, register H (for high) holds the 8 most significant bits; register L (for low) holds the 8 least significant bits.

Register
pair   Registers

B	B	C
D	D	E
H	H	L
PSW	PSW	A

Pointer to Memory M

Fig. 5.2
8080/8085 registers and register pairs.

As you might imagine, distinguishing between register pair B and register B can be confusing. To clarify the distinction, Intel has assigned different mnemonics for instructions that address register pairs than for those that address single registers.

Unlike the registers the PDP-11, only a few of the registers of the 8080/8085 are interchangeable. Several registers have special functions. We have already seen that register A is an accumulator; that is, it accumulates and holds results of arithmetic and logical operations. Register pair H serves as a pointer to memory; when an instruction shows an operand M, it means the memory location whose address is held in H and L. Thus H and L play a special role in working with memory. Registers B, C, D, and E are equivalent for most operations; they are simply general-purpose registers.

The 8080/8085 has two more registers that we can directly affect by our programs—a stack pointer and a program counter. Both are 16 bits long. The **stack pointer (SP)** holds the top address of an area of memory called the stack. The **program counter (PC)** holds the address of the next instruction. We can change the program counter by giving addresses in jump and call subroutine instructions.

Besides its addressible registers, the 8085 has several registers for internal calculations. These include

- An 8-bit instruction register
- Two 8-bit temporary registers—W and Z—that can be used as a pair or individually
- An 8-bit temporary register in the arithmetic and logic unit
- An 8-bit temporary accumulator in the arithmetic and logic unit

Temporary registers W and Z combine with the general-purpose registers, the stack pointer, the condition codes, and the program counter to form the register array shown in Fig. 5.3. Register A and the internal registers of the arithmetic and logic unit are in another part of the CPU.

W Temporary register	Z Temporary register
B	C
D	E
H	L
Stack pointer	
Program counter	

Fig. 5.3
8080/8085 register array.

The program status word of the 8080/8085 holds five **condition codes** or **status flags**—one-bit registers that are set (to 1) or cleared (to 0) to show various conditions. The condition flags of the 8085 are typical of those of most microcomputers. They are:

- Z   (Zero):
       1—last result was zero
       0—last result was not zero

- S (Sign):
    1—last result was negative
    0—last result was positive or zero
- CY (Carry):
    1—last operation had a carry from bit 7 (MSB)
    0—last operation had no carry from bit 7 (MSB)
- P (Parity):
    1—last result had an odd number of 1's (odd parity)
    0—last result had an even number of 1's (even parity)
- AC (Auxiliary Carry):
    1—last operation had a carry from bit 3 to bit 4
    0—last operation had no carry from bit 3 to bit 4

All these bits, except the auxiliary carry, can be tested by program instructions. Be careful how you interpret the Z bit. The Z bit is 1 when the last result was zero. This can be confusing. The CY and AC bits are useful for arithmetic operations; the AC bit is used primarily in decimal arithmetic. The P bit is an **even parity** bit; it tests whether the number of 1's in the last result is an even number—0, 2, 4, 6, or 8. Not all instructions affect all status bits; if in doubt, check on instruction list such as the one in the appendix.

The status flags are arranged in an 8-bit register with three constant bits as follows.

S	Z	0	AC	0	P	1	CY

5.2.2 *Motorola M6800*

The Motorola M6800 was designed after the Intel 8008 but before the 8080 or the 8085. Motorola has since introduced variations of the M6800 carrying numbers of the form M680n and the 16-bit M68000. Some of these variations are software compatible; others are not. We will limit our software discussions to the basic M6800. It is simpler in design than the later Intel microprocessors.

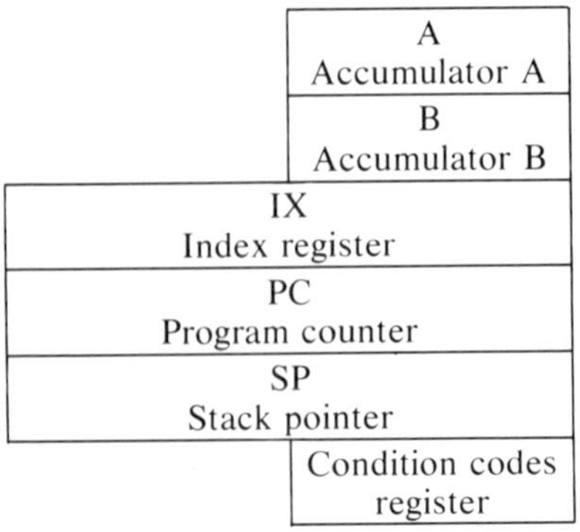

A Accumulator A
B Accumulator B
IX Index register
PC Program counter
SP Stack pointer
Condition codes register

Fig. 5.4
Organization of M6800 microprocessor.

It has fewer registers and fewer basic instruction types. Its timing is also simpler. However, it has more addressing modes than the 8085. Thus its basic instructions, through fewer, can be more powerful.

Like the 8085, the Motorola M6800 can address 65K locations and provides for 8-bit data. Like the PDP-11 but unlike the 8085, it has no separate input/output instructions. Instead, it addresses input/output devices in the same way as memory. External devices can be assigned any of the 65K addresses. This type of input-output is called **memory mapped input/output**.

The programmable registers of the M6800 are highly specialized. As shown in Fig. 5.4, they are:

- Two 8-bit accumulators, A and B.
- A 16-bit program counter.
- A 16-bit stack pointer.
- A 16-bit index register for storing an address.
- An 8-bit status register that holds six flags.

As in the 8085, the stack pointer (SP) holds the top address of an area of memory called the stack. The program counter (PC) holds the address of the next instruction. The index register is the only one that is new to us. An **index register** is designed to save part of an address. A desired address can then be calculated as the sum of the contents of the index register plus some other number. Data stored in sequence can easily be accessed by setting an index register equal to the first address and adding 1, 2, 3, . . . to it. We will see examples of this in programs later.

The two accumulators are almost identical. One instruction—the instruction to move flag values between the status register and accumulator A—is valid only for accumulator A. A few other instructions treat the two accumulators differently.

The M6800 has six status flags; they are:

- C (Carry-Borrow):
    1—last result had a carry from bit 7 (MSB)
    0—last result had no carry from bit 7 (MSB)
- V (Overflow):
    1—last result had 2's complement overflow
    0—last result did not have 2's complement overflow
- Z (Zero):
    1—result of last arithmetic operation was zero
    0—result of last arithmetic operation was not zero
- N (Negative):
    1—last result was negative
    0—last result was positive or zero

- I (Interrupt Mask Bit):
  1—CPU cannot respond to interrupt requests
  0—CPU can respond to interrupt requests
- H (Half Carry):
  1—last result had a carry from bit 3 to bit 4
  0—last result had no carry from bit 3 to bit 4

Three status flags—the zero, the carry (or carry-borrow), and the negative (or sign) flags—are the same on the PDP-11, the 8085, and the M6800. Both microprocessors have an auxiliary carry or half carry for decimal arithmetic. Both the PDP-11 and the M6800 have an overflow bit. The other flags vary. We will see examples of their use later. For now it is important to know that not all instructions affect all status flags. As with the 8080/8085, we will need to consult a list of instructions to see which instructions affect which flags.

The flags are located in the status register as shown below.

1	1	H	I	N	Z	V	C

While we are discussing the M6800, we should note its memory organization. Unlike the 8085, which can access any memory location in the same amount of time, the M6800 can access locations $0–255_{10}$ more quickly and with shorter instructions than other locations. For this reason system designers usually place RAM for data storage in the first 256 memory locations. Another hardware feature causes the computer to restart after power is turned on at the address stored in the two highest memory locations. Thus it is usually desirable to place ROM that contains programs in the high end of memory. The external device addresses and additional RAM and ROM may be anywhere in memory. Hence a system with 4K bytes of memory might be organized as shown in Fig. 5.5.

5.2.3 *Zilog Z-80*

We can learn about the excellence of a design by comparing it with a variation. The same people who designed the 8080A for Intel also designed the Z-80 for Zilog. In fact, they planned the Z-80 to be an enhancement of the 8080. To do this they made sure that it included all 8080 instructions, so that it would be software compatible with the 8080. Though they changed the mnemonics, they kept the same machine codes. Thus if you are working with the Z-80, you should be able to execute on it any of the 8080 programs in this book, once they are converted to numeric code. Because the 8080 did not use all 256 combinations of 8 bits, the Zilog designers had some unused codes available. They could have designated the unused codes for specific instructions, thus adding a few more instructions. Instead, they chose to use the extra codes as signals showing that special Z-80 codes are to be found in the next byte. As a result they added a large number of 16-bit instructions, some of them very powerful ones.

Addresses

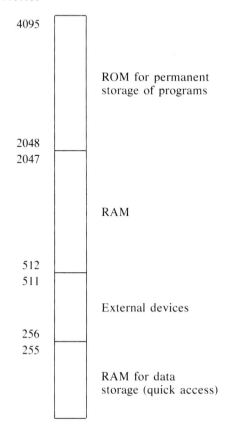

Fig. 5.5
Memory organization for the M6800.

The Zilog designers also improved the architecture of the processor by adding registers. As shown in Fig. 5.6, the Z-80 has two sets of the 8-bit programmable registers—A, B, C, D, E, H, L, and PSW. The duplicate set can easily save copies of these registers while the processor services an exter-

PSW′	A′
B′	C′
D′	E′
H′	L′

PSW	A
B	C
D	E
H	L
SP Stack pointer	
PC Program counter	
IX Index register X	
IY Index register Y	

Fig. 5.6
Z-80 programmable registers.

nal device. The Z-80 also has two index registers, thus allowing indexed addressing.

The Z-80 has other improvements that we will be better prepared to understand later. These include some of the hardware improvements of the 8085. In addition, bus use is markedly different. More recently Zilog has introduced the 16-bit Z8000, which has 16 general-purpose registers and an extensive instruction set.

5.2.4 *Mostek MCS6500*

The Mostek MCS6500 is an enhancement of the Motorola M6800, but the relationship between the two is different from that between the Z-80 and the 8080. Their CPUs are much alike, yet their instructions differ in ways that are not immediately obvious. M6800 programs will not in general execute on a 6500 without subtle changes.

As noted above, the architecture of the two CPUs is much the same. See Fig. 5.7 for the programmable registers of the 6500. One difference between the M6800 and the 6500 is that the 6500 has just one accumulator. Another is that it has two 8-bit index registers instead of one 16-bit index register. The 6500 stack pointer is also only 8 bits wide.

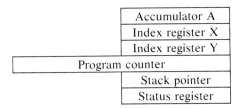

Fig. 5.7
MCS6500 programmable registers.

The M6800 and the 6500 also differ in bus use and other hardware features. We will comment on these and on some of the differences in instructions later in the book.

5.3 *Instruction Formats*

Now that we know something about the organization of the 8085 and the M6800, we are ready to learn about their instructions. We will look at some basic instructions both in their assembly language and in their machine language forms. In **assembly language** we can use symbolic addresses or **labels,** such as A (8085) or ACCA (M6800) for a register. We can also use **mnemonic** instructions—abbreviations that are easy to remember—such as ADD for add and CMP for compare.

In **machine language** we write numeric addresses and instructions. The numeric information can be binary, octal, or hexadecimal. We will use hexadecimal here because a large number of microcomputers provide hexadecimal keyboards and displays. In addition, using hexadecimal will be a change of pace from the octal shown for the PDP-11. Thus we will show addresses such as 11FF and instructions such as 0A.

Instructions have two basic parts. The **operation code** (commonly called **op code**) names the action or operation that the computer will perform. For example, the mnemonic ADD tells a microcomputer to add, and JMP tells it to jump. The **operand** is the data to be acted on. An instruction may give the value or the address of the data. Thus the statement JMP 002A might tell a micro-computer to jump to memory location 002A. Some instructions have no operands. The 8085 instruction HLT (halt the computer) and the M6800 instruction SWI (software interrupt) need no operands. Some instructions, such as moving data into a register, require two operands.

Each part of an instruction is represented inside the computer by a field of one or more bits. We can represent a general instruction as

Op code	Operand

Computers that have 16-bit words (for example, the PDP-11) can often afford to arrange instructions in neat fields. Microcomputers, which typically have 8-bit words, are more cramped for space and require greater cleverness in instruction design. In some cases one or more operands will be implied; in other cases the number of possible operands will be restricted more than would be necessary on a 16-bit or larger machine.

Variable-length instructions are needed to perform a variety of operations. Both the 8085 and the M6800 offer instructions of one, two, and three bytes. This is done because 8 bits is not enough to specify a large number of instructions. Much more can be done with 16 or 24 bits. Of course, the longer instructions do take more time to execute. Hence, wherever possible, the instructions are kept to 8 bits. The flexibility obtained by using three lengths of instructions is good. However, the programmer must be alert to differences in lengths, especially in applications where timing is critical.

In all instructions of both the 8085 and the M6800, the main purpose of the first byte is to name the operation to be performed. Simple operands, such as those held in registers, may be stated or implied in the first byte. The M6800, which applies several modes of addressing to a small set of instructions, also shows the addressing mode in the first byte. The second and third bytes can give data, show memory addresses, or (for the 8085) name external devices.

5.3.1 *Intel 8080/8085 Formats*

The format of 8085 instructions of different lengths is shown in Fig. 5.8. The single-byte instruction of Fig. 5.8(a) is primarily operation code. There are two types of two-byte instructions, shown in Fig. 5.8(b). In the first type, the second byte gives data; in the second type, it gives a device code or port

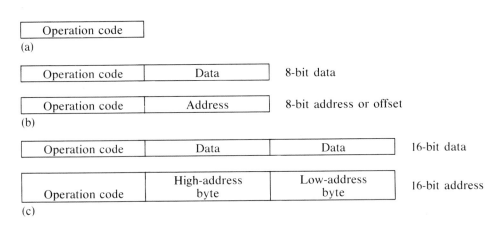

Op code

(a)

Op code	Data byte

8-bit data

Op code	Port number

I/O instruction

(b)

Op code	Data byte	Data byte

16-bit data

Op code	Low-order byte	High-order byte

16-bit address

(c)

Fig. 5.8
8085 instruction format. (a) Single-byte instruction. (b) Two-byte instructions. (c) Three-byte instructions.

number for external devices. The two types of three-byte instructions of Fig. 5.8(c) specify either 16 bits of data or a 16-bit memory address in their second and third bytes. Memory addresses for the 8080/8085 are given with the low-order byte first and the high-order byte second. Thus the address 1245 would be shown in an instruction as 4512. Watch this order carefully—it's easy to make mistakes! More recently designed microcomputers, such as the M6800, show addresses more conveniently, with the high-order byte first.

5.3.2 *Motorola M6800 Formats*

The M6800 also has one-, two-, and three-byte instructions (see Fig. 5.9). As in the 8080/8085, the single-byte instructions are essentially operation code. There

Operation code

(a)

Operation code	Data

8-bit data

Operation code	Address

8-bit address or offset

(b)

Operation code	Data	Data

16-bit data

Operation code	High-address byte	Low-address byte

16-bit address

(c)

Fig. 5.9
M6800 instruction formats. (a) Single-byte instructions. (b) Two-byte instructions. (c) Three-byte instructions.

are two types of two-byte instructions; in one type, the second byte gives 8-bit data; in the other type, it shows an 8-bit address or offset (partial address). Similarly, there are two types of three-byte instructions. In one type, the second and third bytes provide 16 bits of data; in the other type, they name a 16-bit address. The M6800 shows addresses in the same order as we would read them; the high-order byte is first and the low-order byte second. Thus the address 1245 is shown as 1245.

5.3.3 *Assembly Language Formats*

Before moving on to look at some simple programs, we will consider the format of assembly language instructions. As you will recall from Chapter 1, an assembly language program can be translated (assembled) into machine language code by another program, called an **assembler**. The translation process is not at all mysterious, only time-consuming. We can **hand assemble** a program ourselves, and in this chapter we will illustrate hand assembly as we go along. In practical applications, however, you will normally write only an assembly language program (or **source** program) and then use an assembler to convert it to the machine language program (**object** program).

The assembler for a microcomputer may execute on the microcomputer itself (**self-assembly**) or it may execute on another, probably larger, computer (**cross-assembly**). Microcomputer assembly language programs are often cross-assembled on large computers. The reasons for this are the relatively small memories and slow execution times of microcomputers. However, decreases in memory costs and improvements in microcomputers are making self-assembly more common.

When microcomputer assembly language programs are to be cross-assembled, the format of the assembly language program is dictated by the requirements of the cross-assembler. That is, the cross-assembler, rather than the microcomputer itself, determines the format of the microcomputer assembly language program. We will use this to justify our selection of a single assembly language format for both the 8085 and the M6800 programs. That format more closely resembles Intel's than Motorola's; however, the differences are minor. Because cross-assemblers are relatively easy to write—students frequently write them—we could modify an existing cross-assembler to process programs written to our format.

Each assembly language statement may have four fields—label, op code, operand, and comment.

- The **label** gives a symbolic address for an instruction.
- The **op code** (**operation code**) shows the operation to be performed.
- The **operand** gives data or address information.
- The **comment** allows the programmer to explain the statement.

Our assembler will use **free fields**; that is, we may insert any number of blanks between fields. For convenience in reading programs (rather than as a requirement for computer acceptability) we will always align the fields in columns. The assembler needs some punctuation to delimit or set off fields. The rules for separating fields and operands for our assembler are:

1. The label for an instruction, if present, must be followed by a colon.
2. There must be at least one space between the op code and any operand.
3. If two operands occur in one statement, they must be separated by a comma. (We also prefer to insert a space between the comma and the second operand, for readability.)
4. Each line of comment must be preceded by a semicolon.

In the M6800 the registers A and B may be considered part of the operation code, although they are actually operands. Motorola shows A and B separated by one space from operation codes. We will follow this convention.

Examples of assembly language statements, taken from both the 8085 and the M6800, are:

Label	Op code	Operand	Comment
LOOP:	ADD	M	; ADD CONTENTS OF M TO A (8085)
	ADD A	42H	; ADD CONTENTS OF 42 TO A (M6800)
CNEXT:	CMP	C, 0	; COMPARE C WITH 0 (8085)
SECND:	LDA B	5AH	; LOAD B WITH CONTENTS OF 5A (M6800)
			; JUST A COMMENT

Note the use of capitals throughout the instructions and comments. This is the form in which assembly language programs must be prepared in order to be read by the computer.

In the examples above, a trailing H designates hexadecimal. Thus 42H means 42 hexadecimal. Motorola also uses a leading dollar sign ($) to denote hexadecimal (for example, $42), but we will use only the trailing H. Both the M6800 and the 8085 have a **default decimal convention** for numbers; that is, numbers that are not designated otherwise by some special character are assumed to be decimal. Thus 42 by itself means 42 decimal.

We will now inspect each field in more detail.

The label field is optional. The purpose of a label is to provide a convenient way of addressing a statement. During assembly the assembler constructs a **label table** that shows the hexadecimal address associated with each label. Then instructions can reference that address with commands such as JMP LOOP, an 8085 instruction meaning "transfer control to the address called LOOP."

For our purposes labels may be one to six characters long. The first character must be a letter; the others may be letters or numbers. No spaces may occur within a label. We may not use as labels any names that our microcomputer reserves for special purposes, such as operation codes. To help make our programs clear and readable, we will try to pick meaningful names.

Valid labels include LOOP, FIRST, LAST, and SPOT2. Labels such as ADD, PROGRAM, 12A, A 1, and 4-F are invalid. (Can you see why each of these is invalid?)

The op code field shows the mnemonic for the operation to be performed. There's not much room for imagination here. We must select one of the operation codes of the microcomputer that we are using.

The operand field gives information needed to carry out the operation. As we have already indicated, an instruction may have zero, one, or two operands. The information given by them may be a register or register pair (the latter only for the 8085), data, or a memory address. Addresses may be either numeric, such as 1200H, or symbolic, such as LOOP, but the labels used as symbolic addresses must always be identified elsewhere in the program.

The comment field simply documents the program. Comments may be continued from one line to another, so long as a semicolon precedes each line of the comment. The assembler does not translate comments; it merely reads them, stores them, and finally reprints them.

In addition to the standard instructions of each microcomputer, an assembler also needs some special instructions that give it information about how to assemble the program. These special instructions are called **pseudoinstructions**. They are only messages to the assembler; they are not translated into machine code. For the simple programs that we will show in this chapter, we will need only two pseudoinstructions.

ORG is an **origin** pseudoinstruction. When followed by an address, it tells the assembler to begin assembling at that address. Thus the statement

```
ORG   1300H
```

means "start assembly at memory address 1300 hexadecimal." The ORG pseudoinstruction always shows the address in the normal order, with the highest-order digits first.

END, not surprisingly, is the END pseudoinstruction. It shows the end of all instructions and data of a program. Hence it tells the assembler to stop processing statements. Can you see how END differs from a halt instruction, which tells the CPU to stop?

5.4 *Some Programming Examples*

We are now ready to study some simple programs. We are deliberately presenting programs before listing all the instructions of our two microcomputers because it is both clearer and more interesting to look at instructions as they occur in programs. We will look at both the 8085 and the M6800 programs for three problems, those that were flowcharted in Chapter 3. By comparing programs for the two microcomputers we will soon appreciate the differences between them.

Besides showing the assembly language programs, we will show the resulting machine code programs; that is, for each instruction we will show its hexadecimal address, which takes up its first byte, and its hexadecimal code, which occupies one, two, or three bytes.

5.4.1 Addition of Three Numbers

The flowchart for adding three numbers was shown in Fig. 3.1. In Table 5.1 we show the corresponding assembly language program for the 8085. Note that the label field does not appear in Table 5.1 because it is not needed in this program.

Table 5.1
Intel 8085 assembly language program for adding three numbers

Op code	Operand	Comment
		; NUMBERS TO BE ADDED ARE IN B,
		; C, AND D
		; SUM IN A
ORG	1000H	; START IN LOCATION 1000 HEX
MVI	A, 0	; INITIALIZE SUM TO 0
ADD	B	; ADD FIRST NUMBER
ADD	C	; ADD SECOND NUMBER
ADD	D	; ADD THIRD NUMBER
HLT		; STOP
END		

The numbers to be added are assumed to be in registers B, C, and D. The ORG 1000H pseudoinstruction shows that we should start assembling the program at memory location 1000. Because this is a pseudoinstruction, it will not be translated into machine code to be stored at that location. Hence we will begin by translating and storing the first real instruction of the program starting at location 1000 hexadecimal.

This first instruction is

```
MVI   A, 0
```

The mnemonic MVI stands for MoVe Immediate. The operands A, 0 mean that the immediate data 0 is to be moved to register A. The result of the operation is to clear the sum to 0 before proceeding to add the three numbers. This instruction takes two bytes; the second byte is for the 8-bit data of 0.

To hand assemble we refer to a table of 8085 operation codes and find that the code for the first byte, MVI A, is 3E. We store that in location 1000. The second byte will be 00; we store it in 1001. The first two lines of our assembled program, omitting comments, now look as follows.

Hex address	Hex instruction	Op code	Operand
1000	3E	MVI	A, 0
1001	00		

The next four instructions in Table 5.1 are all single-byte ones. The mnemonic ADD simply means "add to A the contents of the register shown as an operand." The mnemonic HLT is short for HALT. The program ends with the END pseudoinstruction, which, like the ORG pseudoinstruction, will not be stored. To hand assemble, we look up the machine codes for these four instructions and store them in the next four locations:

Hex address	Hex instruction	Op code	Operand
1002	80	ADD	B
1003	81	ADD	C
1004	82	ADD	D
1005	76	HLT	

This completes the hand assembly. The resulting program is shown in Table 5.2. This program was easy to hand assemble for two reasons. First, there was only one instruction that took more than two bytes. Second, there were no labels and thus no references to labels. We will deal with the complications presented by labels shortly.

Table 5.2
Intel 8085 program for adding three numbers

Hex address	Hex instruction	Op code	Operand	Comment
				; NUMBERS TO BE ADDED
				; ARE IN B, C, AND D
				; SUM IS IN A
		ORG	1000H	; START IN LOCATION
				; 1000 HEX
1000	3E	MVI	A, 0	; INITIALIZE SUM TO 0
1001	00			; TWO-BYTE INSTRUCTION
1002	80	ADD	B	; ADD FIRST NUMBER
1003	81	ADD	C	; ADD SECOND NUMBER
1004	82	ADD	D	; ADD THIRD NUMBER
1005	76	HLT		; STOP
		END		

Now let us look at the M6800 program to add three numbers, shown in its assembled form in Table 5.3. Because the M6800 does not have enough registers to store the three numbers to be added, we will store them instead in memory, choosing, as the comment shows, memory locations 00, 01, and 02. We will accumulate the sum in accumulator A and, as indicated by ORG 10H, we will start the program in location 10 hexadecimal. On the M6800 we wish to

Table 5.3
M6800 program for adding three numbers

Hex address	Hex instruction	Label	Op code	Operand	Comment
					; NUMBERS TO BE ADDED
					; ARE IN LOCATIONS 00
					; TO 02
					; SUM WILL BE IN ACCA
			ORG	10H	; START IN LOCATION 10H
10	4F		CLR A		; INITIALIZE SUM TO 0
11	9B		ADD A	00H	; ADD FIRST NUMBER
12	00				
13	9B		ADD A	01H	; ADD SECOND NUMBER
14	01				
15	9B		ADD A	02H	; ADD THIRD NUMBER
16	02				
17	3F		SWI		; SOFTWARE INTERRUPT
			END		

keep the program in the first 256 locations of memory because we can then use **direct addressing,** which requires two-byte instructions only. To access the rest of memory we would need to use what Motorola calls **extended addressing,** which requires three-byte instructions. To keep our program as short as we can, we prefer direct addressing.

The first instruction to be translated is CLR A, meaning "Clear accumulator A to start the sum at 0." This is a single-byte instruction; its machine code, 4F, can be stored in the first location, 10 hexadecimal.

10   4F   CLR A

The next three instructions each take two bytes. The mnemonic ADD A means "add to A the contents of the memory location shown in the next byte." The code for ADD A is 9B; the second byte of each instruction is the address of the number to be added. Thus the next six lines of the program read:

11	9B	ADD A	00H
12	00		
13	9B	ADD A	01H
14	01		
15	9B	ADD A	02H
16	02		

The last instruction that needs to be translated is SWI, meaning "software interrupt." Its hexadecimal code is 3F. The M6800 uses this instruction instead of a halt. We will discuss its function later when we consider interrupts.

Comparing the two programs, we note that the 8085 program took six bytes while the M6800 program required eight bytes. Because the M6800 has few registers, it must usually address memory more frequently. Since memory references take two to three bytes as compared to one byte for a register reference, we can expect the M6800 to use more memory for programs like this one.

5.4.2 *Addition of the Absolute Values of Three Numbers*

Our next project is a program to add the absolute values of three numbers. The main feature of this problem is that decisions must be made and different actions taken based on those decisions. To do this we need instructions that change the normal sequence of program execution—instructions that transfer control to some instruction other than the one that comes next after the current instruction. These are usually called BRANCH, JUMP, or SKIP instructions. (The capitalized words refer to instruction types, not exact instructions for the 8085 or the M6800.) More generally we can think of them as transfer instructions. BRANCH and JUMP instructions basically transfer control to the address shown in the operand field. For example, the instruction (for some hypothetical computer)

BRANCH LOOP

transfers control to the location with the symbolic address LOOP. SKIP instructions do not require an address because they merely direct the computer to skip one instruction.

JUMP, BRANCH, and SKIP instructions may be unconditional or conditional. **Unconditional** transfer instructions always transfer control to the address shown (or implied in the case of SKIP). **Conditional** transfer instructions are more interesting; they direct the computer to test one or more condition flags and to take one of two actions depending on the flag settings. They have the general form

BRANCH CONDITION ADDRESS

This generalized instruction means:

- If CONDITION is true, transfer control to the location named ADDRESS.
- If CONDITION is false, proceed with the next instruction in sequence.

With this general explanation as background, let us look at the transfer instructions of the 8085 and the M6800.

The 8085 has a three-byte unconditional jump instruction JMP in which the last two bytes show the 16-bit destination of the jump. In its generalized form (using the abbreviation addr for the address), the instruction and its meaning are:

JMP　addr　　JuMP (to address)

The 8085 has eight conditional jump instructions, each taking three bytes. These instructions and their meanings are as follows.

JC　　addr　　Jump (to address) if Carry (CY = 1)
JNC　addr　　Jump (to address) if No Carry (Cy = 0)
JZ　　addr　　Jump (to address) if Zero (Z = 1)
JNZ　addr　　Jump (to address) if Not Zero (Z = 0)
JM　　addr　　Jump (to address) if Minus (S = 1)
JP　　addr　　Jump (to address) if Positive (S = 0)
JPE　addr　　Jump (to address) if Parity Even (P = 1)
JPO　addr　　Jump (to address) if Parity Odd (P = 0)

The 8085 also has a unique single-byte unconditional jump instruction that transfers control to the location addressed by the HL register pair.

PCHL　　load Program Counter from HL

The M6800 has a large number of branch instructions, all of which employ **relative addressing**. Instead of showing the absolute address of a memory location—that is, its actual address—relative addressing shows the distance from the branch instruction to the location. Let's see how this works.

First we note that the M6800 allows one byte for relative addresses. This byte is interpreted as a 2's complement number. Hence relative addressing can reach forward 127 bytes or backward 128 bytes from the current location. Next we need to know that the program counter is automatically incremented by 2 whenever a branch instruction—a two-byte instruction—is executed. Hence the reference point for calculating the relative address is not the address of the branch instruction but is two bytes higher. We can express the relation between the absolute address of desired destination and the address of the branch instruction as follows.

D = destination of branch instruction
B = address of first byte of branch instruction
R = 8-bit 2's complement offset stored in second byte of branch instruction
$D = (B + 2) + R$

Solving for R, we find

$R = D - (B + 2)$.

The range of D is limited to

$(B + 2) - 128 \le D \le (B + 2) + 127$.

Examples 5.1 and 5.2 show how to calculate relative addresses for branch instructions.

Example 5.1. Branch destination

Task: The first byte of a branch instruction is stored in location $1A08_{16}$. The second byte shows a relative address of 121_{16}. Find the absolute address of the destination of the branch instruction.

Procedure: $D = (B + 2) + R$

$D + (1A08 + 2) + 121$

$D = 1B2B_{16}$

Example 5.2. Relative address

Task: The first byte of a branch instruction is stored in location $2C74_{16}$. The destination of the branch is $2C02_{16}$. Find the offset R.

Procedure: $R = D - (B + 2)$

$R = 2C02 - (2C74 + 2)$

$R = -74_{16}$ expressed in 8-bit 2's complement

$R = 10001100_2$

$R = AC_{16}$

As noted above, the M6800 has a large number of branch instructions—one unconditional and 14 conditional instructions. Eight of the conditional branches depend on the settings of one condition flag each; the other six depend on the settings of two or more flags each. All take two bytes; all use relative addressing. Thus the branch instructions of the M6800 are shorter and more varied than those of the 8085. However, they cannot access all of memory; three-byte jump instructions are supplied to access locations that cannot be reached by branch instructions. The M6800 branch instructions are as follows.

BRA	BRanch Always (branch unconditionally)
BEQ	Branch if EQual (to zero) (Z = 1)
BNE	Branch if Not Equal (to zero) (Z = 0)
BCS	Branch if Carry Set (C = 1)
BCC	Branch if Carry Clear (C = 0)
BPL	Branch if PLus (N = 0)
BMI	Branch if MInus (N = 1)
BVS	Branch if oVerflow Set (V = 1)
BVC	Branch if oVerflow Clear (V = 0)
BLT	Branch if Less Than (zero)
BLE	Branch if Less than or Equal (to zero)
BGE	Branch if Greater than or Equal (to zero)
BGT	Branch if Greater Than (zero)
BLS	Branch if Lower or Same
BHI	Branch if HIgher

Details of the operations of these branch instructions may be found in M6800 programming manuals.

Having learned about transfer instructions, we can now proceed to the programs for adding the absolute values of three numbers. The Intel 8085 program is shown in Table 5.4. Several commands need explanation.

At address 1022 we find the instruction

```
CMP  B, 0
```

This means "compare the contents of B with the value of 0." It is a two-byte command with the value 0 (or any other 8-bit number) as the second byte. Its effect is to subtract the value shown (here 0) from the contents of the register named (here B) and to set the condition flags accordingly. The result of the subtraction is not available—just the settings of the status flags. This instruction is needed to change the flags because the previous instruction, MVI A,0, did not affect the flags.

The next instruction

```
JP   BPOS
```

tells the program counter to advance to the location labeled BPOS if the result of the comparison—that is, the contents of B—is positive or zero. This label has not yet appeared in the program so we do not at first know what address to assign to it. Thus for the moment we leave two bytes for the address and move on to the next instruction. When we later encounter BPOS as a label at memory location 102B, we can return to 1025 and 1026 and store 2B and 10, respectively.

After the branch instruction we encounter

```
SUB B
```

Because of the preceding JP instruction, the computer will read this instruction only if the contents of B are negative. The SUB operator performs a 2's complement subtraction from A—just what we need to get the absolute value of the contents of B. After this instruction we find an unconditional jump

```
JMP  CNEXT
```

to the location that begins the processing of the number in C. As before, we do not at first know the hexadecimal equivalent of the label CNEXT, so we must save two bytes for it and enter it in those locations later.

If the contents of B are positive or zero, we must add them before we proceed to inspect the contents of C. The numbers in registers C and D are handled in exactly the same way as the number in B. Do you understand the branching and how to determine hexadecimal addresses? The program ends with a HLT instruction and an END pseudoinstruction.

The M6800 program for adding the absolute values of three numbers,

Table 5.4
Intel 8085 program for adding absolute values of three numbers

Hex address	Hex instruction	Label	Op code	Operand	Comment
					; NUMBERS ARE IN B, C, D
					; SUM IS IN A
			ORG	1020H	; START AT 1020 HEX
1020	3E		MVI	A, 0	; INITIALIZE SUM TO 0
1021	00				
1022	B8		CMP	B, 0	; COMPARE B WITH 0
1023	00				
1024	F2		JP	BPOS	; IF B IS POSITIVE,
					; GO TO BPOS
1025	2B				; LOW BYTE OF ADDRESS
1026	10				; HIGH BYTE OF ADDRESS
1027	90		SUB	B	; B IS NEGATIVE,
					; SUBTRACT B
1028	C3		JMP	CNEXT	; GO TO CNEXT
1029	2C				
102A	10				
102B	80	BPOS:	ADD	B	; B IS POSITIVE, ADD B
102C	B9	CNEXT:	CMP	C, 0	; COMPARE C WITH 0
102D	00		JP	CPOS	; IF C IS POSITIVE,
					; GO TO CPOS
102E	34				
102F	10				
1030	91		SUB	C	; C IS NEGATIVE,
					; SUBTRACT C
1031	C3		JMP	DNEXT	; GO TO DNEXT
1032	35				
1033	10				
1034	81	CPOS:	ADD	C	; C IS POSITIVE,
					; ADD C
1035	BA	DNEXT:	CMP	D, 0	; TEST D
1036	00		JP	DPOS	; IF POSITIVE, GO TO
					; DPOS
1037	3D				
1038	10				
1039	92		SUB	D	; D IS NEGATIVE,
					; SUBTRACT
103A	C3		JMP	LAST	; GO TO LAST
103B	3E				
103C	10				
103D	82	DPOS:	ADD	D	; D IS POSITIVE, ADD
103E	76	LAST:	HLT		
			END		

shown in Table 5.5, is similar to the 8085 program. The main difference is that the M6800 uses two-byte branch instructions with relative addressing instead of three-byte branch instructions with absolute addressing. We have already

Table 5.5
M6800 program for adding absolute values of three numbers

Hex address	Hex instruction	Label	Op code	Operand	Comment
					; NUMBERS ARE IN LOCATIONS
					; 00 to 02, SUM WILL BE IN
					; ACCA
			ORG	20H	; START IN LOCATION 20H
20	4F		CLR	A	; INITIALIZE SUM TO 0
21	D6		LDA B	00H	; LOAD FIRST NUMBER IN B
22	00				; DIRECT ADDRESS
23	2A		BPL	FPOS	; IF POSITIVE, GO TO FPOS
24	03				; RELATIVE ADDRESS
25	10		SBA		; NUMBER IS NEGATIVE,
					; SUBTRACT B
26	20		BRA	SECND	; GO TO SECOND
27	01				; RELATIVE ADDRESS
28	1B	FPOS:	ABA		; NUMBER IS POSITIVE,
					; ADD B
29	D6	SECND:	LDA B	01H	; LOAD SECOND NUMBER IN B
2A	01				; DIRECT ADDRESS
2B	2A		BPL	SPOS	; IF POSITIVE, GO TO SPOS
2C	03				; RELATIVE ADDRESS
2D	10		SBA		; NUMBER IS NEGATIVE,
					; SUBTRACT B
2E	20		BRA	THIRD	; GO TO THIRD
2F	01				; RELATIVE ADDRESS
30	1B	SPOS:	ABA		; NUMBER IS POSITIVE,
					; ADD B
31	D6	THIRD:	LDA B	02H	; LOAD THIRD NUMBER IN B
32	02				; DIRECT ADDRESS
33	2A		BPL	THPOS	; IF POSITIVE, GO TO THPOS
34	03				; RELATIVE ADDRESS
35	10		SBA		; NUMBER IS NEGATIVE,
					; SUBTRACT B
36	20		BRA	LAST	; GO TO LAST STATEMENT
37	01				; RELATIVE ADDRESS
38	1B	THPOS:	ABA		; NUMBER IS POSITIVE,
					; ADD B
39	3F	LAST:	SWI		; SOFTWARE INTERRUPT
			END		

discussed this. A second difference is that the M6800 does not need comparison instructions before its conditional branches for this problem. With the 8085 we had to insert a comparison instruction before each conditional branch because we had no other way to set the condition flags for the register contents. With the M6800 we can move data from memory into an accumulator (here ACCB) with the instruction LDA B ("load accumulator B"). This automatically changes the N and Z flags accordingly. We can then test the N flag with

```
BPL   FPOS
```

and advance to the location labeled FPOS if the contents of accumulator B are positive or zero. As in the preceding example, we have not at this point seen FPOS in the label field. Thus we save one byte for the relative address. In due course we see that FPOS occurs three bytes after the instruction that follows BPL FPOS; thus we calculate the relative address as 03 and enter it at the place we saved for it.

If the contents of memory location 00 prove to be negative, we perform a 2's complement subtraction of ACCB from ACCA with the instruction

```
SBA
```

The result stays in accumulator A. Thus we effectively add the absolute value of the contents of ACCB to ACCA. After the subtraction we branch unconditionally to the location labeled SECND to start processing the second number.

If the contents of memory location 00 are positive, we simply add them to ACCA as we did in our first M6800 program. We handle the next two numbers in the same way. Be sure that you understand the branches. The program ends as before with a software interrupt and an END pseudoinstruction.

5.4.3 *Addition of N Numbers*

Our third program is for adding N numbers, as flowcharted in Fig. 3.3 for N equal to 100. We will use a loop for the repeated summing of $X(I)$. A **loop,** as we have seen, is a program statement or group of statements that is executed repeatedly. We usually have a **counter** to keep track of the number of times we go around the loop. We start by initializing the counter to the desired number of counts. Each time we go through the loop, we decrement the counter after we have completed the basic calculation of the loop. When the counter becomes zero, we leave the loop.

The numbers to be added are stored in consecutive locations in memory. We use a pointer to access them. A **pointer** is a device (usually a register) that holds the memory address of the desired data. Before entering the loop, we initialize the pointer to the address of the first number. Inside the loop we first add the number to which the pointer is pointing. Then we increment the pointer to the next number. You may be wondering how we add the number to which the pointer points. Each of our microcomputers has a different method so we will discuss them separately.

The 8085 solution is shown in Table 5.6. To save space we will write each instruction on a single line regardless of whether it has one, two, or three bytes. We will show the resulting hex code from left to right. Thus 210020 at location 1062 means 21 in 1062, 00 in 1063, and 20 in 1064.

Table 5.6
Intel 8085 program for adding 100 numbers

Hex address	Hex instruction	Label	Op code	Operand	Comment
					; NUMBERS TO BE ADDED ARE
					; STORED IN LOCATIONS 2000H
					; TO 2063H
			ORG	1060H	; START AT 1060H
1060	3E00		MVI	A, 0	; INITIALIZE SUM TO 0
1062	210020		LXI	H, 2000H	; POINT HL TO FIRST NUMBER
1065	0E64		MVI	C, 64H	; SET COUNTER C TO 100
1067	86	LOOP:	ADD	M	; ADD NUMBER
1068	23		INX	H	; ADVANCE POINTER
1069	OD		DCR	C	; DECREMENT COUNTER
106A	C26710		JNZ	LOOP	; IF NOT 0, REPEAT LOOP
106D	76		HLT		; STOP WHEN C IS 0
			END		

Most of the instructions in this program are familiar, but a few are new. The command

```
LXI H, 2000H
```

establishes the HL register pair as our pointer and initializes it to location 2000, where the first number is stored. It acts just as the MVI instruction does, except that it moves two bytes of data to a register pair instead of one byte to a single register. An MVI instruction is adequate to initialize the counter because a number less than 256_{10} is needed.

We choose the HL register pair rather than the BC or the DE pair because it is designed to be a pointer to memory. The 8085 has a large number of instructions that operate either on any of the 8-bit registers or on a memory location designated M. That memory location is the one to which the HL register pair is currently pointing. That is, M is the memory location whose address is in the HL register pair. Thus the first loop instruction

```
ADD M
```

adds the contents of that memory location to A. Then the pointer is incremented by 1 with the command

```
INX H
```

This increments HL as a register pair. Finally, the counter is decremented by 1 with the command

```
DCR C
```

This sets the condition flags, which may then be tested by the conditional jump

```
JNZ LOOP
```

Table 5.7
M6800 program for adding 100 numbers

Hex address	Hex instruction	Label	Op code	Operand	Comment
					; NUMBERS ARE STORED IN
					; CONSECUTIVE LOCATIONS
					; STARTING IN 1040H
					; SUM WILL BE IN ACCA
					; MEMORY LOCATION 0A HAS 10
					; LOCATION 0B HAS 40
					; ACCB WILL BE A COUNTER
			ORG	50H	; START IN 50H
50	4F		CLR	A	; INITIALIZE SUM
51	DE0A		LDX	0A	; INITIALIZE INDEX REGISTER
					; FROM 0A AND 0B
53	C664		LDA	B, #64H	; INITIALIZE COUNTER
					; WITH 100
55	AB00	LOOP:	ADD	A, X	; ADD NUMBER
57	08		INX		; INCREMENT INDEX REGISTER
58	5A		DEC	B	; DECREMENT COUNTER
59	2EFA		BGT	LOOP	; IF NOT DONE, REPEAT LOOP
5B	3F		SWI		; SOFTWARE INTERRUPT
			END		

As a result, the loop operations are continued until the contents of counter C are 0, when the program concludes with a halt.

The M6800 program for adding 100 numbers, shown in Table 5.7, uses indexed addressing to obtain the numbers to be added. In **indexed addressing**, the hexadecimal address depends on the contents of the index register. The M6800 has several forms of indexed addressing. Here we will use the simplest form. The hexadecimal address will be the contents of the index register, denoted X. We can think of the index register in this case as being a pointer to memory, much as the HL register pair is for the 8085. In more complex forms of indexed addressing we can specify a number or symbol to be added to the contents of the index register to form the desired address.

Again, to shorten the listing of this program we show each instruction on one line regardless of the number of bytes needed. For example, the second instruction of the program takes two bytes. It is shown starting at memory location 51 and containing DE0A. This means that DE is stored in location 51 and 0A in 52. The mnemonic

```
LDX  0A
```

sets the index register equal to the contents of memory locations 0A and 0B. These locations are assumed to hold 10 and 40, respectively. Thus the index register is initialized to 1040, the address of the first of the 100 numbers.

The counter, accumulator B, is initialized to 100_{10} with the command

```
LDA   B, #64H
```

The pound sign, #, shows **immediate addressing**, meaning that 64 is to be interpreted as data, not as an address.

The basic loop operation is

```
ADD   A, X
```

The number whose address is in the index register X is added to accumulator A. The next instruction

```
INX
```

increments the index register by 1 so that it holds the address of the next number to be added. Then the counter (accumulator) is decremented by 1 with the command

```
DEC   B
```

The branch instruction

```
BGT   LOOP
```

transfers control back to the location labeled LOOP so long as the counter is greater than 0. When the counter equals 0, the program ends with a software interrupt.

The M6800 program requires the same number of instructions as the 8085 program. The M6800 program appears to be two bytes shorter, but two bytes are needed to store the first address of the list of numbers. Thus the two programs take the same amount of memory.

5.4.4 *A Subroutine for Adding N Numbers*

As a final example, let us see how we would write a subroutine to calculate the sum of *N* numbers. We will assume that we are somewhere in the middle of a main program as shown in Tables 5.8 and 5.9 for the 8085 and M6800, respectively. A subroutine titled ADDN will calculate the sum of *N* numbers.

The first thing we need is a mechanism to pass the number *N* from the main program to the subroutine. A simple way to transfer the value of *N* is to place it in a register. Hence we will place *N* in register C for the 8085 and in ACCB for the M6800. If we had several values to transfer, we would need other ways to **pass parameters** (exchange information) between the main program and a subroutine. We will examine this topic later.

We **call** (transfer control to) the subroutine ADDN with the instructions

```
JSR    ADDN    (M6800)
CALL   ADDN    (8085)
```

Both of these are unconditional instructions. The 8085 also has conditional call instructions that work much like conditional jump instructions. If the condition is met, the subroutine is called; otherwise the next instruction in sequence is executed. These call instructions are listed later in the chapter. The M6800 does

Table 5.8
Intel 8085 program with subroutine for adding N numbers

Hex address	Hex instruction	Label	Op code	Operand	Comment
					; PROGRAM SEGMENT SHOWING
					; USE OF SUBROUTINES
					; MAIN PROGRAM
					; N STORED IN REGISTER C;
					; STARTING ADDRESS IN HL;
					; RESULT IN A
1100	CD0012		CALL	ADDN	; CALL SUBROUTINE
1103		NEXT:			; NEXT INSTRUCTION IN MAIN
					; PROGRAM
		ADDN:	ORG	1200H	; SUBROUTINE STARTS IN 1200H
					; HL HAS BEEN SET TO FIRST
					; ADDRESS IN MAIN PROGRAM
					; C HAS BEEN SET TO NUMBER
					; OF NUMBERS IN MAIN PROGRAM
1200	3E00		MVI	A, 0	; INITIALIZE SUM TO 0
1202	86	LOOP:	ADD	M	; ADD NUMBER
1203	23		INX	H	; ADVANCE POINTER
1204	0D		DCR	C	; DECREMENT COUNTER
1205	C20212		JNZ	LOOP	; IF NOT 0, REPEAT LOOP
1208	C9		RET		; RETURN TO NEXT INSTRUCTION
					; IN MAIN PROGRAM WHEN 0

Table 5.9
M6800 program with subroutine for adding N numbers

Hex address	Hex instruction	Label	Op code	Operand	Comment
					; PROGRAM SEGMENT SHOWING
					; USE OF SUBROUTINES
					; MAIN PROGRAM
					; N IS STORED IN ACCB
					; ADDRESS OF FIRST NUMBER
					; IS IN X
80	BD1200		JSR	ADDN	; CALL SUBROUTINE ADDN
		NEXT:			; NEXT INSTRUCTION IN MAIN
					; PROGRAM
		ADDN:	ORG	1200H	; ADDN BEGINS IN 1200H
1200	4F		CLR	A	; INITIALIZE SUM
1201	AB00	LOOP:	ADD	A, X	; ADD NUMBER
1203	08		INX		; INCREMENT INDEX REGISTER
1205	5A		DEC	B	; DECREMENT COUNTER
1206	2EFA		BGT	LOOP	; IF NOT DONE, REPEAT LOOP
1208	39		RTS		; RETURN FROM SUBROUTINE
					; TO NEXT INSTRUCTION

not have conditional call instructions. Instead, one can precede unconditional call instructions with conditional branch instructions to achieve a similar end. The M6800 also has a branch-to-subroutine instruction (BSR) that uses relative addressing.

Each subroutine ends with a **return** instruction. In the examples here, the return instructions are unconditional. The codes are

```
RET    ( 8085 )
RTS    ( M6800 )
```

Conditional return instructions are also available for the 8085.

The purpose of a return instruction is to transfer control back to the instruction in the main program immediately following the call instruction. We may call subroutines as many times in a program as we like. Each time after the subroutine is executed, control returns to the instruction immediately following that instruction which called the subroutine. You may wonder how the computer knows the correct return address. There are several ways in which the return address may be saved; we will look at some of them in a later chapter.

5.5 *A Closer Look at 8080 and 8085 Instructions*

Now that we have seen how to write several programs, let us pause to examine the instructions we have used so far and to consider other instructions. Our objective is to be sure that we understand the instructions well enough to program with them in both machine and assembly language. Hence we will examine both the mnemonic and the hexadecimal forms of the instructions. In this section we will consider only 8080 and 8085 instructions; in the next section we will consider only M6800 instructions.

Before looking at the instructions, let us review some of the features of 8080/8085 instructions. They may be one, two, or three bytes long, with the operation code in the first byte. Many instructions perform the same basic operation on any of seven registers or on the memory location whose address is in the HL register pair; hence we can expect to find instructions occurring in sets containing seven or eight variations that depend on the register chosen. The 8080/8085 has separate input/output instructions.

We will first consider all instructions that are common to the 8080 and the 8085. At the end of this section we will look at the additional instructions of the 8085.

Various schemes have been devised for categorizing instructions. All such schemes tend to be arbitrary. Our scheme divides instruction types into four main groups:

1. Data movement

2. Data operations

3. Program control

4. Miscellaneous

Within each main group we may further subdivide these categories according to the registers, memory, immediate data, or input/output devices with which they deal.

5.5.1 *Data Movement Instructions*

One of the major tasks within a program is to move data from memory to a register or between devices or registers. Data must usually be moved to a desired register before it can be processed. Thus data movements represent overhead in a program; they precede or follow the useful operations of a program. We will consider five types of data movement:

- Within a single register.
- Between two registers.
- Between a register and memory.
- Between an input/output device and a register.
- With an immediate operand.

Moving data within a single register The 8080/8085 does not have many instructions to move data within a single register. The only such operation it offers is rotation, and that operation affects only the accumulator (register A) and the carry flag. We will in fact consider the carry flag in this case as an extension of the accumulator. There are four rotate instructions. They are all single-byte instructions and do not require an operand because the accumulator is the implied operand. Two of the four rotations include a carry bit. This bit, one of the five condition codes of the 8085, can be thought of as a one-bit register just to the left of the accumulator; thus nine bits are rotated. The other two rotations do not include the carry bit; only eight bits are rotated. All rotations involve moving the included bits one position to the left or right, with the bit moved out at one end and back in a circle to the other end. In the first two rotations the carry bit is set equal to the leftmost (high-order) or rightmost (low-order) bit of the accumulator, respectively, before the rotation. See Fig. 5.10. The four rotate instructions are as follows.

Hex code	Assembly code	Meaning
07	RLC	Rotate accumulator Left without Carry
0F	RRC	Rotate accumulator Right without Carry
17	RAL	Rotate Accumulator Left (with carry)
1F	RAR	Rotate Accumulator Right (with carry)

You may well feel that these mnemonics might make more sense if the ones with C were switched with those without C; however, we have to make do with what the manufacturer has supplied, so be careful. It takes some thought to

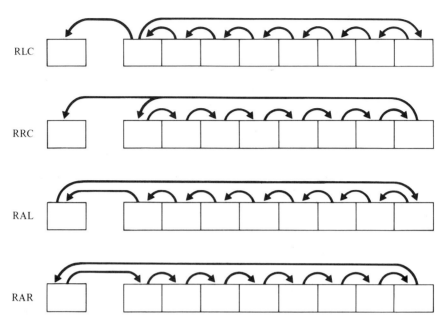

Fig. 5.10
8085 rotation instruction.

remember that RLC does not mean "rotate left through the carry," but that RAL does.

Moving data between registers In contrast to the limited movements it allows within a register, the 8085 allows a wide range of data movements between registers. The most important instruction in this class is the move instruction. It is a single-byte instruction of the form

MOV   dst, src   MOVe byte from source register to destination register

The lower-case letters src and dst in this generalized formulation of the instructions stand for the two operands—the source and the destination of the transfer, respectively. They may be any two of the 8-bit registers—A, B, C, D, E, H, or L. Movement from one register back to itself, for example, MOV E, E, is a null operation; it consumes time but otherwise accomplishes nothing.

The hexadecimal code for any move operation can be calculated by knowing its format.

0 1	dst	src
7 6	5 4 3	2 1 0

A standard octal code applies for the destination and source as well as for registers in other instructions. This code is as follows.

Code	Register	Code	Register
0	B	4	H
1	C	5	L
2	D	6	M
3	E	7	A

Example 5.3: Hexadecimal Code for MOV

Task: Calculate the hexadecimal code for the instruction MOV D, A.
Procedure: From the preceding table we see that the octal code is 127. Using the procedures given in Chapter 2 (Section 2.5), we find that the 8-bit binary code is 01010111 and that the hexadecimal code is 57.

We can describe the general move operation symbolically as

dst ← src

By this notation we mean that the *value* on the right is transferred to the *location* on the left. This is a **nondestructive transfer**; the value of the source is not changed.

We will not describe all instructions here in this way, but we do so in the appendix. This shorthand notation gives a brief and accurate description. You should try to describe any 8085 instruction with this notation to check your understanding of the instruction.

There are no comparable instructions for moving data between any two register pairs. However, there are a few limited single-byte instructions for data movement between specific register pairs. For example,

EB   XCHG   eXCHanGe contents of registers D and E with contents of
                                registers H and L
                                D ← H; E ← L; H ←D; L ← E
F9   SPHL   load SP from H and L (leaving H and L unchanged)

Moving data between a register and memory The 8085 has a number of rather specialized instructions for moving data between some register or register pair and memory.

There are two single-byte instructions for moving data between the accumulator and the memory location whose address is in register pair. The register pair, denoted rp in our generalized formulations, may be either B or D; it cannot be H or SP. The two instructions are:

0A(B) or 1A(D)   LDAX rp   LoaD Accumulator from the memory
                                                    location addressed by rp
02(B) or 12(D)   STAX rp   STore the contents of the Accumulator
                                                    at the memory location addressed by rp

To describe these instructions symbolically, we use parentheses ( ) to denote ''contents of.'' Thus LDAX rp can be described as

A ← (rp)

The value of the location whose address is the contents of rp is moved to the accumulator. Similarly, STAX rp can be described as

(rp) ← A

The value of the accumulator is stored at the location whose address is the contents of rp.

Two more single-byte instructions allow moving data between a register pair and the top of the stack. We will assume that you know something about stacks, perhaps from operating a calculator. Later, when we discuss subroutines in greater detail, we will define stack operations more carefully. For the moment we can think of a stack as an area of memory having last-in, first-out access. That is, the last two bytes to be stored on the stack are at the top and will be moved from the stack before any bytes stored earlier. The stack pointer SP always points to the top two bytes of memory in the stack; more exactly, the top two bytes are in the memory location addressed by the stack pointer and the memory location whose address is one more than that given by the stack pointer. Data is POPped (transferred) from these two locations. Data PUSHed (stored) on the stack goes into the locations with addresses one and two less than the contents of SP. The register pair rp designated may be B, D, H, or PSW. (Remember that the program status word PSW consists of A and the flags.) The register contents are stored in the stack with the high-order byte in the higher numbered memory location. When the register pair is PSW, the contents of A are stored in the higher numbered location.

PUSH   rp   PUSH contents of rp onto stack
POP   rp   POP contents of top of stack to rp

After a PUSH, the stack pointer is decremented by 2. After a POP, it is incremented by 2.

The hexadecimal code for PUSH and POP involves a two-bit code for register pairs as follows.

Code	Register pair
0	B
1	D
2	H
3	PSW

The binary format for PUSH and POP instructions is

| 1 | 1 | rp | 0 | X | 0 | 1 | X = 1 for PUSH, 0 for POP
 7   6   5 4   3   2   1   0

The same coding for register pairs was used for the LDAX and STAX instructions. Can you figure out their formats?

A similar register pair coding is used for other instructions, with 3 denoting SP instead of PSW. Usually we can determine from the nature of the instruction whether the stack pointer or the program status word is a more appropriate operand.

Example 5.4: Stack operations

A brief example may clarify these instructions. Suppose SP holds the address 4A5C hexadecimal. Suppose B holds A0 hex and C holds B1 hex. The instruction

PUSH B

loads B1 into location 4A5B and A0 into 4A5A. SP is decremented by 2 to 4A5A; the contents of B and C are not changed. After this move, the instruction

POP D

moves the contents of 4A5A, namely B1, to E and the contents of 4A5B, namely A0, to D. These two instructions, thus, have moved the contents of register pair B to pair D.

Suppose the next instruction is

PUSH PSW

We recall that register pair PSW consists of A and the five condition codes. Specifically, the 8-bit register for the condition codes has the following form.

S	Z	0	AC	0	P	1	CY
7	6	5	4	3	2	1	0

Suppose the accumulator holds E7, and the parity and carry condition codes are 1 while all others are 0, resulting in 07 hex. Then the result of the instruction is to move E7 into 4A5B and 07 into 4A5A; the contents of the accumulator and the condition codes are not changed. Figure 5.11 shows contents of registers and memory during these operations.

A somewhat unusual single-byte instruction exchanges the single byte at the top of the stack with the contents of register pair HL:

E3   XTHL   eXchange Top of stack with HL

Note how XTHL differs from SPHL, which loaded the stack pointer from H and L but left H and L unchanged. Here two 16-bit values are exchanged—the contents of the memory locations at the top of the stack and the contents of the H and L registers.

Hexadecimal address	Hexadecimal memory contents	Hexadecimal address	Hexadecimal memory contents
4A59	Empty	4A59	Empty
4A5A	Empty	4A5A	B1
4A5B	Empty	4A5B	A0
4A5C	Top of stack	4A5C	Former top

Registers	Contents	Registers	Contents
B	A0	B	A0
C	B1	C	B1
D	22	D	22
E	33	E	33
PSW		PSW	
A		A	
(a)		(b)	

Hexadecimal address	Hexadecimal memory contents	Hexadecimal address	Hexadecimal memory contents
4A59	Empty	4A59	Empty
4A5A	B1	4A5A	07
4A5B	A0	4A5B	E7
4A5C	Top of stack	4A5C	Former top

Registers	Contents	Registers	Contents
B	A0	B	A0
C	B1	C	B1
D	A0	D	A0
E	B1	E	B1
PSW	07	PSW	07
A	E7	A	E7
(c)		(d)	

Fig. 5.11
Results of PUSH and POP operations: (a) Before PUSH B. (b) After PUSH B. (c) After POP D. (d) After PUSH PSW.

Two three-byte instructions allow transferring data between H and L and any memory location. The last two bytes of the instruction give the 16-bit memory address of the low-order byte. The address of the high-order byte is one greater. In the assembly language instruction we usually provide the address in hexadecimal. The instructions are:

22	SHLD	addr	Store H and L Direct in memory location addr
2A	LHLD	addr	Load H and L Direct from contents of memory location addr

For example, suppose H contains 11 hex and L contains 77 hex. The instruction

```
SHLD 12EEH
```

will store the contents of H, namely 11H, in 12EF and the contents of L, namely 77H, in 12EE.

Two more three-byte instructions allow transferring data between the accumulator and any memory address. As in the preceding instructions, the last two bytes give the memory address. Because the accumulator can hold only one byte, only one memory address is needed. The instructions are:

32	STA	addr	STore Accumulator direct in memory location addr
3A	LDA	addr	LoaD Accumulator directly from memory location addr

Moving immediate data The capability of loading immediate data allows us to initialize registers easily. There are two move or load immediate instructions—one each for registers and for register pairs. For register pairs a three-byte instruction is needed to provide 16 bits of immediate data.

LXI   rp, data   Load rp Immediate with data

0	0	rp	0	0	0	1
7	6	5 4	3			0

Register pairs B, D, H, and SP may be named; pair PSW may not be used in this instruction.

A two-byte instruction is needed to give 8 bits of immediate data to a single register.

MVI   reg, data   MoVe Immediate data to reg

0	0	reg	1	1	0
7	6	5 3	2		0

For the register, any of A, B, C, D, E, H, L, or M may be given; M is the memory location addressed by register pair H.

Input/output movement The last two data movement instructions are the two-byte instructions for moving data between input or output ports and the accumulator. We will examine them quickly. The second byte gives the port number of the input or output device.

D3	IN	port	INput data to A from port
DB	OUT	port	OUTput data from A to port

5.5.2 *Data Operation Instructions*

Computers perform two types of data operations—arithmetic and logical. Arithmetic operations include addition and subtraction, incrementing and decrementing, and special adjustments. Logical operations include complementation, AND, OR, and EXCLUSIVE OR. Some of these operations take one operand, others take two. We will first consider arithmetic operations.

Arithmetic operations Data operations can involve one register, two registers, or one register and immediate data. Only memory location M, addressed by H and L, can be part of any arithmetic operations. If we wish to calculate with data elsewhere in memory, we must first move the data to a register.

Single-register arithmetic operations The contents of any 8-bit register or M (the memory location addressed by H and L) can be incremented or decremented by 1 with single-byte instructions.

INR   reg   INcrement Register by 1

0 0	reg	1 0 0
7 6 5	3 2	0

DCR   reg   DeCrement Register by 1

0 0	reg	1 0 1
7 6 5	3 2	0

Similar single-byte instructions for register pairs are:

INX   rp   INcrement register pair

0 0	rp	0 0 1 1
7 6 5 4 3		0

DCX   rp   DeCrement register pair

0 0	rp	1 0 1 1
7 6 5 4 3		0

Two-register arithmetic operations We can add or subtract the contents of any register or M with the contents of A. The carry bit may or may not be part of the register or M. These single-byte instructions are as follows.

ADD   reg   ADD register or memory to accumulator

1 0 0 0 0	reg
7	3 2 0

ADC   reg   ADd register or memory and Carry to accumulator

1 0 0 0 1	reg
7	3 2 0

SUB   reg   SUBtract register or memory from accumulator

1 0 0 1 0	reg
7	3 2 0

SBB   reg   SuBtract register or memory with Borrow from accumulator

1 0 0 1 1	reg
7	3 2 0

ADD simply adds two 8-bit numbers. The carry bit is set if there is a carry from the highest-order bits of the addition; otherwise it is reset. For example, if D holds FFH and A holds 01H, the instruction ADD D results in 00 in A and 1 in the carry.

ADC adds the carry bit to the lowest-order bit of the sum of the register and the accumulator. The carry bit is set if there is a carry out of the highest-order bits of the sum. It is most useful when a previous addition resulted in a carry. For example, if the carry is 1, E holds FFH, and A holds 01H, then the results of ADC E are that carry is 1 and A holds 01.

SUB subtracts two 8-bit numbers. It sets the carry bit if there is *no* carry from the highest-order bit position. The reason for this is that the carry is considered to be a borrow bit. If there is no carry from the highest bit position, a borrow has occurred. Otherwise the carry is reset. For example, if A holds 2EH, and E holds 2EH, then SUB E results in 0 in A and 0 in the carry.

SBB subtracts the contents of the register and the carry bit (considered to be a borrow) from the accumulator. It is most useful when a previous subtraction has produced a borrow. After the subtraction, the carry bit is set if there was a carry out of the high-order position, meaning that a borrow occurred. Otherwise it is reset. Suppose D holds 3, A holds 5, and the carry is 1. The results of SBB D is that A holds 1 and the carry is 0.

The 8085 provides decimal arithmetic, as illustrated by programs in a later chapter. A necessary part of decimal arithmetic is a **decimal adjustment**. It corrects the sum of any binary addition of two decimal numbers in A. As explained in Chapter 2, it provides the correct binary code whenever the sum exceeds 9 or the carry is 1. We usually make this adjustment after any decimal addition. The single-byte instruction is

27   DAA   Decimal Adjust Accumulator

Binary addition (2's complement) may also be done on the contents of register pairs. A single-byte instruction adds the contents of any of register pairs B, D, H, or SP to the contents of H and L, leaving the sum in H and L.

DAD rp Double ADd the contents of rp	0 0	rp	1 0 0 1
to H	7 6	5 4 3	0

Immediate arithmetic operations Exactly similar arithmetic operations can be done with immediate data and the accumulator. Two-byte instructions are needed; the second byte holds the immediate data.

C6	ADI	data	ADd Immediate data to accumulator
CE	ACI	data	Add Carry plus Immediate data to accumulator
D6	SUI	data	SUbtract Immediate data from accumulator
DE	SBI	data	Subtract with Borrow Immediate data from accumulator

Logical operations Logical operations also can involve one register, two registers, or one register and immediate data. We will consider them in that order.

Single-register logical operations The 8085 performs a few logical operations on single registers. It can complement the accumulator but cannot set or clear it without using immediate data. It can set or complement the carry bit but cannot reset it. The single-byte instructions for these actions are:

2F	CMA	CoMplement Accumulator
37	STC	SeT Carry
3F	CMC	CoMplement Carry

Two-register logical operations The 8085 can perform AND, OR, and EX-CLUSIVE OR between any register or M and the accumulator. It can also compare the contents of any register to those of the accumulator and set condition codes accordingly. The single-byte instructions are as follows.

ANA	reg	ANd register or memory with Accumulator							

ANA reg ANd register or memory with Accumulator

1	0	1	0	0	reg
7			3	2	0

ORA reg OR register or memory with Accumulator

1	0	1	1	0	reg
7			3	2	0

XRA reg eXclusive oR register or memory with Accumulator

1	0	1	0	1	reg
7			3	2	0

CMP reg CoMPare register or memory to accumulator

1	0	1	1	1	reg
7			3	2	0

The results of the first three operations are left in the accumulator. The accumulator can be cleared quickly by XRA A. (Why?) In the comparison the contents of the register or memory are internally subtracted from the accumulator, leaving both unchanged. The result may change condition codes.

Logical immediate operations The same four logical operations can be made with immediate data and the accumulator. Two bytes are necessary; the second gives the immediate data. The instructions are:

E6	ANI	ANd Immediate with accumulator
F6	ORI	OR Immediate with accumulator
EE	XRI	eXclusive oR Immediate with accumulator
FE	CPI	ComPare Immediate with accumulator

As with the preceding instructions, the results of ANI, ORI, and XRI are placed in the accumulator. The CPI comparison internally subtracts the immediate data from the accumulator and affects only condition codes—not the accumulator.

5.5.3 *Program Control Instructions*

The 8085 has three main types of program control instructions: (1) jumps, (2) subroutine calls, and (3) subroutine returns. It also has one special program control instruction, the single-byte halt instruction:

76   HLT   HaLT

When this instruction is encountered, the program counter is incremented to the address of the next instruction in sequence. The CPU enters the STOPped state, and the program ends.

The jumps and subroutine calls and returns can be either unconditional or conditional on four of the condition codes. These are as follows.

• CY (carry bit)—equals value of carry bit; depends on results of arithmetic operation

- Z (zero bit)   —equals 1 if result of certain instructions is 0, otherwise equals 0
- S (sign bit)   —equals sign of most significant bit of result of certain instructions
- P (parity bit) —equals 1 if number of 1 bits in a byte is even; otherwise equals 0

No jumps, calls, or returns depend on the status of the fifth condition code—the auxiliary carry, AC. It is used only in arithmetic operations (notably in decimal arithmetic) and is not accessible to the programmer.

Jump instructions The 8085 has a unique single-byte unconditional jump instruction that transfers control to the location addressed by the H and L registers:

E9   PCHL   load Program Counter from H and L

It also has a more conventional three-byte unconditional jump instruction in which the last two bytes state the destination of the jump:

C3   JMP   addr   JuMP (to address)

It also has six conditional jump instructions, each taking three bytes.

DA	JC	addr	Jump (to address) if Carry (CY = 1)
D2	JNC	addr	Jump (to address) if No Carry (CY = 0)
CA	JZ	addr	Jump (to address) if Zero (Z = 1)
C2	JNZ	addr	Jump (to address) if Not Zero (Z = 0)
FA	JM	addr	Jump (to address) if Minus (S = 1)
F2	JP	addr	Jump (to address) if Positive (S = 0)
EA	JPE	addr	Jump (to address) if Parity Even (P = 1)
EO	JPO	addr	Jump (to address) if Parity Odd (P = 0)

Subroutine call instructions The 8085 has one unconditional and six conditional subroutine call instructions. Each require three bytes—the last two for the subroutine address. A subroutine call instruction transfers control to the subroutine and pushes the return address—the location after the subroutine call instruction—on the stack addressed by SP. The range of possible conditions is the same as for jumps.

CD	CALL	sub	CALL subroutine
DC	CC	sub	Call subroutine if Carry
D4	CNC	sub	Call subroutine if No Carry
CC	CZ	sub	Call subroutine if Zero
C4	CNZ	sub	Call subroutine if Not Zero
FC	CM	sub	Call subroutine if Minus
F4	CP	sub	Call subroutine if Plus
EC	CPE	sub	Call subroutine if Parity Even
E4	CPO	sub	Call subroutine if Parity Odd

The 8080 also has a special purpose, single-byte subroutine call. It is

RST   exp   ReSTart at location 8 × exp

1	1	exp	1	1	1
7	6	5 3	2		0

The operand exp is an expression that must equal a digit from 0 to 7. When RST is executed, the address of the next instruction in sequence is pushed on the stack. Control is transferred to the location whose address is 8 times the digit. RST is usually used to store eight 8-byte subroutines in the first 64 words of memory. They service interrupts.

Subroutine return instructions Not surprisingly, the subroutine return instructions offer a similar selection of conditions. However, each subroutine return instruction requires just one byte. The return address does not need to be named by the instruction, because it has been saved on the stack by the subroutine call instructions. On return the address is automatically popped from the top of the stack into the program counter. Thus control transfers to the instruction following the subroutine call. The subroutine return instructions are as follows:

C9	RET	RETurn
D8	RC	Return if Carry
D0	RNC	Return if No Carry
F8	RM	Return if Minus
F0	RP	Return if Plus
E8	RPE	Return if Parity Even
E0	RPO	Return if Parity Odd

5.5.4 *Miscellaneous Instructions*

The 8085 has three single-byte instructions that are not among the three preceding categories. They are

FB	EI	Enable Interrupts
F3	DI	Disable Interrupts
00	NOP	No OPeration

EI and DI, respectively, allow the CPU to recognize interrupts or prevent it from doing so. NOP does nothing except to consume time and memory. What other instructions act as NOP?

Most 8085 instructions are summarized in Table 5.10 (see pp. 134–135).

5.5.5 *8085 Addressing Modes*

While the 8085 does not have as many addressing modes as the PDP-11, it nonetheless has several useful modes. They are more closely related to specific instructions in the 8085 than in the PDP-11 or in the M6800. Most 8085 instructions are associated with only one addressing mode, instead of with eight or twelve as in the PDP-11. The modes are:

- Direct addressing.
- Direct register and register pair addressing.
- Indirect register pair addressing.
- Stack pointer addressing.
- Immediate addressing.

Direct addressing When an instruction supplies the effective memory address it has **direct addressing**. For example,

```
LDA 0AB0H
```

has direct addressing. It means that the accumulator should be loaded from the contents of memory location AB0. The effective memory address is AB0; the operand is the contents of AB0.

Similarly, the instruction

```
SHLD 108H
```

uses direct addressing. It causes the contents of H and L to be stored in memory location 108 and 109.

What other 8080/8085 instructions have direct addressing?

Direct register and register pair addressing If an effective address is a register or register pair, the addressing mode is **direct register** (or register pair) **addressing**. The operand is the contents of the register or register pair. For example, in

```
DCR E
```

E is the effective address; the contents of E which will be decremented by the instruction are the operand.

Similarly, in

```
DAD B
```

the effective address is register pair B. The contents of B and C are added to those of the H and L registers. We could say that there are two effective addresses—register pairs B and H. The latter is implied by the instruction. The 8085 has such implied addresses in many instructions, and we will not choose to regard implied addresses as a separate addressing mode. What is the most common implied address?

Indirect register and register pair addressing Some instructions use a register pair, usually H, to point to a memory location. The effective address is the contents of the register pair—the memory location addressed by the register pair. The operand is the contents of that memory location. Such instructions have **indirect register pair addressing**. Whenever M is given in the operand field

Table 5.10
Summary of 8080 and 8085 instructions*

Instruction		Possible operand(s)	Byte(s)	Explanation
INR	reg	A, B, C	1	INcrement Register
DCR	reg	D, E, H L, M	1	DeCrement Register
MOV	dst, src		1	MOVe source to destination
ADD	reg		1	ADD register to A
ADC	reg		1	ADd register to A with Carry
SUB	reg		1	SUBtract register from A
SBB	reg		1	SuBtract register from A with Borrow
ANA	reg		1	ANd register with A
XRA	reg		1	eXclusive oR register with A
ORA	reg		1	OR register with A
CMP	reg		1	CoMPare register with A
MVI	reg, data	8 bits	2	MoVe Immediate data to register
CMC			1	CoMplement Carry
STC			1	SeT Carry
CMA			1	CoMplement Accumulator
DAA			1	Decimal Adjust Accumulator
RLC			1	Rotate accumulator Left without Carry
RRC			1	Rotate accumulator Right without Carry
RAL			1	Rotate Accumulator Left (through carry)
RAR			1	Rotate Accumulator Right (through carry)
ADI	data	8 bits	2	ADd Immediate
ACI	data		2	Add with Carry Immediate
SUI	data		2	SUbtract Immediate from A
SBI	data		2	SuBtract Immediate with Borrow
ANI	data		2	ANd Immediate to A
ORI	data		2	OR Immediate with A
XRI	data		2	eXclusive oR Immediate with A
CPI	data		2	ComPare Immediate with A
STA	addr	16 bits	3	STore A in address
LDA	addr		3	LoaD A from address
STAX	rp	B or D	1	STore A in location addressed by rp
LDAX	rp		1	LoaD A from location addressed by rp
PUSH	rp	B, D, H, or PSW	1	PUSH contents of rp on stack

* In addition to these instructions the 8080/8085 provides for conditional jumps, calls, and returns as discussed in Section 5.5.3.

Table 5.10 (Continued)

Instruction		Possible operand(s)	Byte(s)	Explanation
POP	rp	B, D, H, or PSW	1	POP top of stack to rp
DAD	rp	B, D	1	Double ADd rp to HL
INX	rp	H or SP	1	INcrement rp
DCX	rp		1	DeCrement rp
LXI	rp, data	B, D, H, or SP, 16 bits	3	Load Immediate data to rp
XCHG			1	eXCHange HL and DE
XTHL			1	eXchange HL with top of stack
SPHL			1	Load SP from HL
SHLD	addr		3	Store HL in addr and addr + 1
LHLD	addr		3	Load HL from addr and addr + 1
PCHL			1	load PC from HL
EI			1	Enable Interrupts
DI			1	Disable Interrupts
IN	port	8-bits	2	INput to A from port
OUT	port		2	OUTput from A to port
NOP			1	No OPeration
HLT			1	HaLT
RST	exp	0-7	1	ReSTart at 8 × exp
JMP	addr	⎰ 16	3	JuMP to address
CALL	sub	⎱ bits	3	CALL subroutine
RET			1	RETurn from subroutine

of an instruction, the effective address is M, which is the contents of the H and L registers. Although a symbol for effective address is shown in the instruction, this is not direct addressing. The actual addressing mode employed inside the computer is indirect register pair addressing. The contents of H and L must be examined; then the actual memory location can be inspected.

For example, the instruction

```
INR M
```

incremented the contents of the memory location addressed by H and L.

Two instructions address memory with either the B and C or the D and E registers. They are STAX and LDAX.

Stack pointer addressing **Stack pointer addressing**, used by PUSH and POP instructions, is a modification of indirect register pair addressing. The stack pointer is the register pair. After the address has been calculated and the operation performed, the stack pointer is either incremented by 2 (for POP) or decremented by 2 (for PUSH).

Immediate addressing As we have noted in reviewing 8085 instructions, a large number of them take immediate operands. Thus they have immediate addressing. There is no effective address; the operand—either 8 or 16 bits—is given directly. For example,

```
ADI 23H
```

means that the hexadecimal number 23 should be added to A.

With these addressing modes and a little cleverness, we can accomplish almost any operation we wish, although less easily, perhaps, than we might on the PDP-11. We will sorely miss indexed addressing, which is available on some microcomputers, such as the M6800. Lacking relative addressing, we will program in absolute code, rather than in position-independent code.

5.5.6 Additional 8085 Instructions

The 8085 has only two instructions that the 8080 does not. Both deal with processing interrupts. We will defer a full explanation until we discuss interrupts in detail. The instructions are:

20	RIM	Read Interrupt Mask
30	SIM	Set Interrupt Mask

5.6 M6800 Instructions

The M6800 has a relatively small number of basic instructions that are varied by employing different addressing modes. The instructions may be one, two, or three bytes long. Sometimes a single instruction can have any of these lengths, depending on the addressing mode chosen. Because addressing modes are so central to M6800 instructions, we will discuss those modes before examining instruction types.

5.6.1 Addressing Modes

The M6800 has seven addressing modes, some of which we have already seen. The modes are:

- Direct addressing.
- Extended addressing.
- Accumulator addressing.
- Inherent addressing.
- Immediate addressing.
- Relative addressing.
- Indexed addressing.

Direct and extended addressing An instruction that supplies the memory address has **direct addressing**. The M6800 has two types of direct addressing. In the first, called direct addressing by Motorola, an 8-bit address is the second byte of the instruction. In the second, called **extended addressing** by Motorola, a 16-bit address is the second and third bytes of the instruction. Direct addressing can reach only the first 256_{10} locations in memory; extended addressing can reach higher addresses. For example, the instructions

LDA A 44H

and

LDA A 2120H

illustrate direct and extended addressing, respectively. Accumulator A is loaded from the contents of location 44 by a two-byte instruction or from the contents of location 2120 by a three-byte instruction.

Accumulator addressing If an effective address of an instruction is an accumulator, the addressing mode is **accumulator addressing**. This mode is similar to direct register addressing (or just register addressing) for the 8085. The instruction

LDA A 44H

illustrates accumulator addressing as well as direct addressing. Having two addressing modes in the same instruction is termed **dual addressing**. Note that here we separate A (showing accumulator addressing) from 44H (showing direct addressing) by a space. Motorola commonly uses one or more spaces to separate addresses in dual addressing. In programs we frequently show a comma separating two addresses, in accordance with a common practice of Intel and other companies.

Inherent addressing When the operation code names the operands, the addressing mode is considered to be **inherent addressing**. For example,

ABA

means to add the contents of accumulators A and B and store the sum in accumulator A. The operands are inherent in the operation code. The 8080/8085 has a similar addressing mode, but Intel does not specifically identify it. We considered such instances as implied addressing for the 8085 and did not regard it as a separate addressing mode.

Immediate addressing In **immediate addressing** the operand—rather than its address—is stated. The immediate operand is preceded by a pound sign (#). For example,

ADD A #42H

means "add 42 hexadecimal to accumulator A."

Relative addressing Instructions with **relative addressing** show an offset that must be added to the address of the next instruction to yield the absolute address of the instruction. This addressing mode was discussed in detail in the section on branch instructions.

Indexed addressing With **indexed addressing** the address is determined in part from the contents of index register X. Typically the instruction shows an offset that is added to the contents of the index register to yield the effective address. For example,

```
LDA A 8,X
```

means load accumulator A from the contents of the location whose address is the sum of the contents of the index register plus 8. If the index register holds 2400H, the effective address is 2408H.

5.6.2 *Data Movement Instructions*

We will follow the same classification scheme for M6800 instructions as we did for the 8085. That is, we will divide instructions into four categories:

- Data movement.
- Data operation.
- Program control.
- Miscellaneous.

We will further subdivide the data movement category into three subparts:

- Moving data within a single register.
- Moving data between registers.
- Moving data between a register and memory or an input/output device.

Because of its different architecture, the M6800 does not have the two separate types of instructions that the 8085 had within this category. That is, since the M6800 uses memory mapped input/output, there are no special instructions for moving data between a register and an input/output device. Instead, the instructions for moving data between a register and memory suffice. The M6800 also has no special instructions for moving immediate data; instead, the immediate addressing mode is applied to basic data movement instructions.

Because of the applicability of several addressing modes, a single M6800 instruction may have many hexadecimal codes. For simplicity we will usually not show all combinations. Instead we will choose one, corresponding ordinarily to accumulator addressing for accumulator A.

Moving data within a single register The M6800 has five instructions for moving data within a single register. All five instructions can operate on accumulator A or accumulator B as well as with both extended and indexed addressing. Thus data can be moved within a memory location as well as within an accumulator. All five instructions affect the carry as well.

The first two instructions are rotations:

49　ROL　ROtate Left
46　ROR　ROtate Right

For both rotations the carry flag can be thought of as a one-bit extension to the left of the accumulator or memory. The rotation then involves 9 bits, with the contents of each bit shifted one location to the left or right as shown in Fig. 5.12.

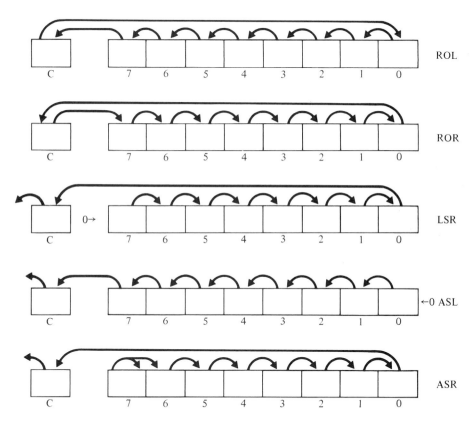

Fig. 5.12
M6800 rotate and shift instructions.

The third instruction is a right logical shift.

44　LSR　Logical Shift Right

A **logical shift** moves bits along a register in one direction. Bits shifted off at one end are lost; 0's are shifted in at the other end. In this right logical shift the carry flag is viewed as an extension to the right of bit 0. The value of bit 0 is moved to the carry; the previous value of the carry is lost; a 0 is entered into bit 7; and the remaining values are shifted one bit to the right. Why can this be thought of as either an 8-bit or a 9-bit logical shift?

The last two instructions are arithmetic shifts. An **arithmetic shift** is intended to accomplish arithmetic operations, typically multiplication and division. The M6800 arithmetic shifts differ from more typical arithmetic shifts in that the carry bit is affected and the sign bit is handled differently in the left shift. The shifts can be seen in Fig. 5.12. We will comment on them separately.

Although called an arithmetic shift, the operation

48 ASL Arithmetic Shift Left

is actually a logical left shift. The carry flag can be considered a one-bit extension to the left of the register or memory. A 0 is placed in bit 0; the contents of bits 0 through 6 move one place to the left; the value of bit 7 is moved into the carry; the previous value of the carry is lost.

The operation

47 ASR Arithmetic Shift Right

is a true right arithmetic shift corresponding to division by 2. The value of bit 7—the sign bit—stays constant. The contents of bits 7 through 1 are shifted one place to the right. The contents of bit 0 are moved into the carry; the value of the carry is lost.

The hexadecimal codes shown for these five instructions were for accumulator A. To adapt them for accumulator B or for extended or indexed addressing, the first digit should be changed from 4 to 5, 7, or 6, respectively.

Moving data between registers Due to its small number of registers the M6800 has just six instructions for moving data between registers. All employ inherent addressing. These six occur in three pairs for moving data between (a) accumulators A and B, (b) accumulator A and the processor condition code register, and (c) the index register and the stack pointer.

The first pair of instructions is:

16 TAB Transfer from accumulator A to accumulator B
06 TBA Transfer from accumulator B to accumulator A

In each case the contents of one accumulator are moved to the other, leaving the contents of the first accumulator (the source) unchanged. Earlier we showed a notation in which an arrow ← means "transfer the value on the left to the location on the right." With this notation we can describe TAB as

B ← A

This transfer is nondestructive; the contents of the source, accumulator A, stay as they were.

To understand the second pair of instructions,

06	TAP	Transfer from accumulator A to the processor condition code register
07	TPA	Transfer from the processor condition code register to accumulator A

we should quickly review the organization of the processor condition code register. It uses six bits of the 8-bit status register as shown below.

H	I	N	Z	V	C
5	4	3	2	1	0

Hence in the transfers only six bits of the accumulator are transferred, namely bits 5 through 0. The TPA instruction sets bits 6 and 7 of the accumulator to 1. We can adapt our descriptive notation by adding subscripts to show bits:

TAP $P \leftarrow A_{5-0}$
TPA $A_{5-0} \leftarrow P; A_{7-6} \leftarrow 1$

The next two instructions differ from the other transfers in that the data transferred are incremented or decremented in the transfer. Contents of the source register are not changed in either transfer. Abbreviating the stack pointer as SP and the index register as X, we can describe these transfers as

30	TSX	Transfer from Stack pointer to indeX register
		$X \leftarrow SP + 1; SP \leftarrow SP$
35	TXS	Transfer from indeX register to Stack pointer
		$SP \leftarrow X - 1; X \leftarrow X$

Moving data between a register and memory The M6800 has three instructions for moving data from memory to a register (**loading** a register) and three instructions for moving data from a register to memory (**storing** data in memory). The most powerful instructions deal with accumulators A and B. Because of their importance we show all the addressing modes and their hexadecimal codes.

	LDA	LoaD Accumulator		
86	A immediate		C6	B immediate
96	A direct		D6	B direct
B6	A extended		F6	B extended
A6	A indexed		E6	B indexed

	STA	STore Accumulator		
97	A direct		D7	B direct
B7	A extended		F7	B extended
A7	A indexed		E7	B indexed

The other four instructions provide for transfers between memory and the stack pointer and index register. Because both of these registers are 16 bits long, the transfers affect two memory locations. In all cases the memory locations are the one addressed in the instruction and the one with the next higher address. Two separate transfers are needed. The first is between the more significant byte of the register and the memory location named. The second is between the less significant byte of the register and the next higher memory location. For example, consider LDS with a direct address of M. Let the address of the next higher location be M + 1.

9E   LoaD Stack pointer

$$SP_{15-8} \leftarrow M$$
$$SP_{7-0} \leftarrow M+1$$

The other three instructions with the hexadecimal code for direct addressing shown are:

DE	LDX	LoaD indeX register
9F	STS	STore Stack pointer
DF	STX	STore indeX register

5.6.3 *Data Operations*

The M6800 has a large number of instructions for arithmetic operations and a smaller number for logical operations.

Arithmetic operations There are three basic addition instructions. The first uses inherent addressing:

1B   ABA   Add accumulator B to accumulator A

$$A \leftarrow B + A$$

The other two are more general. They can operate on accumulator A or accumulator B with immediate, direct, extended, or indexed addressing. In each case the accumulator named holds one operand and stores the result. We illustrate each for direct addressing with accumulator A. Then, because of their importance, we show the hexadecimal codes for the first digit of each instruction.

9B   ADD   ADD (without carry)

$$A \leftarrow A + M$$

99   ADC   ADd with Carry

$$A \leftarrow A + M + C$$

All ADD codes have B as the second digit. All ADC codes have 9 as the second digit. Codes for the first digit for these instructions and also for several other arithmetic and logical instructions are:

8	A immediate	C	B immediate
9	A direct	D	B direct
B	A extended	F	B extended
A	A indexed	E	B indexed

Similarly, there are three basic subtraction instructions. The first has inherent addressing:

10	SBA	Subtract accumulator B from accumulator A
		$A \leftarrow A - B$

The next two resemble the two multipurpose addition instructions. Coding is shown for direct addressing with accumulator A.

90	SUB	SUBtract
		$A \leftarrow A - M$
92	SBC	SuBtract with Carry
		$A \leftarrow A - M - C$

We usually think of subtraction as involving a borrow, not a carry. However, the carry can be used as a borrow so that we do not need a borrow flag. Can you convince yourself of this? If not, you can read more about arithmetic operations later.

The coding of the second digit of SUB is 0; the coding of the second digit of SBC is 2. The codes for the first digit are the same as for addition.

A decimal adjust instruction affects only accumulator A. It corrects the result of binary addition to the proper decimal sum as explained in Chapter 2. We will examine its use in a later chapter.

19	DAA	Decimal Adjust A

Six instructions increment or decrement the contents of various registers by 1. Four employ inherent addressing and operate on either the index register or the stack pointer.

34	DES	DEcrement Stack pointer	$SP \leftarrow SP - 1$
09	DEX	DEcrement indeX register	$X \leftarrow X - 1$
31	INS	INcrement Stack pointer	$SP \leftarrow SP + 1$
08	INX	INcrement indeX register	$X \leftarrow X + 1$

The remaining two instructions can operate on accumulator A or accumulator B or can use extended or indexed addressing. We illustrate them for accumulator A. The first digit should be changed to 5, 7, or 6 for accumulator B or for extended or indexed addressing, respectively.

4A	DEC	DECrement
4C	INC	INCrement

Logical operations Three basic logical operations can be performed on two operands. Direct, immediate, extended, and indirect addressing can be used with accumulators A and B. Codes for the first digit of these instructions are the same as for addition instructions. We illustrate direct addressing with accumulator A. In each case the accumulator named holds one operand and stores the result.

94	AND	logical AND	A ← A AND M
98	EOR	Exclusive OR	A ← A XOR M
9A	ORA	OR Accumulator	A ← A OR M

Three logical (or arithmetic) operations can be performed on a single operand. All three use the familiar first digits of 4 for accumulator A, 5 for accumulator B, 7 for extended addressing, and 6 for indexed addressing. For accumulator A these operations are:

4F	CLR	CLeaR	A ← 0
43	COM	COMplement	A ← $\overline{A}$ (each bit is complemented)
40	NEG	NEGate	A ← $\overline{A}$ + 1

The last four logical operations let us set or clear two condition flags—the carry and overflow flags. They are:

OC	CLC	CLear Carry
OA	CLV	CLear oVerflow
OD	SEC	SEt Carry
OB	SEV	SEt oVerflow

5.6.4 *Program Control*

Five instructions allow comparisons. The simplest compares the contents of accumulators A and B by subtracting B from A without altering either, and affects flags N, Z, V, and C accordingly:

| 11 | CRA | CompaRe Accumulators |

The second compares the contents of the index register with the contents of two memory bytes and sets or clears the Z flag accordingly. Addressing modes and their corresponding first digits are immediate (8), direct (9), extended (B), and indexed (A). The more significant byte of the index register is compared with the addressed byte; the less significant byte of the index register is compared with the next higher memory byte (address one higher). For direct addressing the instruction is

| 9C | CPX | ComPare indeX register |

The third instruction tests the contents of accumulator A (first digit 4), accumulator B (5), an extended memory address (7), or an indexed memory address (6) to see whether they are 0 and sets the N and Z flags accordingly. For accumulator A, the instruction is

4D   TST   (Set flags Z and N according to A $-$ 0)

A more powerful comparison instruction allows us to compare the contents of accumulator A or B and memory using immediate, direct, extended, or indexed addressing with the same first-digit coding as for addition. For direct addressing with ACCA the instruction is

91   CMP   CoMPare

A more complex comparison lets us logically AND the contents of accumulator A or B with memory and set the N and Z flags accordingly. Thus we can test any bits of the memory location that we like by first placing in the accumulator the bit pattern we desire for a mask. A 0 in a bit position masks the corresponding bit of the memory location; a 1 extracts or displays the corresponding bit. Coding of the first digit is the same as for the compare instruction, and the same addressing modes are available. For direct addressing with accumulator A the instruction is

95   BIT   BIT test

The M6800 allows many possibilities for branching, based ordinarily on the results of the preceding comparison instructions. All branch instructions have relative addressing. We looked at them earlier in the chapter, but will list them again briefly here with their hexadecimal codes.

24	BCC	Branch if Carry Clear (C = 0)
25	BCS	Branch if Carry Set (C = 1)
27	BEQ	Branch if EQual (to zero) (Z = 1)
2C	BGE	Branch if Greater than or Equal (to zero)
2E	BGT	Branch if Greater Than (zero)
22	BHI	Branch if HIgher
2F	BLE	Branch if Less than or Equal (to zero)
23	BLS	Branch if Lower or Same
2D	BLT	Branch if Less Than (zero)
2B	BMI	Branch if MInus (N = 1)
26	BNE	Branch if Not Equal (to zero) (Z = 0)
2A	BPL	Branch if PLus (N = 0)
20	BRA	BRanch Always
28	BVC	Branch if oVerflow Clear (V = 0)
29	BVS	Branch if oVerflow Set (V = 1)

An alternative to the BRA instruction is a jump instruction that can be used with either extended addressing (first digit 7) or indexed addressing (first digit 6). Its advantage is a 16-bit memory address:

7E   JMP   JuMP

Three instructions allow transferring to or from subroutines. The first uses either extended addressing (first digit B) or indexed addressing (first digit A); the other two have inherent addressing.

BD	JSR	Jump to SubRoutine
8D	BSR	Branch to SubRoutine
39	RTS	ReTurn from Subroutine

Two instructions involve stack operations. We will discuss stacks in detail later. For the moment we note that a stack is an area of memory in which data are stored in a last-in, first-out manner. A stack pointer holds the address where the next data may be stored. Storing data on the stack, or **pushing**, is accompanied by decrementing the stack pointer. Removing data from the stack, or **pulling** (called **popping** on most other computers), is accompanied by incrementing the stack pointer. Either accumulator may be the source of a push or the destination of a pull. We show both codings.

36 for A	37 for B	PSH	PuSH accumulator contents onto stack
32 for A	33 for B	PUL	PULl data from stack

5.6.5 *Miscellaneous Instructions*

Like the 8085, the M6800 has a no-operation instruction that consumes time and memory but otherwise does nothing:

01	NOP	NO oPeration

It also has five instructions dealing with interrupts—events or devices that cause the computer to stop processing its current program in order to deal with the interrupt. We will discuss interrupts in detail later. For the moment we simply list the five instructions. Two of them deal with setting or clearing an interrupt mask bit in the condition code register in order to enable or disable the microprocessor's interrupt handling capability:

OE	CLI	CLear Interrupt mask
OF	SEI	SEt Interrupt mask

The remaining three concern processing the interrupt itself:

3F	SWI	SoftWare Interrupt
3B	RTI	ReTurn from Interrupt
3E	WAI	WAIt for interrupt

5.7 *Instructions of the Z-80 and the Mostek MCS6500*

In this section we will briefly look at some of the additional instructions of the Zilog Z-80 and the Mostek MCS6500. We have two purposes. First, if you are using one of these processors rather than the 8085 or the M6800, you will want to know about its extra features. Second, even if you are not using one of these processors, you will learn something by seeing an augmented instruction set.

5.7.1 *Z-80 Instructions*

The Z-80 includes all 8080 instructions as a subset. Although they have different mnemonics, the same hexadecimal codes are used. As we noted earlier in the chapter, the Z-80 has an extra copy of all basic 8080 programmable registers as well as two 16-bit index registers. It also has an interrupt vector register and a memory refresh counter. To obtain additional instructions the Z-80 has taken unused 8080 operation codes, such as CB, and used them to signal that a special Z-80 operation code is in the next byte. Hence all new Z-80 instructions require at least two bytes. In this quick overview we will not specify hexadecimal codes but will simply describe the major new addressing mode instructions.

The Z-80 has added two more addressing modes, similar to those we saw in the M6800. Because of the added index registers, it has a number of memory reference instructions with indexed addressing. Using indexed addressing frees the BC and DE register pairs for other operations. Indexed addressing can be supplemented by a one-byte displacement, allowing 8-bit relative addressing. This type of relative addressing differs from that of the M6800, which is relative to the contents of the program counter; in the Z-80 relative addressing relates to the contents of a 16-bit index register.

As you will recall, the 8085 does not have an overflow flag. The Z-80 has added an overflow flag and also a subtract status flag. The parity flag serves as an overflow flag when binary arithmetic is being done. Then parity is of no interest, while overflow is important; thus this double use makes sense. The subtract flag distinguishes between decimal addition and subtraction when the decimal adjust instruction is used.

Two new instructions deal with blocks of memory. A block compare instruction allows searching a block of memory—that is, several consecutive bytes—for a given value. A block move instruction allows moving a block from one area of memory to another or to an output port.

Other added instructions deal with testing or altering contents of registers and memory. Improved interrupt logic and added instructions result in easier handling of interrupts.

5.7.2 *Mostek MCS6500 Instructions*

Comparing the 6500 with the M6800 is more difficult than comparing the Z-80 with the 8080/8085. The Z-80 is closely related to the 8080; its instruction set consists of 8080 instructions plus some others. The 6500, while related to the M6800, has less in common with it. The two processors share a similar design and have many common instructions, but they differ in many important respects. We cannot simply take a program written for the M6800 and run it on a

6500 without making changes. In our discussion here we will look at a few interesting features of the 6500 but will not consider all the differences.

We note first that the 6500 has different addressing modes. Its indexed addressing uses two 8-bit index registers X and Y instead of one 16-bit index register. It has two modes of index addressing. In one, the contents of either index register are added to the second byte of the instruction; in the other, they are added to the second and third bytes of the instruction. The 6500 also has **indirect** addressing, in which the second and third bytes of an instruction are interpreted as the address of a memory location whose contents are the desired address. We will examine indirect addressing in a later chapter.

The 6500 has two new status flags. A **break** status flag is set whenever a software interrupt is executed. A **decimal mode** flag is set whenever decimal arithmetic is being performed. The programmer writes a set decimal mode instruction when decimal arithmetic is to be performed and a clear decimal mode instruction when arithmetic should return to binary. The programmer does not need to be concerned with the details of decimal calculations.

5.8 *Running a Machine Language Program*

Microcomputers vary considerably in the input and output devices they offer users. Inputs may be from toggle switches, thumb wheels, octal or hexadecimal keyboards, or full typewriterlike keyboards. Outputs may be lights, octal or hexadecimal displays, oscilloscopes, or typed copy. If your microcomputer has either toggle switches and lights or a full keyboard with hard copy output, you may learn more about its use by reading the last section of Chapter 4 (on running the PDP-11) than by reading this section.

Since there is no single illustration that can cover all variations, we will take a middle approach. We will assume that the input of our microcomputer consists of a hexadecimal keyboard along with some special keys called function keys. The output consists of a six-digit display, with four digits for addresses and two for data. The method by which the individual digits are shown is known as seven-segment display, because any digit can be shown by lighting or not lighting each of seven segments. This produces what looks like a squared-off 8 when all segments are lit. (See Fig. 5.13.) Associated with the keyboard is a simple **monitor** that senses the switches and executes the desired functions. We will assume that our microcomputer allows recording of programs and data onto a magnetic tape cassette and that such programs can later be loaded into memory from the cassette.

Functions of the keys (see Fig. 5.13) are as follows.

LOAD MEM   Loads two bits of data into desired memory location and then advances to the next memory location; when first used, both address and memory are loaded via the

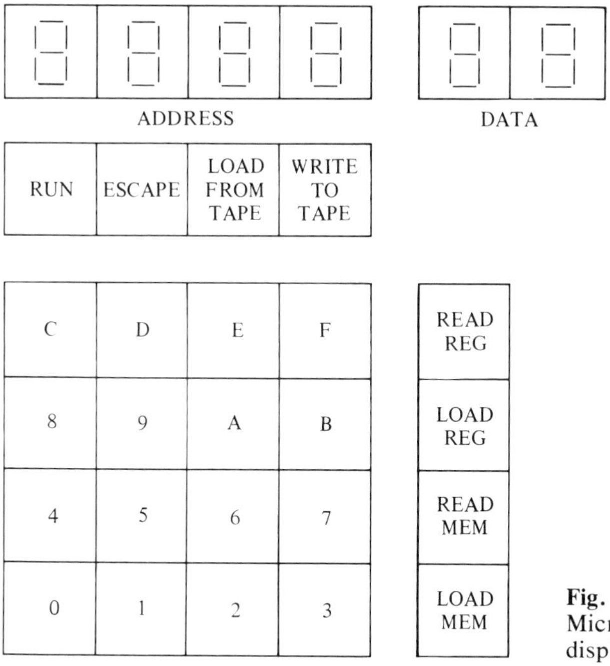

ADDRESS   DATA

RUN	ESCAPE	LOAD FROM TAPE	WRITE TO TAPE

C	D	E	F	READ REG
8	9	A	B	LOAD REG
4	5	6	7	READ MEM
0	1	2	3	LOAD MEM

Fig. 5.13
Microcomputer keyboard and display.

	hexadecimal keys; thereafter only the data need be entered.
READ MEM	Displays the value of the previously entered memory location and then advances to the next memory location.
LOAD REG	Enters two digits into the specified register.
READ REG	Displays the contents of the specified register.
WRITE TO TAPE	Records on magnetic tape the contents of memory between an entered starting address and an entered final address.
LOAD FROM TAPE	Loads memory between a specified starting address and a specified final address with data from magnetic tape.
ESCAPE	Allows escape from any function.
RUN	Runs program starting from specified address.

Your microcomputer may have a different selection of functions, but it probably will include most of these. You may also have some functions that help to find errors in your program. We will deal with this topic in the next chapter.

Table 5.11
Procedure for loading and running Intel 8085 program for adding three numbers

Hexadecimal keys	Function keys	Comment
10003E	READ MEM	Starting address and first instruction
	LOAD MEM	Loads instruction and advances
00		
	LOAD MEM	
80		
	LOAD MEM	
81		
	LOAD MEM	
82		
	LOAD MEM	
76		Last instruction
	LOAD MEM	
B13		First number for B
	LOAD REG	
C21		Second number for C
	LOAD REG	
D32		Third number for D
	LOAD REG	
1000		Starting address
	READ MEM	Go to starting address
	RUN	
A		
	READ REG	Examine sum in A

As an example of the use of this system, consider the procedure shown in Table 5.11 for loading and running a simple Intel 8085 program, the one that appeared in Table 5.2. After we specify the starting address, we load instructions into memory by alternately keying the instructions on the hexadecimal keyboard and pushing the LOAD MEM key. Because this program works with data in registers, after we have loaded the instructions we must also load the registers. When all data and instructions have been entered, we return to the starting address and run the program. Then we can inspect the sum in the accumulator by the read register function.

5.S *Summary*

Most 8-bit microcomputers have four main parts, which may be implemented as separate chips or may be combined on one or two chips. These parts are the CPU for control and arithmetic functions, ROM for permanent storage of programs and constant data, RAM for temporary storage of data, and interface logic for connection with external devices. The parts are interconnected by a data bus, a control bus, and an address bus.

The Intel 8080/8085 has seven 8-bit programmable registers that may be combined into register pairs. The M6800 has two 8-bit accumulators and a 16-bit index register and stack pointer. Both microcomputers have a 16-bit program counter and a condition codes register for carry, sign, zero, and selected other functions. The Zilog Z-80 and the Mostek 6500 are variations of the 8080 and M6800, respectively, offering more flexible architecture and extra instructions.

Instructions have two basic parts. The operation code names the action or operation that the computer will perform. The operand names the value to be operated on. Microcomputers with 8-bit words typically have instructions that may be one, two, or three bytes long.

Assembly language instructions have four fields. The label names the statement's address. The operation code shows the operation to be performed. The operand gives data or address information. The comment allows the programmer to add explanatory material.

Assembly language programs may be hand-assembled, with the programmer translating symbols and mnemonics to numeric values, they may be self-assembled (translated on the computer they were written for), or they may be cross-assembled (translated on a larger computer). During assembly an assembly language source program is translated to a machine language object program.

Pseudoinstructions are messages to the assembler that are not translated into machine code. Important pseudoinstructions are the origin instruction, showing the starting address, and the end instruction, showing that the program and all its data are complete.

Simple programs may be implemented in straight-line fashion. More complex programs require branching instructions that may be conditional or unconditional. Procedures that will be performed at more than one point may be programmed as modules termed subroutines, which may be called by the main program whenever needed.

Instructions may be arbitrarily categorized as being designed for data movement, data operations, program control, and miscellaneous. In general, only data operation instructions perform basic operations for the problem to be solved. Data movement instructions simply transfer data to various locations in preparation for operational instructions. Program control instructions direct the execution of the program.

The 8080/8085 offers direct, register, indirect, stack pointer, and immediate addressing. The M6800 has direct, extended, accumulator, inherent, immediate, relative, and indexed addressing. We will discuss these addressing modes in greater detail in later chapters.

Loading and executing a program can be done readily on a microcomputer with a hexadecimal keyboard and seven-segment displays.

Key Terms

accumulator addressing
address bus
arithmetic shift
assembler
assembly language
auxiliary carry
call
carry
comment
conditional transfer
control bus
cross-assembly
data bus
decimal adjustment
default decimal convention
direct addressing
even parity
extended addressing
field
flag
free fields
hand assembly
immediate addressing
index register
indexed addressing
inherent addressing
interface
interrupt
interrupt mask
isolated input/output
label
label table
load
logical shift
loop

machine language
memory-mapped input/output
mnemonic
monitor
nondestructive transfer
object program
operand
operation code (op code)
origin
overflow flag
parity
passing parameters
pointer
port
program counter (PC)
program status word (PSW)
pseudoinstruction
RAM
register addressing
register pairs
relative addressing
return instruction
ROM
self-assembly
sign flag
software compatible
source program
stack
stack pointer (SP)
stack pointer addressing
store
subroutine
unconditional transfers
upward compatible
zero flag

5.R *References*

Many helpful books cover the material of this chapter. One of the most readable is Osborne (1978), a good general introduction to microcomputers. Leventhal (1978) presents information on 6800 and 8085 programming in two separate books. Other useful texts are Hilburn and Julich (1977), Klingman (1977), and Korn (1978). A more advanced book, stressing instrumentation, is

Peatman (1977). The user's manuals for the microcomputer that you are using are invaluable references.

5.1 What are the main parts of a microcomputer?

5.2 What buses does a microcomputer have?

5.3 Describe the registers of the 8085 and M6800.

5.4 Describe the condition codes of the 8085 and M6800.

5.5 What are the four parts of an assembly language statement? Which are optional?

5.6 Why do 8-bit microcomputers have instructions of different lengths?

5.7 What is the main purpose of the first byte of an 8-bit microcomputer instruction?

5.8 Why do assembly language programs have pseudo-instructions?

5.9 Explain how to hand assemble a program.

5.10 What are the four main groups of instructions and their purposes?

5.11 Describe the addressing modes of the 8085.

5.12 Describe the addressing modes of the M6800.

Section 5.3

5.1 State whether the following names are valid labels:
   a) START   e) CONSTANTINOPLE
   b) 100A   f) ONE A
   c) HALT   g) END
   d) JMP   h) TWICE

Section 5.4

5.2 Modify the program of Section 5.4.1 to add five numbers. Show both machine and assembly language forms.

5.3 Write an assembly language program to test three numbers to determine how many are zero. For the 8085 assume the numbers are stored in registers B, D, and E; keep the count in C. For the M6800 assume the numbers are stored in memory locations 60H, 61H, and 62H; keep the count in ACCB.

5.4 Calculate the destinations of M6800 branch instructions with first byte stored at memory location $2A17_{16}$ and the following offsets.
   a) 21_{16} b) FF_{16} c) AB_{16} d) 76_{16}

5.5 Calculate the offset needed to branch from M6800 memory location $096A_{16}$ to the following locations.
a) $0A12_{16}$ b) 0900_{16} c) $08AF_{16}$ d) $09F0_{16}$

Section 5.6

5.6 Write an assembly language program for Problem 3.1 (absolute values).

5.7 Write an assembly language program for Problem 3.2 (overflow).

5.8 Write an assembly language program for Problem 3.4 (loops).

5.9 Write an assembly language program for Problem 3.6 (sorting). For the 8085 assume A, B, and C are in B, D, and E, respectively. For the M6800 assume they are in memory locations 50, 51, and 52.

System Software

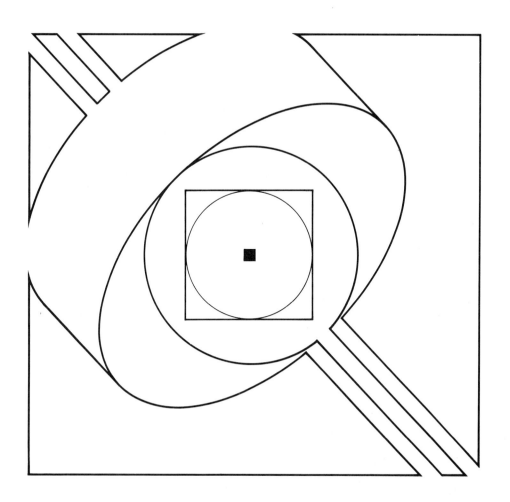

6.1 *Introduction*

To prepare and use assembly and high-level language programs, we need several other programs. As a minimum, we would like an editor that allows us to make changes in our programs easily. For assembly language programs we need an assembler to convert the source program, written in assembly language, to an object program, written in machine code. (For high-level language programs we need similar conversion programs, called interpreters or compilers, but we will defer that discussion until the chapter on high-level languages.) Because our program will probably not execute correctly the first time, we need debugging programs to help us find our mistakes. In addition to the foregoing, we may need a loader to load these programs into memory. We may also want a simulator to simulate hardware and software operations.

All these programs are examples of **system software**—programs that help us use the computer itself, as opposed to programs that are designed to process data for the user. In all but the simplest computer systems each of the programs just described will be run under the control of a monitor or executive program. The **monitor** is the controlling element of the computer's **operating system**, a group of system programs. Because the monitor will control use of other system software, we will begin our discussion with the monitor.

6.2 *Monitors*

The monitor is the center of communications for the computer. It recognizes commands from the computer's control panel or keyboard and calls and controls other system and user programs. A monitor may be as simple as a few hundred bytes of code that control a dozen control panel functions or it may be a complex program with the capability of dealing with real-time events on a wide variety of input/output devices. Advanced monitors can allocate computer resources to several programs that reside in the computer at one time.

Monitor functions may include any of the following:

- Scan keyboard or terminal and identify commands.
- Display output.
- Assign input/output devices.
- Control other systems programs.
- Allocate resources to user programs.
- Resolve priorities.
- Determine time and date.
- Transfer information between memory and input/output devices.

In this section we will look at several representative monitors.

We will look first at a PDP-11 monitor that is typical of many minicomputer monitors. This monitor is designed to work with floppy disk storage. We will discuss disks later, in the chapter on memory. For the moment we can think of a floppy disk as something like a 45 rpm record on which information can be stored.

We will address commands to the monitor via a Decwriter, a typewriterlike terminal. Other minicomputer and microcomputer systems might instead use a terminal with a **cathode ray tube (CRT)** display, which looks much like a TV screen. CRT terminals are more convenient to use unless a hard copy (printed paper) output is needed. Either a Decwriter or a CRT terminal is preferable to a Teletype—the former mainstay of the communications industry—which is slow and noisy, and requires using troublesome paper tapes.

The PDP-11 system that we will study deals with information stored as **files**—blocks of information, such as a program or data, that begin with a file header and end with an end-of-file mark. We will be able to create files for programs that we are processing and later delete them to free space on the disk for other programs. We can name a file with any one to six letters or digits. If we like, we can follow its name with a period (.) and three more characters called an **extension**. For example, we could have a file named SLOAN with an extension ONE, resulting in SLOAN.ONE. If several people are to be using a system, it is best to select a distinctive file name rather than something like MYFILE. You should pick a file name that you're sure you will remember—both for ease of reference when you are using the file and for ease of deletion when you are finished with it.

We will interact conversationally with the monitor. Specifically, we will end each command to the monitor by typing a carriage return (CR) so that the monitor will recognize that we have completed an instruction to it, and then the monitor will execute our command, typically with some clattering of the floppy disc. When it has finished, the monitor will in turn prompt (signal) us that it is ready for a new command. Alternatively, it may request more information before executing the command. Its basic **prompts** are a period (.) and an asterisk (*), usually appearing in the first column of a new line. (The asterisk is generally created by programs, not by the monitor.)

Depending on our PDP-11 system, the monitor may be either a single-job or a foreground/background monitor. A **single-job monitor** handles just one program at a time. It executes that program until either the program finishes or the user interrupts the program from the console. A **foreground/background** monitor handles two independent programs that are in memory at the same time. One program, called the **foreground program**, has priority. It runs until it gives control to the other program, called the **background program**. Then the background program can run until the foreground program needs to resume control. In most of the following discussion we will assume that we are using the simpler single-job monitor. However, we will show some commands that work only on a foreground/background monitor.

Let's look at how we can get into the monitor mode on our PDP-11. We must first place the disk containing the monitor into the floppy disk controller. Then we must turn on the PDP-11, as we discussed in the last section of Chapter 4. We turn the power knob to ON, and depress the CONTROL and BOOT switches. We call this procedure **booting** the system. The computer then responds with four six-digit octal numbers—the contents of registers R0, R4, R6, and R7—and a dollar sign, for example,

```
157400   176400   173400   000030$
$
```

The computer is now in the machine language mode, in which machine language programs can be entered and run as discussed in Chapter 4. To get into the monitor mode we must now type

```
DX  (CR)
```

The computer responds with the name of the operating system, skips a few lines, and gives a prompt. For example,

```
RT-11SJ   V02C-02
```

We may now type a command to the monitor beside the period.

Suppose that in file SLOAN.ONE we have a source program that we wish to assemble. SLOAN.ONE is a symbolic file with instructions and data stored as ASCII characters. In the following paragraphs we will show the steps needed to assemble and run the program. The names of the commands used in this description are idiosyncratic and pertain only to a particular PDP-11 monitor, but the procedure is much the same as for any other disk operating system. Note that in each line of the dialog the beginning period or asterisk is placed there by the computer; the user does not type them.

The name of the assembler we will use is MACRO. We call it by typing beside the period

```
.R MACRO (CR)
```

The computer returns an asterisk. To assemble the program we now type beside the asterisk

```
*SLOAN.OBJ,SLOAN.LST=SLOAN.ONE (CR)
```

The extension OBJ means object program; LST means listing. The command tells the assembler that our object program and listing should be derived from the symbolic file input SLOAN.ONE. If our program is assembled correctly, the computer responds with a message like the following:

```
ERRORS DETECTED:   0
FREE CORE:   1800.   WORDS
```

These statements mean that no errors were detected and that a lot of memory was left.

If, instead, the assembler found errors it would show the number of errors. To examine them you would type

```
*,TT:=SLOAN.ONE/C:R:M:P:S:C:E
```

This would produce the source listing and several tables. The instruction ,TT is a basic print command. The letters appearing after the slash (/) are optional—as is the slash—and are called switches. The switches have the following meanings.

C   Print the following listings
S   User-defined tables such as labels
R   Registers used and their assigned names
M   Macros
P   Permanent symbols such as instructions
C   Control sections
E   Error codes

If no switches are chosen, just the source listing and a symbol table (see Section 6.4) will be printed.

Assuming that the assembler found errors, we will wish to correct our program by using the editor. To get into the editor mode, we type

```
.R EDIT (CR)
```

We then can edit our program as described in the next section.

When the program has been assembled correctly, we will want to create an **absolute element** that we can run, as contrasted with the **relocatable element** that is the output of the assembler. To do this, we must first return to monitor mode by typing a control C; that is, we must type a C while holding down the CTRL key. The result looks like any other C on paper but signals the monitor that we have finished using whatever program we have been using—in this case, the assembler:

```
.C
```

Then we call the **linker**, the program that will create an absolute element, by typing

```
.R LINK (CR)
```

To link our program we type

```
*SLOAN.SAV,SLOAN.MAP=SLOAN.OBJ
```

This tells the linker to construct an absolute element (SAV) and map (MAP)

from the relocatable element (OBJ). The names of the extensions SAV, MAP, and OBJ are all dictated by the format of the monitor. We will explain more about the linker later, in the section on loaders. After the linker has finished its processing it returns a prompt, and we then type a request for printed output:

```
* TT:=SLOAN (CR)
```

The computer responds

```
RT-11 LINK  V04=04  LOAD  MAP
SECTION ADDR  SIZE  ENTRY  ADDR  ENTRY  ADDR  ENTRY  ADDR
.ABS.  000000  001000
       001000  00XXXX
TRANSFER ADDRESS = 001000
HIGH LIMIT = XXXXXX
```

This information tells us that our assembled program has been assigned a starting address of 1000 and that its last address is XXXXXX (where XXXXXX are the octal numbers of the address).

Next we exit from the linker with a control C and load the program. We type

```
.C
.R SLOAN.SAV (CR)
```

Now our absolute element is loaded into memory, but the monitor is still active. We wish to run our machine language program in the way discussed in Chapter 4. To do so, we must abandon the monitor by turning the system off and rebooting it. Then, as described in Section 4.6.2, we can type

```
$L 1000 (CR)
$S
```

to load the program counter with 1000 and start executing the program.

Monitor commands for the PDP-11, including several we have not discussed, are summarized in Table 6.1.

6.2.2   *INTELLEC 8I Monitor for the 8080*

Our next example is a microcomputer monitor, the monitor for the INTELLEC 8I, a system development tool for Intel 8080 microcomputer users. The INTELLEC 8I system also includes an editor and an assembler.

The INTELLEC 8I monitor is implemented on eight PROM (programmable read-only memory) modules, each holding up to 256 bytes. (We store programs in PROM while we are developing them because we can erase and reprogram PROM as often as we like. Later after we have completely tested our programs, we may have them placed in ROM, which cannot be reprogrammed.) The monitor is designed to be used with the INTELLEC 8I front panel and a Teletype. Its starting address of the monitor is 3800_{16}. Like the PDP-11 monitor, this monitor is file-oriented and conversational. The monitor

Table 6.1
PDP-11 monitor commands

Command	Name	Meaning
ASS	ASSIGN	Assign a name to a device.
SET	SET	Change device characteristics.
GE	GET	Load program of file into memory.
B	BASE	Set base address for relocation.
E	EXAMINE	Examine contents of memory.
D	DEPOSIT	Deposit values into locations.
SAV	SAVE	Save memory contents in file.
R	RUN	Run a background program.
ST	START	Execute a program at specified address.
RE	REENTER	Start program at reentry address.
DAT	DATE	Enter indicated date or print current date.
TIM	TIME	Enter indicated time or print current time.
IN	INITIALIZE	Initialize background program.
CLO	CLOSE	Save files for background program.
LOA	LOAD	Load device handler into memory.
UNL	UNLOAD	Free device handler from memory.
FRU	FRUN	Run foreground program.
SUS	SUSPEND	Stop executing foreground program.
RSU	RSUME	Resume executing foreground program.

and other system software use the first 16 bytes of memory for temporary storage. Hence the user should avoid those locations for applications programs.

To access the monitor, we must turn the INTELLEC 8I on, turn the Teletype on in its line position, and jump to address 3800. To do the last we place a "jump to 3800" command (C30038H) in the first three locations of the system and press RESET. The exact sequence is:

1. Press MEM ACCESS, enabling the memory access.
2. Set all address, data, and instruction switches to 0.
3. Press LOAD, setting the console address register to 0.
4. Set Address/Instruction/Data switches (0,1,6, and 7) to C3H.
5. Press DEP, placing C3 in location 0.
6. Press INCR to increment the address register to 1.
7. Set Address/Instruction/Data switches to 0.
8. Press DEP, loading 00 into location 1.
9. Press INCR.
10. Set Address/Instruction/Data switches to 38H.
11. Press DEP to load 38H into location 2.
12. Press RESET to start executing the monitor.

Each command we give the monitor consists of a single letter typed on the Teletype that may be followed by one or more arguments, such as device names or memory addresses. Each command ends with a carriage return (CR) or space. Arguments must be separated by spaces or by commas. When the monitor has finished processing a command and is ready for another, it prompts us with a period (.). If the monitor detects a mistake we made in typing a command, it will prompt instead with an asterisk (*). We should then retype the command.

Before using the monitor or any other system programs, we will usually assign input/output (I/O) devices. The INTELLEC recognizes four logical types of I/O devices; all are character-oriented; their basic unit of information is a character, not a bit. The types are:

- Console—An interactive device used for both input and output; for example, a Teletype or CRT.

- Reader—An input device that transfers data on command and signals when it reaches an end-of-file condition; for example, a Teletype keyboard or paper tape reader.

- Punch—An output device that accepts a character from the system and records it on some external medium; for example, a Teletype punch.

- List—An output or high-speed punch device that accepts a character from the system and records it on an external medium in a form we can read; for example, a Teletype or CRT.

Each of these four logical types of devices may have any one of four physical devices actually associated with it at any time. Each logical type has a two-bit field that shows its current assignment. An I/O status byte stored in memory holds the assignments.

	List		Punch		Reader		Console	
I/O status byte	7	6	5	4	3	2	1	0

We will not consider all the details of these assignments. When the system is reset, the I/O status byte is set to 00H, resulting in the Teletype being selected for all logical devices.

Let's suppose that we wish to assemble a program that we have punched on paper tape. After entering the monitor, we must load the assembler, which is also stored on paper tape. Rather than loading it via the slow Teletype paper tape reader, we choose to load it via a high-speed paper tape reader. We must first assign this special reader to the logical reader by typing

```
.AR = P (CR)
```

The initial A is for the assign command, R is for reader, and P is for paper tape reader. Remember that the monitor supplies the initial (prompting) period.

We also choose to assign a separate high-speed punch to simplify assembly. Hence we type

.AP = P (CR)

We will use the Teletype as our logical console and list devices. We do not need to assign it because this is the **default** assignment (the assignment that occurs when no other is specified).

Next we execute a read command by typing

.R (CR)

The assembler will be loaded into memory. After it has been completely loaded, the monitor will prompt us for a "go to 0010" command (10 is the starting address of the assembler). We type

.GO010 (CR)

The INTELLEC assembler then begins operating. It is a two-pass assembler, meaning that it needs to read the source paper tape twice, as we will explain in the section on assemblers. We load the paper tape with our assembly language source program into the paper tape reader. Then we type "1" on the Teletype. The input tape is then read in, and the assembler proceeds with its first pass. When it is finished, it types

. P =

on the Teletype. Now we must reload our assembly language program into the paper tape reader and type "4" on the Teletype. This causes the assembler to proceed with its second pass. When it has finished, it prints a listing of the program, including any error messages, and it sends the machine language object program to the logical punch device—the high-speed punch.

If the assembler found any errors, we will wish to edit our program using the text editor. To use it, we follow the same procedure as with the assembler. We load its paper tape into a tape reader and type a "go to 0010" command.

If our program assembled correctly, we will want to load it into memory. We take the machine language object tape produced by the assembler and load it into our paper tape reader. We then type a read command on the Teletype:

R (CR)

We are then ready to execute our program. If the starting address is any location other than 0, we must load a "jump to starting address" instruction, following the same procedure as we used to jump to 3800 for the monitor.

The INTELLEC monitor has some instructions that the PDP-11 monitor lacked. Some of these deal with PROM. We can program a PROM module that has been placed in a special socket on the INTELLEC with a special "program PROM" command. Similarly, we can load memory from a PROM with a "transfer PROM to memory" command. We can compare the contents of 256 bytes of a PROM plugged into that socket with the contents of memory. If the

Table 6.2
INTELLEC monitor commands

Letter	Command	Meaning
A	ASSIGN I/O DEVICE	Assign actual device to logical device.
B	PUNCH INBNPF FORMAT	Punch tape in special binary format.
C	COMPARE PROM WITH MEMORY	Compare 256 bytes and print mismatches.
D	DISPLAY IN HEXADECIMAL FORMAT	Display memory contents in hexadecimal.
E	END	Create end-of-file mark (60 null characters).
F	FILL MEMORY	Load data into memory.
G	GO TO	Go to specified address.
H	HEXADECIMAL ARITHMETIC	Print sum and difference of arguments.
L	LOAD BNPF FORMAT	Load from BNPF tape memory.
M	MOVE	Move a block of memory.
N	PUNCH NULL	Punch 60 null characters.
P	PROGRAM PROM	Program PROM from memory.
R	READ HEXADECIMAL TAPE	Read hexadecimal tape into memory.
S	SUBSTITUTE	Display and modify memory.
T	TRANSFER PROM TO MEMORY	Load memory from PROM.
W	WRITE HEXADECIMAL	Punch hexadecimal tape from memory.
X	EXAMINE REGISTERS OR MEMORY	Display and modify registers.

contents of PROM and memory do not match exactly, the address, PROM data, and memory data are printed for every mismatch.

Other unusual monitor commands are those for performing hexadecimal arithmetic (sum and difference of two numbers supplied as arguments), loading tapes punched in BNPF (binary) format, punching BNPF tapes, punching end-of-file marks, and punching null characters. The monitor instructions are summarized in Table 6.2.

6.2.3 *A Keyboard Monitor for the M6800*

As an example of a very simple monitor, we will look at the JBUG monitor for the M6800. It resides in a 1K × 8-bit ROM and controls the keyboard and display. Its prompt is a dash that appears in the rightmost digit of the display. The JBUG monitor controls eight functions:

M   Display and change memory contents.
E   Escape for current operation.
R   Display register contents.
G   Start executing program.
P   Punch from memory to tape cassette.
L   Load into memory from tape cassette.
N   Trace one instruction.
V   Set and remove breakpoints.

The last two commands deal with debugging, as we will describe in a later section. Notice how simple these commands are compared with those of the previous two monitors. The JBUG monitor stands by itself: it does not call other programs such as assemblers or editors, but only its own subroutines. Use of the monitor differs little from the example of machine language programming for a microcomputer given in Chapter 5. Thus we will not give another example here.

6.3 *Editors*

Preparing computer programs often involves changes of a ''cut-and-paste'' nature. An **editor** can help us change programs quickly and easily; it enables us to create and change symbolic programs, such as assembly language programs, by turning a teleprinter or CRT keyboard into a sophisticated typewriter or word processor. A good editor can locate symbols, correct them, add or delete characters and lines, and read or print data. It is especially helpful in preparing paper tape programs, since the program can be edited until it is correct before punching the tape; thus errors in punching on unforgiving paper tape are avoided.

Using an editor is simple. We type commands that tell the editor to create and delete characters or lines that it stores in a working area called a **buffer**, which may be either a part of computer memory or storage inside the CRT terminal. The lines of text may be numbered decimally for easy reference. Some editors deal only with lines; some deal only with characters; some deal with both lines and characters.

An editor operates either in command mode or in text mode. It starts in **command mode**, waiting for a command. The user types the desired command code and ends the command with a special signal, such as an ESCAPE key. In command mode, the editor interprets all statements as requests. The editor carries out the command and then enters **text** or **input mode**, in which it interprets all characters as text to be treated as instructed by the preceding command. The editor returns from text mode to command mode when the user hits special end-of-text keys.

Typical editor commands include:

- READ—Read a block of text from a peripheral device into the buffer.
- INPUT—Input a string of characters.
- DELETE—Delete a string of characters.
- INSERT—Insert a string of characters before a designated line.
- CHANGE—Replace one string of characters with another.
- FIND—Find the first or next occurrence of a specified character string.
- PRINT—Print the contents of the buffer.
- PRINT N—Print the next *N* lines.
- MOVE—Move a group of adjacent lines to a new location.
- VERIFY—Print the current line.
- KILL—Kill the contents of the buffer.

The editor has a pointer that shows the current line or character in the buffer, that is, the line or character being edited by the user. Editor commands that move the pointer include:

- BEGIN—Move the pointer to the beginning of the buffer.
- NEXT—Move the pointer to the beginning of the next line.
- LAST—Move the pointer to the beginning of the preceding line.
- GO TO TEXT—Move the pointer to the point that follows the given text.
- END—Move the pointer to the end of the buffer.
- FORWARD—Move the pointer forward one character position.
- BACK—Move the pointer backward one character position.
- ADVANCE N—Move the pointer forward *N* lines.

Sophisticated CRT terminals used for editing usually have the pointer shown on the screen as a cursor or underline, _, that can be moved rapidly up, down, right, and left by keys with arrows to quickly correct any part of the text on the CRT display. CRT terminals are more convenient for editing than teleprinters because incorrect lines and characters can be easily removed from the display so that the corrected copy appears. Sophisticated CRT editors feature **scrolling**—rapid moving of the screen over a large body of text. The display acts as a window for the buffer.

With teleprinters, the initial correction must be done by striking out the incorrect copy with a RUBOUT key, which usually appears as a backward slash (\) in print, while it deletes the last character in the buffer. Repeated rubouts delete from right to left. For example, the printed statement

```
THUS IS \\\\\IS IS AN EXAMPLE
```

is stored in the buffer as

```
THIS IS AN EXAMPLE
```

The contents of the buffer can be printed when desired to show the edited text.

Editors differ in their power and flexibility. Good editors are conversational and give clear diagnostics. Large computers usually have sophisticated editors with elaborate commands and file manipulation capabilities. Complex programs for mini- and microcomputers can be edited rapidly with such editors. In fact, microcomputer programs are frequently edited on large computers before being cross-assembled. Most minicomputer editors (that is, editors that are used on-line with a minicomputer) have few commands and limited buffer space. However, they are usually adequate for most minicomputer programs.

6.3.1 *A PDP-11 Editor*

We use the PDP-11 text editor to create and change ASCII source files, such as programs. The editor can read ASCII files from storage devices (such as disks), change them, and write them back into storage or list them on a printer. Each file is considered by the editor to be divided into logical units called pages. A page is about 50 to 60 lines long. The editor reads one page at a time from an input file into its buffer so that the page can be edited.

As we saw in our discussion of the PDP-11 monitor, we call the editor by typing

```
.R EDIT (CR)
```

The editor program then responds with a prompting asterisk to show that it is in command mode.

While the editor is in command mode, it interprets anything we type on the keyboard as a command. We end each command by typing the escape key (SEL) twice, which results in the printing of two dollar signs ($$). The editor then executes the command and returns another prompt. If we should make an error in entering a command, the editor will find the error when it tries to execute the command and will give us an error message and a prompt.

Text-handling commands We enter text mode by typing a command that must be followed by a text string. To return to command mode, we press the escape key once, resulting in a single dollar sign ($). Commands that must be followed by text are:

I	Insert following text.
$\pm n$D	Delete n characters forward ($+n$) or backward ($-n$) from the pointer.
$\pm n$K	Kill (delete) n lines.
$\pm n$C	Change n characters by replacing them with following text.
$\pm n$X	Exchange n lines by replacing them with following text.

Pointer commands The text-oriented commands just discussed show the dual nature of the PDP-11 text editor. It can deal with either characters or lines. We see this feature also in the set of commands that let us move the pointer. These commands are:

B   Move the pointer to the beginning of the buffer.
±*n*J   Jump the pointer forward (+) or backward (−) *n* characters.
±*n*A   Advance the pointer forward or backward *n* lines.

Search commands Sometimes we want to locate a particular character or string of up to 40 characters in the buffer. For this we may use the basic search command:

*n*G   Place the pointer after the *n*th occurrence of the given text.

The basic G command confines the search to the text currently in the buffer. If *n* instances of the text are not in the buffer, the editor prints an error message. Variations of the G command permit searching the entire input file by reading additional pages as needed into the buffer.

Input/output commands An important group of commands transfer text between the buffer and input/output devices. They include:

R   Read from the input device to the buffer.
±*n*W   Write *n* lines from the buffer to the output file.
±*n*N   Write *n* pages from the input file to the output file.
±*n*L   List *n* lines.
V   Verify the current line by printing it.
EF   End the current output file.
EX   Exit from editing.

Before we can use these commands we must specify device and file names. Suppose we have an existing file called SLOAN.ONE on the system. We can open this input file so that we can read it by the command

```
ERSY:SLOAN.ONE $$
```

Later, to read it to an output file, we should open an output file with the command

```
EWSY:SLOAN.ONE
```

Consider a simple example of use of the editor. Suppose we wish to create a file for a simple program that will add two numbers. We can proceed as follows.

```
.R EDIT (CR)                          Call the editor.
*ISUM = %0; SUM IS REGISTER 0         Insert text.
MOV  R1, SUM
ADD  R2, SUM
HLT
.END
$$                                    Return to command mode.
```

There are a few problems in this program as we have typed it, which we will now correct. We note that we have misspelled HALT. One way to solve this problem is to take the following actions.

```
*B$$              Move pointer to beginning.
*GHLT$$           Find HLT, pointer follows T.
* -2J$$           Back pointer two spaces.
*IA$$             Insert A.
*V$$              Verify current line.
HALT              Editor prints corrected line.
```

We next note that we have used R1 and R2 without defining them. Hence we write

```
*B$$              Move pointer to beginning.
*A$$              Advance one line.
*IR1 = %1         Insert two lines.
R2 = %2
$$                Return to command mode.
```

Next we may decide to add a title.

```
*B$$                                Move to beginning.
*I; A PROGRAM TO ADD TWO NUMBERS    Insert text.
$$                                  Return to command mode.
```

If we are now satisfied with our program, we may list it.

```
*B$$                                Move to beginning.
*/L$$                               List entire buffer.
; A PROGRAM TO ADD TWO NUMBERS

SUM = %0
R1 = %1
R2 = %2
MOV  R1,  SUM
ADD  R2,  SUM
HALT
.END
```

Finally, we may create an output file on the system for this program.

```
*B$$                      Move to beginning.
*EWSY:SLOAN.TWO $$        Write to output.
*EX $$                    Leave editor.
```

Note that we frequently had to type a B command to reposition the pointer to the beginning of the buffer. If we had not done this, the pointer would be located just after the last character on line we had edited. We also had to reposition the pointer with a B command before writing our program into an output file. Otherwise, because the pointer was at the end of the program after

Table 6.3
PDP-11 editor commands

Command	Name	Meaning
±nA	ADVANCE	Advance pointer n lines.
B	BEGINNING	Move pointer to beginning of buffer.
±nC	CHANGE	Replace n characters by following text.
±nD	DELETE	Delete n characters.
EF	END FILE	End current output file.
EX	EXIT	Exit from editor.
nG	GET	Place pointer after nth occurrence of text.
I	INSERT	Insert text.
nJ	JUMP	Move pointer n characters.
±nK	KILL	Delete n lines.
±nL	LIST	List n lines.
±nN	NEXT	Write buffer and input to output.
R	READ	Read from input device to buffer.
V	VERIFY	Print current line.
±nW	WRITE	Write n pages to output file.
±nX	EXCHANGE	Replace n lines by text.

execution of the last command, nothing would have been written into the output file.

PDP-11 editor commands are summarized in Table 6.3. Variations of most of these commands are possible, and commands may be strung together with a single escape between them. Your PDP-11 manual suggests ways of making the most effective use of the commands.

6.3.2 *INTELLEC Editor*

The INTELLEC text editor provides an interesting contrast to the PDP-11 editor. It is designed to work with text read into a memory area called the **workspace** from either the system console or the system reader. (Recall from the discussion of the INTELLEC monitor that the system recognizes logical devices called consoles, which are input/output devices, and readers, which are input devices only.) The output of the editor is a punched paper tape.

Because the carriage return character (CR) must be punched at the end of each line on the tape, the editor does not regard a carriage return as a signal to go from one mode to another; it treats a carriage return as it would any other character. To change modes, we end commands to the editor with two ES-CAPE or ALT MODE characters; one or both of these appear on any input device that we might use. We will show these characters as dollar signs ($$). We can also type a BREAK in the middle of a command to stop the command and return to text mode.

The editor treats both lines and characters. It has a buffer pointer that is always located between two characters. As we type each line, the editor automatically supplies a line feed character for the punch after each carriage

Table 6.4
INTELLEC editor commands

Command	Name	Meaning
A	APPEND	Append text to workspace.
B	BEGINNING	Move buffer pointer to start of workspace.
±nC	CHARACTER	Move buffer pointer n characters.
±nD	DELETE	Delete n characters.
E	END	Punch workspace and input tape.
F string	FIND	Find string.
I string	INSERT	Insert string.
±nK	KILL	Delete n lines.
±nL	LINE	Move buffer pointer n lines.
N	NULL	Write 60 null characters.
S str1\$ str2\$	SUBSTITUTE	Substitute string 2 for string 1.
±nT	TYPE	Type n lines on the Teletype.
±nW	WRITE	Punch n lines from the workspace.
Z	END OF WORKSPACE	Move buffer pointer to end of workspace.
n command string	\$\$	Execute command string n times.

return. The editor then regards the space between two line feed characters as a line. A character is any ASCII character, including carriage return and line feed.

The editor allows writing command strings containing several consecutive commands. A command string can be executed n times by typing n and then placing angle brackets < and > about the string. This procedure, called command iteration, may be nested up to eight levels; that is, we may have repeated command strings inside repeated command strings up to a depth of eight.

Whenever we work with a Teletype, we may use its TAB character (produced by typing I while holding CTRL down) to make our listing more readable. It works much like tabs on a typewriter, except that we can't change the tab stops, which are located eight positions apart.

Most of the INTELLEC editor commands look like those of the PDP-11 editor. One exception is a command to write 60 null characters, needed as header for paper tapes in the system. The commands are summarized in Table 6.4.

6.4   *Assemblers*

As we have noted earlier, an **assembler** is a program that converts an assembly language program into a machine language program. The assembly language

Table 6.5
Examples of symbol tables

a) For the PDP-11

Symbol table

COUNT =%000001	LOOP 000012R	N 000026R	
POINT =%000002	STADR 000030R	STORE 000032R	
SUM =%000000			

b) For the 8080

* 01

A 0007	B 0000	C 0001	D 0002
E 0003	H 0004	L 0005	LOOP 1067
M 0006	PSW 0006	SP 0006	

program written by the user is called a **source program**, and the machine language program produced by the assembler in response to the source program is called a (binary) **object program**. The main feature that distinguishes assemblers from other programs that convert source programs into object programs (e.g., compilers or interpreters) is that the assembler converts each source program statement into an object program statement. There are a few exceptions to this simple conversion, such as macros, which we will discuss later. We are already aware that one microcomputer instruction can require one, two, or three bytes, and for this discussion we will assume that the machine language statements produced by the assembler may have different lengths. This interpretation is consistent with the output of many assemblers.

The assembler requires a few new devices to carry out the conversion. It contains its own program counter, called a **location counter**, to assign sequential addresses to source statements and to symbolic operands. As the assembler processes each source statement, it increments the location counter according to the length of the instruction. Each time the assembler finds a symbolic label in the label field of a source statement, it assigns the current value of the location counter to that label. A **symbol table** holds the addresses of all symbolic operands. Table 6.5 shows examples of symbol tables. The 8080 symbol table includes numeric assignments for all registers as well as listing any symbols that we define.

6.4.1 *Two-Pass Assemblers*

Most standard assemblers are **two-pass assemblers**, so called because they read or pass through the source program twice. Figure 6.1 shows the basic operations performed during each pass. The main activity of pass 1 is to assign locations to each symbolic label and to each statement. During pass 2, the binary values for each operand from the symbol table and each operation code from an operation code table are assembled to yield one or more machine language statements for each source statement.

Most assemblers also inspect the source program for errors and print error statements. For example, an assembler may detect undefined symbolic operands by noting each symbol found in the operand field that does not appear as a label in the label field. If, say, the program contained the statement JMP LOOP, but LOOP did not appear as a label, the assembler would flag that error. Similarly, the assembler may note any symbolic operands that are assigned two conflicting values. It may also note illegal symbol definitions and operation codes. Thus if we have misspelled an op code, the assembler will alert us. An assembler cannot detect all errors, however. Its task is to search for errors in syntax—we may think of this as grammar and spelling—rather than for errors in program logic. The error statements it prints are called **diagnostics**. Examples are "undefined operand," "END command missing," and "illegal value." Some assemblers provide descriptive messages; others just tag the incorrect line with an error code. Table 6.6 shows error messages for an Intel 8080 assembler.

Table 6.6
INTELLEC assembler error messages

Message	Name	Meaning
A	ADDRESS ERROR	Address of JUMP or CALL instruction out of range.
B	BALANCE ERROR	Unbalanced parentheses or quotes.
E	EXPRESSION ERROR	Poorly constructed expression.
F	FORMAT ERROR	Format error—usually missing or extra operand.
I	ILLEGAL CHARACTER	Invalid ASCII character or number too large.
M	MULTIPLE DEFINITION	Two or more identical labels.
N	NESTING ERROR	Improper nesting of ifs or macros.
P	PHASE ERROR	Value changed between passes 1 and 2.
Q	QUESTIONABLE SYNTAX	Poor syntax—usually omitted op code.
R	REGISTER ERROR	Specified register invalid for operation.
S	STACK OVERFLOW	Assembler's stack overflowed.
T	TABLE OVERFLOW	Assembler's symbol table exhausted.
U	UNDEFINED IDENTIFIER	Symbol in operand field did not appear as label.
V	ILLEGAL VALUE	Value exceeds allowed range.

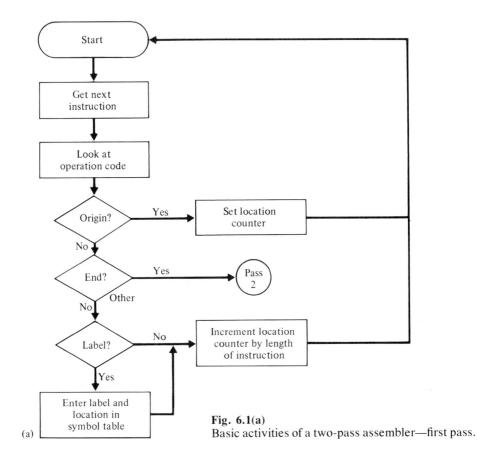

Fig. 6.1(a)
Basic activities of a two-pass assembler—first pass.

(a)

    The assembler must process pseudoinstructions, immediate values, and arithmetic expressions separately. The assembler program provides for correct actions for all pseudoinstructions, via a pseudooperation code table. Thus, for example, it automatically initializes the location counter when it encounters an origin pseudoinstruction. The assembler handles arithmetic expressions in the operand field during the second pass; it recognizes the allowed operators (e.g., $+$, $-$) with their associated operands and produces the correct machine language address.

    To help us understand the assembly process, we might compare it with the procedures we used for hand assembling programs in Chapters 4 and 5. We found we had to make two passes—though not two complete and systematic passes—through any program that had symbolic operands. However, we did not make a symbol table. Instead, we identified the address of each label when it appeared and substituted that address for each operand of the same name.

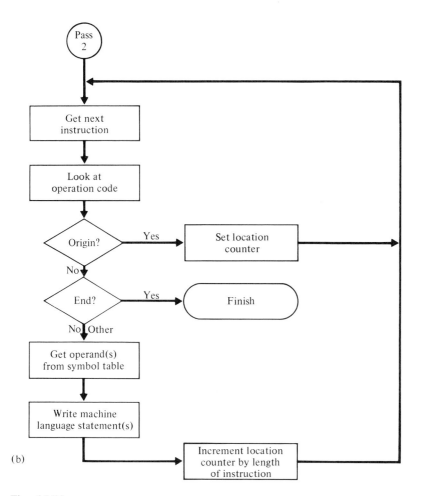

Fig. 6.1(b)
Basic activities of a two-pass assembler—second pass.

Naturally, we had to convert decimal values to binary, octal, or hexadecimal. And catching errors in syntax was up to us. Some errors, such as misspellings, didn't matter so long as we wrote the correct numeric code. Other errors, such as not naming the right number of operands, may have escaped our notice, resulting in an incorrect machine language program.

Assemblers can be absolute or relocatable. An **absolute assembler** assigns an absolute or fixed machine language address to each statement. This suffices for small computers that deal with single special-purpose programs, such as a simple microcomputer used as a controller. For general use, a relocatable assembler is better. A **relocatable assembler** allows relocating programs anywhere within computer memory. To minimize programming time and to maximize efficiency of memory use, programs are often divided into segments that will call on segments of other programs for subroutines. A relocatable assembler allows programs anywhere in memory to call on other program segments or on standard library routines as needed. Relocatable assemblers are used with relocating loaders, to be described in Section 6.5.3.

Two-pass assemblers read the source program from start to end on both passes. The more powerful small computers store the source program in memory as it is read from a tape reader or other input device on the first pass; then, on the second pass, the program can be reread from memory. A large amount of memory is usually needed for storing the source program, since it is stored in the form of ASCII characters, each of which requires one byte of memory. Thus the storage space required for the source program, the assembler, and the object program is too great for the smallest computers. They usually require that the source program be read on both passes from some external source, usually a paper tape reader or a cassette tape recorder. The object program does not need to be retained in memory in a two-pass assembler; it can be outputted—for example, punched on paper tape—as it is prepared in the second pass, one instruction at a time.

6.4.2 *One-Pass Assemblers*

A **one-pass assembler** eliminates the nuisance of passing the source program through the assembler twice. It does this by constructing a forward reference table in addition to a symbol table. A **forward reference** is a symbolic operand that has not yet appeared in a label field. For example, suppose one instruction in our program is JUMP DOWN, where DOWN is a label several lines later. DOWN is a forward reference.

When a forward reference occurs in the source program, the assembler assigns it to the **forward reference table** along with the address at which it was encountered. The assembler then assembles an instruction using the assigned address with an indirect address bit. When the undefined symbol finally appears in the label field, it can be placed in the symbol table along with its absolute address. The forward reference table points to the absolute address via indirect addressing. When the object program is run, all forward references are executed by indirect addressing during the run, with the aid of the forward reference table. The disadvantage of assembling a program in this way is that the use of indirect addressing increases execution time and memory requirements.

A variation of this scheme replaces the forward reference table with a **jump table**. With this approach we are restricted in our use of symbolic operands. All symbolic operands except operands in JUMP statements must appear as labels before they appear as operands. The only forward references, then, are for JUMP statements. All forward-referenced jumps are implemented as two-stage jumps using the jump table. Other solutions are also possible.

6.4.3   *Macro Assemblers*

Macros are powerful devices to increase the scope and simplicity of an assembly language program. We will discuss programming with macros in Chapter 8. For the moment we may think of macros as instructions that we define and then use much as we would any other assembly language instruction. Not all assemblers can handle macros; those that can are called **macro assemblers**. When the assembler encounters the macro definition pseudoinstruction in pass 1, it switches to a macro definition mode and enters the macro name in a **macro definition table**. It then records the macro parameters in an associated list. The assembly language statements that define the macro are also entered into the macro definition table. The only processing done is to replace the formal arguments by special identifiers, such as n, identifying them as the nth arguments.

A macro assembler has a slightly modified assembly process. When it processes an operation code, it first inspects the macro definition table before it looks at the pseudooperation and operation code tables. This order of procedure allows the programmer to redefine some basic operation codes as macros. If the assembler finds the operation code symbol in the macro definition table, it enters macro expansion mode. It copies the assembly language code from the macro definition table, replacing all argument identities by the arguments from the call statement. At the end of the macro definition, it reenters normal assembly operation. Macro expansion normally takes place in both passes when the source program is read from an external medium like paper tape. When the assembler can store the source program in memory, the macro expansion needs to be done only in the first pass. The expanded form of the macro is inserted into the modified source program in the first pass, and the second pass proceeds as usual.

Some macro assemblers feature **conditional assembly**, which allows changing the way a macro is expanded. With conditional assembly, the program can decide what parts of the macro are included or excluded in each expansion. During assembly, a conditional test of the parameters that control the process determines which instructions from the macro definition are included in any given expansion. The controlling parameters are defined and calculated during assembly and are not translated into machine language. Conditional assembly can be used to modify macro expansion if some of the desired parameters are missing. It can also be used to make a macro definition suitable for several different computers that the host computer may be simulating.

6.4.4   *Microcomputer Assemblers*

Microcomputers, because of their small word size and memory, are sometimes more limited in the types of assemblers they can offer than are minicomputers. The more powerful microcomputers usually offer a simple assembler that operates much like the two-pass assembler that we have just discussed. Quite extensive assemblers are available for some microcomputers as part of their development systems.

It is often easier, however, to assemble microcomputer programs on a separate, larger computer to take advantage of the larger computer's greater memory and speed. Thus, as we have noted, microcomputer programs are often assembled via cross-assemblers. **Cross-assemblers** assemble a computer program for one computer on another, usually larger computer. Cross-assemblers for microcomputers often are programmed for large, time-sharing computer systems that the microcomputer user can access. They contrast with **resident assemblers**—programs that use the computer for which the assembly language program is written. The INTELLEC assembler is an example of a resident assembler.

6.5 *Loaders*

While the machine language programs of Chapters 4 and 5 can be entered into the computer using control panel bit switches or a hexadecimal keyboard, we need more advanced inputs to accept programs such as source programs, assemblers, or editors. Specifically, we need loaders to load our programs. Most small computers have several types of loaders, all of which help change the computer from a device that can accept inputs from switches only to one that can accept input from several peripheral devices and relocate the information as desired in memory. Loaders may be separate programs or loading may be one function of the monitor.

6.5.1 *Bootstrap Loaders*

A **bootstrap loader** is a simple program that lets the computer load other loaders so that the computer can "pull itself up by its bootstraps." A typical bootstrap loader is a short series of machine language instructions that the user reads in on the bit switches. The loader is short for user ease and accuracy. After the bootstrap is loaded, more complex loaders can be loaded using the bootstrap loader.

An example is the bootstrap loader for paper tape reader input for the PDP-11. It has 14 instructions, listed in Table 6.7. We do not yet know enough about addressing modes or input/output operations to understand the instructions, but the table does illustrate their brevity and simplicity. The program loads data from paper tape written in a special format into successive bytes of memory, starting with a loading address specified by the tape. A bootstrap loader is usually placed in the highest locations of memory. The one shown here is for an 8K system.

Bootstrap loaders can work only as long as their instructions remain in memory. Careless users may write other instructions into the same locations and destroy the bootstrap loader. To avoid this problem, small computers may

Table 6.7
PDP-11 bootstrap loader

Address	Octal code
037744	016701
037746	000026
037750	012720
037752	000352
037754	005211
037756	105711
037760	100376
037762	116162
037764	000002
037766	037400
037770	005267
037774	000765
037776	177560

protect the loader by providing a switch that prevents others from writing into the same area of memory. Some computers go one step further and have the bootstrap loader written into ROM; it is then a hardware feature.

6.5.2 *Absolute Loaders*

Bootstrap loaders can load simple programs, but they are rigid and inflexible. They may load tapes of a restricted format into only one location. Usually we use the bootstrap loader to load another loader that is more flexible and convenient for loading longer programs. The second loader may be an **absolute loader,** which can load programs into predetermined, fixed addresses anywhere in memory. Via the bootstrap loader, the absolute loader is put into memory, often into the uppermost area of available memory. Then it can be kept there permanently while user programs and other system programs are placed in the lower part of memory. Absolute loaders may be combined with starting addresses so that the program begins executing as soon as it is loaded.

The absolute loader loads absolute programs, which are composed of blocks that have several parts. Division into blocks is helpful in fast, correct loading of long programs. If one block is loaded incorrectly, as happens far too often with paper tapes, then just that block, not the whole program, needs to be reloaded. A typical program block or record has the following elements.

- A start-of-block statement
- The number of bytes or words to be loaded
- The load address
- The information to be loaded
- A check sum for the block

The **start-of-block statement** shows that a block to be loaded follows. The loader ignores information that does not begin in this way; thus information to be loaded, such as a binary object tape from an assembler, can easily be separated from other information, such as a symbol table listing.

The **load address** is the first address of the block to be loaded. Alternatively, on some computers the load address may be specified by means of console switches.

Most loaders check for errors that occur in loading when one or more bits are misread. The most common way of checking uses a **check sum**, which is a count of the number of 1 bits on the tape. The computer compares the check sum with the number of 1's read in the loading process. If the two counts differ, one or more errors have occurred. The incorrect block must then be reloaded. Another checking method is to verify that the check sum plus the bytes in the block add up to zero when added byte by byte, with overflow ignored.

6.5.3 *Relocating Loaders*

Absolute loaders, while more powerful than bootstrap loaders, do not solve all loading problems. Suppose, for example, that we have written and assembled two different assembly language programs that have starting addresses of 300, and that we wish to keep both of them in memory. The obvious solution is to change the starting address of one program to some other address, say 400, and to change other addresses in that program as needed to conform. One way to do this is to reassemble the program with the new starting address; all other addresses will be changed as needed during assembly. A second and better way is to use a relocating loader.

A **relocating loader** can perform the following tasks while it is loading programs:

1. It can automatically change addresses in a program to move it from its assembled starting address to a new starting address; the program will execute properly in the new location.

2. It can load two or more separately assembled programs into nonoverlapping areas of memory. It will adjust memory addresses in one program that refer to labels in another so that cross references among program will be correct.

3. It can search a library for standard functions, such as SIN and TAN, and for user-defined functions that are called by two or more programs.

To see what is needed to change addresses, consider changing the simple PDP-11 program of Table 6.8 from its starting address of 1000 to 1500. What changes must we make? First, the starting address must be changed. We don't need to change any of the instructions because the addresses of A and B

Table 6.8
A simple PDP-11 program to be relocated

Label	Op code	Operand	Comment
	. =	1000	; STARTING ADDRESS = 1000
	MOV	A, %1	; PUT A IN R1
	MOV	%1, B	; STORE THE CONTENTS OF R1 IN B
	MOV	%1, CADDR	; STORE CONTENTS OF R1 IN
			; LOCATION POINTED TO BY CADDR
	HALT		; STOP
A:	6		
B:	7		
C:	1		
CADDR:	C		; THE ADDRESS OF C
	. END		

relative to the instructions stay constant. However, we must change the contents of CADDR: because it holds the address of C.

More generally, if we move a program by a displacement of N locations, we must add that displacement to every word which contains the absolute address of any word in memory. That is, we must add the displacement to words which contain the addresses of other words. Words that are constants, such as A, B, and C in Table 6.8, are not changed during relocation. Address words for relative addresses also are not changed; we can write programs that are relocatable without change by using relative addressing for all references to operands in memory. (We will show how to write such programs in Chapter 7.) Similarly, instructions that refer to registers are not changed because the contents of the registers will be the same no matter where the program is located in memory. Thus relocation involves adding the displacement to some, but not all, of the words in an assembled program.

The loader cannot inspect a word in a program and determine whether it is an instruction, a constant, or an address that must be changed. Therefore, information must be given to the loader from the assembled program to enable the loader to change addresses as needed during relocation. During assembly a relocatable assembler declares the words that have addresses that must be changed during relocation.

The second function of relocating loaders is the loading of two programs that were assembled separately in such a way that they can refer to each other. Such programs are said to have **external references**—references to a program outside the referring program. Pseudoinstructions are needed for external references. For example, the PDP-11 has the external reference pseudoinstruction .GLOBAL. The statement

.GLOBAL X

means that X is a symbol either defined in or used in another program. External or global pseudoinstructions tell the assembler that the addresses are outside the program being assembled. The assembler notes these references and puts this information in the assembled program along with other information for the relocating loader. The assembled program notes each external symbol and lists all addresses referring to that symbol.

Programs that contain locations that can be referenced by external or global pseudoinstructions in other programs have comparable processing. During assembly the symbols and their addresses are listed. When two or more programs with external references are being loaded, the relocating loader places all external references and their corresponding addresses in a symbol table. After all such programs have been loaded, the loader inspects the loader symbol table. It then replaces each reference to an external symbol in any of the programs by its corresponding address. The process resembles the handling of the symbol table during the second pass of the assembler.

The third function of relocating loaders is the establishing and searching of a library. A program **library** is a collection of useful programs that are ordinarily stored outside the computer's main memory, or disks or tape. The library contains such standard algorithms as SIN, TAN, and SQRT and may also contain user-defined programs. The programs are stored in their assembled forms so that they need not be assembled every time they are used. If a loader cannot find an external reference address in its loader symbol table, it searches the library.

A relocating loader prepares a directory that describes all user-defined and standard routines in the library, gives their entry points and locations, lists any other routines needed by a given routine, and shows the length of the routine. It also creates a **load map**, listing all programs that have been loaded, together with their length, location, and any other programs they use.

The actual implementation of relocating loaders differs from computer to computer. For example, suppose a computer uses paging; that is, its memory is divided into equal-sized areas called pages. (This is a topic we will examine in Chapter 7.) In that case addresses on the first page (called the base page) are ordinarily treated differently from other addresses. Thus each program is associated with two displacements—one for the base page and one for the rest of the program. The assembler must tag every relocatable address as either base-page relocatable or program relocatable for the use of the loader. During loading the relocatable loader adds the appropriate displacement to each relocatable address. Other types of relocatable addresses requiring different treatments also occur in certain computers.

Some computers, such as the PDP-11, assign the responsibilities of a relocating loader to two programs—a **linkage editor** (or linker) and a loader. The linkage editor takes the assembler outputs, called **object modules**, and performs three tasks.

1. It relocates object modules and assigns them absolute addresses.
2. It links together modules that reference each other.
3. It produces a load map that shows the assigned absolute addresses.

The output of the linkage editor is a complete load module that may then be loaded by a relatively simple loader.

6.6 *Debugging Programs*

One of the first things a programmer learns is that programs rarely run correctly the first time. Most programs of any length or complexity have logical errors that are, for the most part, detected only when the program is run. Syntactic errors, such as violating the rules of a computer language, are usually detected by compilers or assemblers. But programmers need other software aids to help locate logical errors.

Detecting the existence of logical errors can be difficult, especially when the program includes complicated calculations of the type for which a computer is most useful. Checking values by hand is tedious in such cases. Hence, we may catch only obviously incorrect results. Ideally, we should try to test all possible cases. Often, however, the program is just too large, and we may resort to crossing our fingers and hoping the logic of the program is correct.

Even if we do discover incorrect results, the logical error(s) may not be easy to locate. We can try several methods:

• Dump all memory locations used by the program.
• Rewrite the program to print intermediate results.
• Monitor the program execution with console lights and switches.
• Trace the program as it is executed.
• Use a debugging program.

Dumping memory locations (printing memory contents) allows the programmer to quickly inspect the contents of all desired memory locations in which both instructions and data are stored. The dump may be in binary, octal, or hexadecimal. If a memory dump program is not available in the computer's software routines, we can easily write one. A flowchart of the main features of a simple memory-to-teletypewriter octal dump routine is shown in Fig. 6.2.

A memory dump resembles a snapshot of the contents of memory after a program has been executed. It can help us find errors that end up recorded in memory, but it is not helpful in finding transient errors that occur once in a program and then disappear. For that we need a dynamic technique that shows the contents of memory at several times.

One approach is to include, in our initial writing of the program, instructions to print selected intermediate results. If we are clever or lucky in choosing

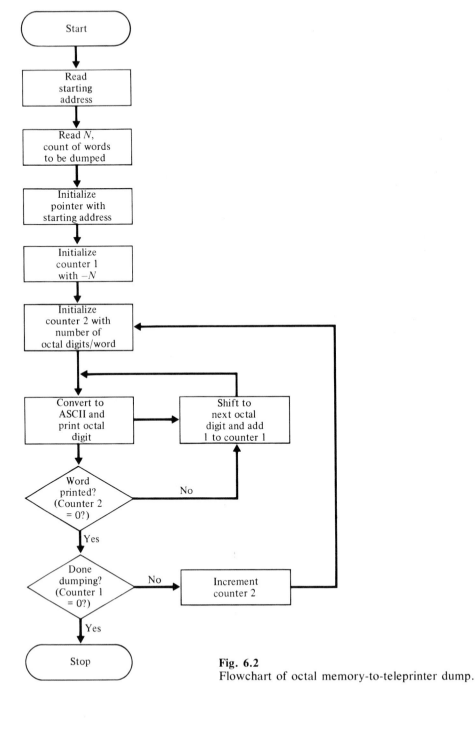

Fig. 6.2
Flowchart of octal memory-to-teleprinter dump.

the intermediate output, we may find the source of errors. Yet it is usually not possible or desirable to print all calculations, and errors may still elude us.

Another, less haphazard, method is to monitor execution of the program step by step. We can do this by repeatedly pressing a single-step switch that stops execution after each cycle and inspecting the contents of registers and memory locations after any step. On some computers, the program can be run at very slow speeds, perhaps a few seconds per cycle. This method, of course, has the disadvantage of being time consuming and tedious. Furthermore, since interpreting console displays can be difficult, it's easy to make mistakes. To shorten the time, we may place halts in the program only after sections that we think need checking and then run the program, examining desired locations at each halt. The method then becomes very similar to the method of printing intermediate results in the program.

A related method that does not require so much of the user's time is to use a **trace program**, which directs the computer to print instructions and data as the user's program is executed. Some computers, such as the PDP-11, have a **trace bit** in the processor status word that helps to trace instructions. When the trace bit (called a T-bit on the PDP-11) is set, it causes a CPU trap after each instruction is executed.

Microcomputers may have trace features that are used with the monitor. For example, consider the trace features of the JBUG monitor for the M6800, described in Section 6.2.3. It has two instructions for debugging—a breakpoint instruction and a trace instruction. The breakpoint instruction lets us insert and later remove up to five **breakpoints**—points at which we want to stop the program so that we can examine results. We can set the breakpoints by entering a four-digit hexadecimal address followed by pressing V for breakpoint. Thus to enter a breakpoint at $12A5_{16}$ we key 12A5 and then press V. Breakpoints will be stored in the monitor until they are all simultaneously cleared by pressing V without previously giving an address.

We ordinarily use the trace instruction in conjunction with breakpoints. It allows us to single-step through the program from any breakpoint by repeatedly pressing N for trace. Each time we press N, the computer executes one instruction and displays the address and the operation code of the next instruction. If we wish, we can examine the contents of all registers through the register display function of the monitor. Good choices for breakpoints are critical points of a program. For example, we might wish to insert breakpoints at the start and end of any loop, to check on the updating of our pointers and counters.

Using breakpoints and then single-stepping is helpful because it allows us to skip over the more straightforward parts of our program. However, the process can still require considerable time, and we would like something more powerful. The most convenient as well as the most powerful aid is a **debugging program**, which can perform the equivalent of a selective memory dump and a program trace automatically. It can be used both for debugging and for close monitoring of programs. On minicomputers, a debugging program is usually used conversationally to let us interact with the computer through a terminal or Teletype. With such a program we can issue commands to do any of the following.

- Start or stop a program at any desired breakpoint.
- Inspect or change the contents of registers and memory.
- Add to or correct the program while it is running.

Typical commands are:

- BEGIN—Start executing a user program at a stated location.
- OPEN—Inspect or change contents.
- CLOSE—Move to another operation.
- BREAKPOINT—Stop executing the program at a stated point.
- PROCEED—Continue execution after a breakpoint.
- SEARCH—Look for a particular bit pattern, such as a certain instruction.
- LIMIT—Limit the memory addresses of a search.

As an example of a minicomputer debugging program, let us consider the On-line Debugging Technique (ODT) for the PDP-11. It is a conversational debugging program that interacts with us and with an object program. It can perform the following actions.

- Display or change the contents of any location.
- Search for bit patterns.
- Search for words that reference a given word.
- Set one or more bytes to a desired value.
- Calculate offsets for relative addresses.
- Run all or part of a program by setting up to eight breakpoints.

Some of its more important commands are:

$n	Open register n to inspect or change contents.
n/	Open contents of location n
(CR)	Close an open location.
addr;B	Set breakpoint at location address.
;B	Clear all breakpoints.
addr;G	Start executing program at location address.
addr;P	Proceed with execution after halting at breakpoint address.

Given these basic commands, let us consider how we might use ODT to debug the simple program for adding three numbers that we wrote in Chapter 4. For convenience we list the program below with its memory addresses but without its original comments.

	. =	500
500	CLR	%3
502	ADD	%0, %3
504	ADD	%1, %3
506	ADD	%2, %3
510	HALT	
	. END	

To test this program we decide to place numbers in each of the registers that the program uses and to check the sum after each addition. To place a number in a register we open the register, read and ignore its current contents, and write the desired number. Then we set breakpoints at each addition step. When the program pauses at the breakpoint, we check register 0 for the sum. Our dialog with ODT runs approximately as shown in Table 6.9. In this table the responses of ODT are underlined to distinguish them from user input.

Most microcomputers and some minicomputers have **simulators** for checking the performance of a system before the hardware has been fully developed. Simulators allow simultaneous development of software and hardware. Their commands include most debugging commands. As their name implies, they

Table 6.9
Example of ODT dialog for debugging a PDP-11 program

Dialog	Comment
*$1/016747 1 (CR)	Open R1 and change contents to 1.
*$2/021606 2 (CR)	Open R2 and change contents to 2.
*$3/012614 3 (CR)	Open R3 and change contents to 3.
*502;B	Set breakpoint at 502,
*504;B	and at 504,
*506;B	506,
*510;B	and 510.
*500;G	Start executing program at 500.
B0;000502	First breakpoint occurs at 502.
*$3/000000 (CR)	Examine R3.
*$;P	Proceed.
B1;000504	Next breakpoint occurs at 504.
*$3/000001 (CR)	Examine R3.
*;P	Proceed.
B2;000506	Next breakpoint occurs at 506.
*$3/000002 (CR)	Examine R3.
*;P	Proceed.
B2;000506	Next breakpoint occurs at 506.
*$3/000002 (CR)	Examine R3.
*;P	Proceed.
B3;000510	Next breakpoint occurs at 510.
*$3/000006 (CR)	Examine R3.
*;P	Proceed.

simulate operation of both hardware and software. They allow us to run programs with register and memory contents initialized to any values we desire and with input/output events simulated. They differ from debugging routines in that simulators generally run on computers other than the one being checked, while debugging routines usually run on their own computers.

Simulators are especially helpful for the debugging of programs that have little input/output interaction. Like debugging programs, they have trace features that print register contents after every instruction or after specified breakpoints. As one might expect, the printing of trace data slows the operation of the simulator. When input or output operations are indicated, the data can be displayed as well. However, operation of the simulator may be further slowed down by too many requests for input data.

Some simulators have trap commands that stop program execution when a given address is reached. Because timing for microcomputers is particularly critical, microcomputer simulators usually display the number of clock cycles for each instruction.

6.S *Summary*

System software permits easy operation of a computer. A monitor controls other system programs. It recognizes commands and data from a keyboard or terminal, displays output, and allocates resources of the system.

An editor is a program that helps the programmer in preparing and correcting a source program. It operates in command mode, accepting commands from the user, or in text mode, receiving text to be edited.

Assemblers convert user-written source programs (assembly language programs) into binary object programs (machine language programs). Assemblers contain location counters for assignment of addresses and symbol tables for compilation of addresses of symbols. Most assemblers examine the source program twice. On the first pass, they construct a symbol table. On the second pass, they assemble the machine language instructions of the object program. One-pass assemblers have a forward reference table to hold undefined operands.

Macro assemblers require construction of macro definition tables. When a macro is called, the assembler replaces the macro by a series of statements in a process called macro expansion. Macros with conditional assembly allow macro expansions to differ as needed, in accordance with the values of controlling parameters.

Microcomputer assemblers may be two-pass assemblers that are much like minicomputer assemblers. Sometimes, however, because of limits on word length and memory, microcomputer assembly programs are prepared on other computers with the aid of cross-assemblers.

Loaders are necessary to load input from sources other than the console bit switches. Bootstrap loaders are simple, manually entered loaders that accept more complex loaders. The more complex loaders include absolute loaders, which store programs into fixed areas of memory, and relocating loaders, which can locate programs according to separately supplied location information.

Debugging routines monitor program execution closely and aid in correcting programs. Simulators are programs that mimic the operation of hardware and software.

Key Terms

absolute assembler	load module
absolute element	loader
absolute loader	location counter
assembler	macro assemblers
background program	macro definition table
booting	macro expansion
bootstrap loader	memory dump
breakpoint	monitor
buffer	object module
cathode ray tube (CRT)	object program
command mode	off-line
compiler	one-pass assembler
conditional assembly	on-line
cross-assembler	operating system
debug routine	prompt
default	relocatable assembler
dump	relocatable element
dynamic debugging program	relocating loader
editor	resident assembler
extension	scrolling
external reference	simulator
file	single-job monitor
foreground/background monitor	single-step
foreground program	source program
forward reference	symbol table
forward reference table	text mode
jump table	trace bit
library	trace program
linkage editor	two-pass assembler
linker	workspace

6.R *References*

Discussions of assemblers and loaders can be found in Booth (1971), Stone (1972), Abrams and Stein (1973), and Gear (1974). Korn (1973) has a good discussion of minicomputer assemblers and loaders. Eckhouse (1975) contains a detailed discussion of PDP-11 system software. Barron (1972) has an especially thorough treatment of assemblers and loaders. Peatman (1977) discusses microcomputer software development. Most minicomputer and microcomputer manuals explain the assemblers, editors, and loaders they feature.

6.Q *Questions*

6.1 What is system software?

6.2 What features does a monitor have?

6.3 How is a file organized?

6.4 What distinguishes a single-job monitor from a foreground/background monitor?

6.5 How do we interact with a monitor?

6.6 What are the modes of operation of an editor? How can we switch between them?

6.7 What advantages do CRT editors have over hard-copy editors?

6.8 Explain the purposes of an editor buffer and pointer.

6.9 Explain the purposes of an assembler location counter and symbol table.

6.10 What are the relative merits of bootstrap, absolute, and relocatable loaders?

6.11 Compare several methods for debugging programs.

Addressing Modes

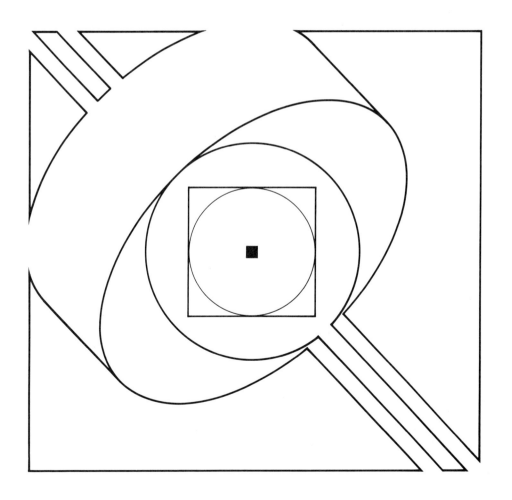

7.1 *Introduction*

One of the most powerful tools in assembly language programming is the set of addressing modes supplied by the computer designer. In earlier chapters we discussed two addressing modes for the PDP-11 and all the addressing modes for the M6800 and the Intel 8085. In this chapter we will try to establish a conceptual structure for considering the addressing modes of any small computer and we will show implementations of certain addressing modes on several mini- and microcomputers. As we will see, we can understand variations of addressing modes without knowing all the details of a computer's architecture. Hence our examples of addressing modes will contain only a minimum of information about architecture.

After establishing a framework for categorizing addressing modes, we will proceed to look in detail at addressing on the PDP-11, a minicomputer with a particularly rich and flexible set of addressing modes. That part of the chapter may not interest you if you are working exclusively with microcomputers. In fact, you may skip the entire chapter on a first reading of the book, so that you may proceed to discussions of other programming concepts. Don't forget, however, that you must at some point master the material in this chapter, because a command of addressing is essential for successful assembly language programming.

7.2 *Addressing Modes*

Although many addressing modes exist, only a few basic concepts are involved. Variety comes from combining a small number of techniques in a large number of ways. In this section we will highlight these techniques and show their combinations and variations. Much of the confusion over addressing modes arises because different computer manufacturers may refer to the same basic mode by three or four different names. In our discussion we will consistently use a few standard names, noting, however, the cases in which certain manufacturers use different names.

Let us start by thinking of the purposes for addresses. Basically there are two. First, addresses of data are needed so that data can be moved and manipulated. Since data may be in a register, in memory, or at an input or output port, we may have to employ several different addressing modes, depending on the location of the data. For example, a computer may have separate instructions and perhaps separate addressing modes for data in memory and for data at input/output ports. Such a scheme, known as **isolated input/output**, contrasts with **memory-mapped input/output**, in which the same instructions and addressing modes can be used for both memory and input/output devices. A second example is a microcomputer that expects data to be in RAM and a program to be in ROM. Such a computer may have addressing modes for data that can operate only on RAM and input/output ports.

The second main purpose for which addresses are needed is for branching. When a program changes the contents of a program counter with a branch instruction, the address is ordinarily another memory address—not a register or an input/output port. Hence a specialized set of addressing modes may be needed for branch addresses. A microcomputer may limit its addressing for this purpose to modes that can access only other ROM locations.

Addressing modes are usually implemented in the following way. The instruction gives the address of an operand and other information—the mode—showing how the address should be changed during execution of the instruction. (More than one operand may be involved, but the procedure is the same.) As the instruction is executed, the following actions take place:

1. The CPU fetches the instruction from memory.
2. The CPU decodes the operand address and the addressing mode.
3. The computer calculates a new operand address, the **effective address**, from the given address and the addressing mode.
4. It executes the instruction with the effective address.

Calculating the effective address does not affect the instruction in memory; it affects only the meaning of the instruction as it is executed.

In discussing addressing we often use the concept of pointing, mentioned in Chapters 4 and 5. A **pointer**—typically a register or a designated memory location—holds the address of some data in which we are interested. More loosely, we can say that the effective address of an operand points to the operand. The effective address is the name of an operand; the operand itself is a value. Thus there are two equivalent statements. We can say either that a location contains the effective address or that the location points to the operand.

To make this idea more explicit, consider the situation illustrated in Fig. 7.1. A register is serving as a pointer. The register holds 4A6B, the effective address of the desired operand, whose value is 2081. Thus the register points to the operand.

Throughout this section on addressing modes, we will frequently refer to the concept of an effective address, abbreviated EA. We can concisely describe

Memory

	Address	Contents
Pointer register	4A69	
	4A6A	
4 A 6 B ⟶	4A6B	2 0 8 1
	4A6C	
	4A6D	
	4A6E	
	4A6F	

Fig. 7.1
A pointer.

an addressing mode by noting the calculation of an effective address in that mode. In simple cases the effective address may be computed from the contents of several registers or memory locations. As in earlier chapters, we will follow the convention that parentheses ( ) denote "contents of."

We can describe two addressing modes quickly without detailing their calculations of effective addresses. For these two modes the concept of effective address is not particularly helpful. **Inherent addressing** occurs when an instruction is applicable to only one operand, usually a register. The effective address is then inherent in the operation code; the computer does not need to calculate it.

Common examples of inherent addressing are shifts and rotations that can be done on only one register. Any small computer that has just one accumulator probably employs inherent addressing for any shifts and rotations. In addition, such computers have inherent addressing for the accumulator in most arithmetic and logical instructions. The PDP-8 and the 8080/8085 use inherent addressing for those instructions and for several others. The 8080/8085 also has instructions that can operate only on the HL register pair and hence show inherent addressing. The M6800, with its two accumulators, has fewer examples of instructions with inherent addressing. Yet it has some instructions (such as decimal adjust) that work on only one accumulator, other instructions that apply only to the index register or only to the stack pointer, and some dual operand instructions that transfer data between two registers with inherent addresses. The PDP-11, with its flexible treatment of registers, has even fewer examples of inherent addressing. It does have some instructions with inherent addressing for one operand—for example, instructions transferring bytes between the processor status word and some other location.

Immediate addressing gives the operand directly, ordinarily in one or more bytes placed just after the operation code. We say that there is no effective address. (Actually, the operand is stored in a memory location, but we do not consider this to be an effective address in the usual sense.) Nearly all small computers designed within the last ten years allow immediate addressing as the quickest way of supplying constants. As seen earlier, the PDP-11, the 8080/8085, and the M6800 all have immediate addressing. The PDP-8, an earlier minicomputer, does not.

In evaluating immediate addressing, we should consider the representation and the range of immediate operands. Ordinarily, immediate operands are represented as 2's complement numbers so that both positive and negative numbers can be efficiently handled. Minicomputers usually devote one word to an immediate operand; hence a 16-bit minicomputer such as the PDP-11 can handle immediate data from -2^{15} to $+2^{15} - 1$. Eight-bit microcomputers may allow only one byte for immediate operands, thus limiting data to a range from -256 to $+255$. Others, like the 8080/8085, provide two types of immediate instructions, one for 8-bit data and the second for 16-bit data, so that they can handle the same range as the PDP-11. (See Fig. 7.2.) Except for complex

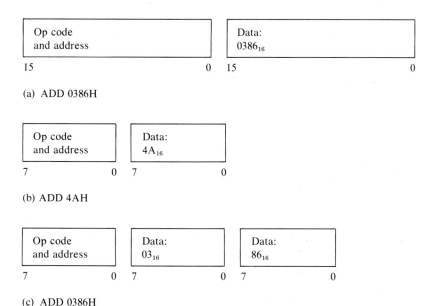

(a) ADD 0386H

(b) ADD 4AH

(c) ADD 0386H

Fig. 7.2
Immediate addressing: (a) 16-bit computer. (b) 8-bit computer with 8-bit data.
(c) 8-bit computer with 16-bit data.

control problems, we are usually content with a fairly small range of immediate
data.

7.3 Direct Addressing

The next addressing modes that we will encounter are direct addressing modes.
In direct addressing the effective address is given directly. It may be a register,
an input/output port, a memory location, or a combination of these. Many
variations are possible, especially when memory is addressed.

Direct register addressing (or simply **register addressing**) names the register
that holds the desired operand. The effective address is the register specified:

EA = register.

Typically, instructions with direct register addressing have a length of only one
byte (for a microcomputer) or one word (for a minicomputer), with a field
designating the register. (See Fig. 7.3.) This mode is sometimes called accumulator addressing or scratchpad register addressing, depending on the type
of register addressed. (A **scratchpad register** is a general-purpose CPU register,
so called because it is used as a scratchpad for temporary storage.) Nearly all
small computers that have more than one addressable register use direct register addressing.

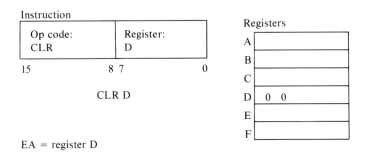

CLR D

EA = register D

Fig. 7.3
Direct register addressing for the instruction CLR D. The effective address is register D.

Direct memory addressing gives the address in memory of the desired operand. The effective address is the given memory address:

EA = memory address.

The main problem with direct memory addressing is that address bits require too much space if the addressing range is to be large. That is, a tradeoff must be made between the size of addressable memory (which should be large) and the length of the instruction (which should be small).

Figure 7.4 shows direct memory addressing implemented with an 8-bit

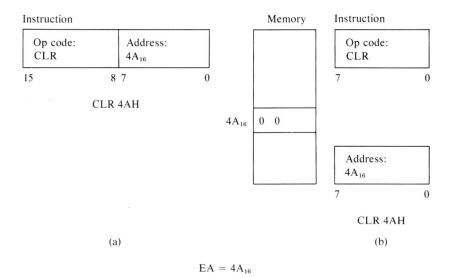

$$EA = 4A_{16}$$

Fig. 7.4
Direct memory addressing for the instruction CLR 4AH. (a) 16-bit computer. (b) 8-bit computer. In both cases the effective address is the given address, $4A_{16}$.

address field for both a 16-bit and an 8-bit computer. The range of possible address is from 0 to 255_{10}. Variations are possible. If an 8-bit field is not needed for the operation code, the 16-bit computer could divide its instruction between a 4-bit operation code field and a 12-bit address field, thus allowing addresses from 0 to 4095_{10}. With an 8-bit computer it is customary to devote one byte to the operation code; therefore, extra addressing space can be gained only by adding another address byte. A three-byte instruction with two address bytes can address up to 64K locations. A 16-bit computer can also add a second word solely for an address field to address up to 64K locations.

Most small computers have some version of direct memory addressing. Consider these examples.

- The Intel 8080/8085 can address up to 64K locations with three-byte instructions in which the last two bytes contain the address.
- The M6800 has similar three-byte instructions using a mode called extended addressing and also has two-byte instructions in which the second byte provides an 8-bit address.
- The PDP-11 has a two-word instruction in which the second word provides a 16-bit address; DEC calls this mode absolute addressing.
- The PDP-8 has a one-word (12-bit) instruction that gives a 7-bit address.

Variations of direct memory addressing involve segmenting memory into blocks called **pages**. This segmentation is conceptual, not physical. The simplest way of paging is to organize memory into fixed pages, each containing perhaps 256_{10} locations, as shown in Fig. 7.5. The first page has memory locations 0 through 155_{10} (FF_{16}) and is known as **page zero**. The next page has

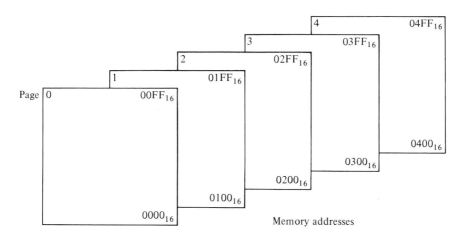

Fig. 7.5
Fixed paging.

addresses from 0100_{16} to $01FF_{16}$, the following from 0200_{16} to $02FF_{16}$, and so on. Page zero can be accessed easily. In fact, for page zero we can define a special variation of direct memory addressing.

Page-zero direct addressing names an address on page zero. An instruction that specifies page-zero addressing and supplies an n-bit address can access any of the first 2^n locations in memory. The effective address is the given address:

EA = address.

For microcomputers an 8-bit address is usually given, allowing access to the first 256_{10} locations. The result is exactly the same as shown in Fig. 7.4(b) for direct memory addressing on an 8-bit computer with an 8-bit address. The M6800 uses this addressing mode but calls it direct addressing, in contrast to its extended addressing instructions, which provide 16-bit addresses.

We could easily extend page-zero direct addressing to addressing on any other page by supplying the page number and address on the page. Doing this, however, requires exactly as many bits as for direct memory addressing, so we save nothing. A better idea comes from noting that most memory addresses needed in a program are located close to the current instruction. In fact, studies have shown that 80–90% of branch addresses are located within 127 addresses of the current instruction. This means that a desired branch address has a good chance of being on the same page as the current instruction. We can call this page the **current page** and consider it to be identified by the high-order bits of the program counter. For simplicity, let us suppose that our pages have 256 locations. If our program counter has a hexadecimal display, then its two highest digits at any time show the number of the current page, while the two lowest digits show a memory location on the current page. Thus we can access any address on the current page by supplying an 8-bit address along with the information that we wish a current-page address. We can let one bit of the instruction, called a **page bit**, show that we wish a current-page address. The page bit can have two values—0 for page zero and C (actually 1) for the current page. We now have another addressing mode.

Current-page direct addressing names an address on the page shown by the program counter. An instruction that specifies current-page addressing by setting the page bit and that specifies an n-bit address can access any of the 2^n locations on the page shown by the program counter. The effective address has the high-order bits of the program counter and the n low-order bits shown by the instruction. Using a subscript to denote bits of a register, we can write

EA = $(PC)_{high}$ + address.

For the case of 8-bit page addresses and a 16-bit program counter, the effective address consists of the highest 8 bits (two hexadecimal digits) from the address given in the instruction:

EA = $(PC)_{15-8}$ + address.

Figure 7.6 shows examples of addressing modes with fixed paging. A 16-bit

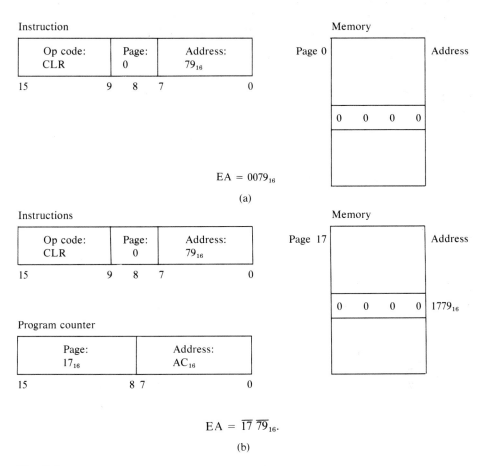

Fig. 7.6
Addressing modes with fixed paging. (a) Page-zero direct addressing. (b) Current-page direct addressing.

instruction is assumed, allowing a 7-bit field for the operation code, one page bit (showing 0 for page zero and C for current page), and an 8-bit address field. As Fig. 7.6(a) shows, page-zero direct addressing yields the given address on page zero as the effective address. Figure 7.6(b) shows that for current-page direct addressing the effective address combines the leftmost digits of the program counter with the address digits of the instruction.

Page-zero direct addressing is sometimes used without current-page direct addressing, as on some microcomputers. But when current-page addressing is used, it usually coexists with page-zero addressing, and a single page bit is required to designate one of the two modes. The PDP-8 is a classic example of a small computer with both page-zero and current-page addressing. Its pages have 128 locations instead of 256.

Paged addressing, a term covering any addressing mode involving paging, can present several problems. A major problem is that paging wastes memory. Ideally, a program should reside on a single page. Thus, if the program is less than 256 locations long, memory is wasted unless another small program of just the right size can also be squeezed onto the same page. Ordinarily, not only the program but also its data should be on the same page, because the program can access only data on the current page and can branch only to addresses on the current page, assuming that current-page direct addressing is the only mode used. You can probably think of solutions to this problem, probably involving other addressing modes. Nonetheless, when current-page addressing is used, programmers do tend to package programs on separate pages, thus wasting some memory space. On sophisticated computers, system software may manage memory efficiently, but on basic microcomputers we may encounter difficulties in storing programs, especially if we need to add a few instructions.

A more subtle problem with current-page addressing is that errors may occur at page boundaries. During execution of instructions, the program counter is usually incremented just after the instruction has been fetched and before address calculations are made. Hence the page number is taken from the incremented program counter. At the page boundary, the incremented page counter will show a page number that is one higher than the page number of the current instruction. For example, an instruction at location FF of page 04 may desire a branch to location 2A of page 04. However, as soon as the instruction is fetched, the program counter will advance to page 05 and thus the branch will actually be made to location 05FF instead of 04FF.

A novel solution to this problem is to use wrap-around pages, a feature illustrated by the SC/MP. This microcomputer has 16 pages of 4096 locations each. The four highest-order bits of its program counter—the page number—are never incremented after instruction fetch. Hence, after reaching the last address on a page, the SC/MP wraps around to the first address on the same page. For example, after $5FFF_{16}$, it goes to 5000_{16}.

We can solve some of the problems of current-page addressing by choosing a different form of paging, as shown in Fig. 7.7. Instead of having pages fixed in

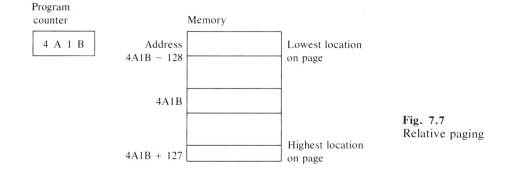

Fig. 7.7
Relative paging

memory, we consider their boundaries to be determined by the contents of the program counter. Thus we can regard memory as one long roll; the contents of the program counter at any given time will dictate a page roughly centered about the address shown in the program counter. In Fig. 7.7, pages are considered to be 256 locations. As explained earlier, the contents of the program counter are incremented just after the instruction is fetched and before the address is calculated. Depending on the computer, the incrementing may be by one, two, three, or four locations. Hence with this new addressing mode the relative page is centered, not about the instruction, but about a point somewhat higher in memory. Given this concept of relative pages, we can define an addressing mode for it.

Relative direct addressing interprets the address field of an instruction as a 2's complement **offset** to be added to the incremented contents of the program counter. The effective address is the sum of the contents of the program counter after incrementing plus the offset:

EA = (PC) + offset.

Microcomputers using relative direct addressing ordinarily have 8-bit offsets, resulting in pages with 256 addresses. The M6800 uses this addressing mode; examples of offset and effective address calculation for the M6800 were given in Chapter 5. An example for a similar 8-bit microcomputer with two-byte instructions is shown in Fig. 7.8. The instruction calling for direct addressing begins in location 2715_{16}; the offset of 31_{16} is stored in 2716_{16}. After incrementing, the program counter holds 2717_{16}; adding the offset yields the desired location of 2748_{16}.

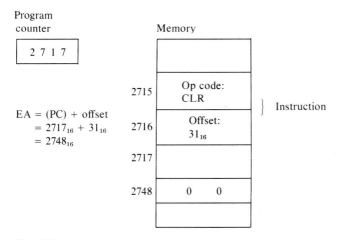

Fig. 7.8
Relative direct addressing. The effective address is the contents of the program counter plus the offset.

Other computers with relative direct addressing accomplish it as follows.

- The PDP-11 provides a 16-bit offset and increments the program counter by 4 before adding the offset.
- The Z-80 has enhanced the 8080 to include two-byte relative jump instructions with 8-bit offsets.
- The SC/MP has two-byte relative jump instructions with 8-bit offsets and wrap-around paging.

Indexed direct addressing obtains effective addresses by adding the contents of one or more **index registers** to an offset supplied by the instruction. In this operation the contents of the index register are not changed. There are many variations of indexed addressing. In its basic form the effective address is just the sum of the contents of an index register and the offset. Some computers have 2's complement offsets; others have unsigned offsets:

EA = (index register) + offset.

Figure 7.9 shows two examples of indexed direct addressing. In the first, a 16-bit computer has a 16-bit offset and a 16-bit index register. The effective address is the sum of the contents of the index register and the offset. If the sum is greater than $FFFF_{16}$, the carry is ignored so that only the first 64K of memory is addressed. This situation is typical of 16-bit minicomputers.

Microcomputers usually save one byte of an instruction by providing only an 8-bit offset, as shown in Fig. 7.9(b). The effective address is the sum of the contents of the 16-bit index register and the 8-bit offset. Any address in memory can be accessed in this way by changing the 8 high-order bits of the index register.

The following examples show how some small computers implement direct indexed addressing.

- The PDP-11 allows any general register to be considered an index register and has a 16-bit offset.
- The SC/MP has three 16-bit registers that may be used in indexed addressing with a signed 8-bit offset.
- The M6800 has one 16-bit index register and an unsigned 8-bit offset.
- The MCS6500, with its two 8-bit index registers, offers two types of direct indexed addressing. In base-page indexed addressing, the contents of one index register are added to the unsigned offset, with the carry discarded if the sum exceeds FF_{16}. In absolute indexed addressing, the contents of an index register are added to a 16-bit address provided in the second and third bytes of an instruction.
- The Signetics 2650 has indexed addressing with any of six 8-bit registers and a 13-bit address provided by the instruction.

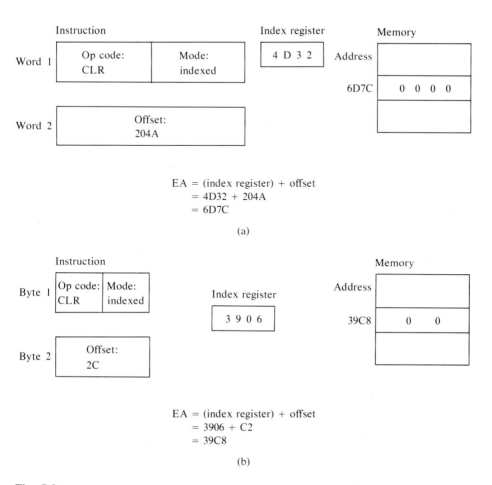

Fig. 7.9

Indexed direct addressing. (a) 16-bit computer with 16-bit index register and 16-bit offset. (b) 8-bit computer with 16-bit index register and 8-bit offset.

Implied addressing treats the contents of a special register as the memory address. It is similar to indexed addressing without an offset. When implied addressing is used for accessing data, the implied register is called a **data counter**. Microcomputers often have this mode. The effective address is the contents of the register:

EA = (register).

Figure 7.10 shows implied addressing with a data counter. Two instructions are required to perform calculations on data stored in memory. The first instruction loads the address of the data into the data counter. The second

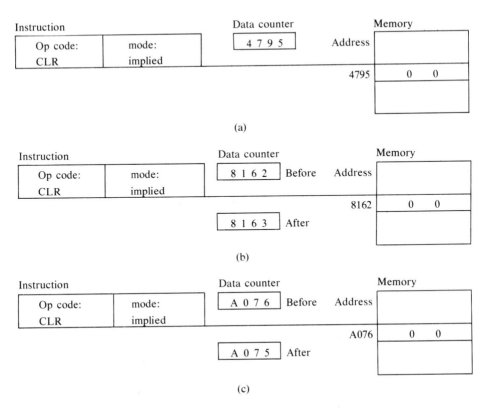

Fig. 7.10
Implied addressing. (a) Simple implied addressing. (b) Autoincrementing. (c) Auto-decrementing.

instruction does the calculation. Usually the first instruction takes two or three bytes for the operation code and address. The second may require just one byte, because the address is implied to be the data counter. Some microcomputers have more than one data counter. Implied addressing requires more memory space and time than direct addressing. (Why?) Microcomputers originally used implied addressing because design of the control unit on a small chip was simpler. They continue to use it now, even though LSI technology has advanced and more efficient direct addressing modes could well be used.

For stepping through data stored in a table it is convenient to automatically increase or decrease the contents of the data counter. With **autoincrementing**, the contents of the data counter are increased by 1; with **autodecrementing** they are decreased by 1. **Autoindexing** is a general term for autoincrementing or autodecrementing. These procedures are shown in Fig. 7.10(b and c) with changes in the data counter occurring after the implied memory location is cleared. When incrementing or decrementing takes place after the basic operation of the instruction is complete, we have **post-indexing**. In the opposite case, when the incrementing or decrementing occurs before the basic operation of the instruction, we have **pre-indexing**.

7.4   *Indirect Addressing*

Nearly all direct addressing modes can be converted to indirect addressing modes by considering the address calculated as a pointer to the effective address. That is, the calculated address is interpreted as the address of the desired address. We will show a few types of indirect addressing; you should be able to construct many more.

Indirect register addressing treats a register as a pointer to the desired data. The register holds an address of the desired data, not the data themselves. The effective address is the contents of the register named:

EA = (register).

The implied addressing mode just discussed can be thought of as a type of indirect register addressing in which the register is implied. Figure 7.11 shows indirect register addressing.

Instruction   Register   Memory

Op code:	Mode:
CLR	indirect

7 A 1 9

Address	
7A19	0 0 0 0

EA = (register)

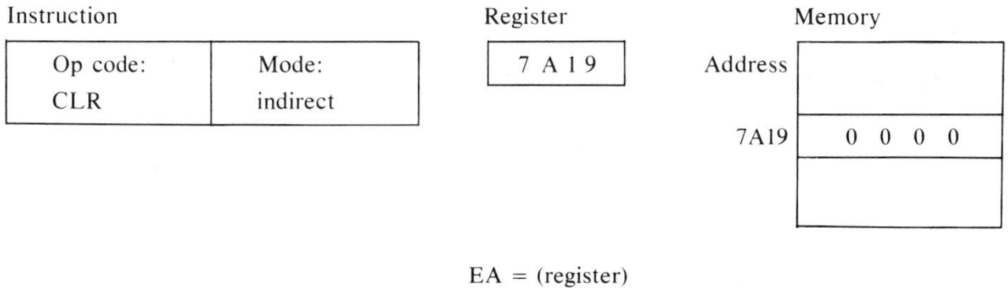

Fig. 7.11
Indirect register addressing.

Indirect memory addressing treats the memory address given as a pointer to the desired memory address. The address given is the address of the address of the desired data. The effective address is the contents of the memory location named by the given address:

EA = (address).

Examples of indirect memory addressing are shown in Fig. 7.12. In the first case, a 16-bit computer with an 8-bit address field can have a 16-bit memory address with indirect addressing, but only an 8-bit address with direct memory addressing. (Why?) In the second case, an 8-bit computer has three-byte instructions, giving 16 bits for both the given and effective addresses.

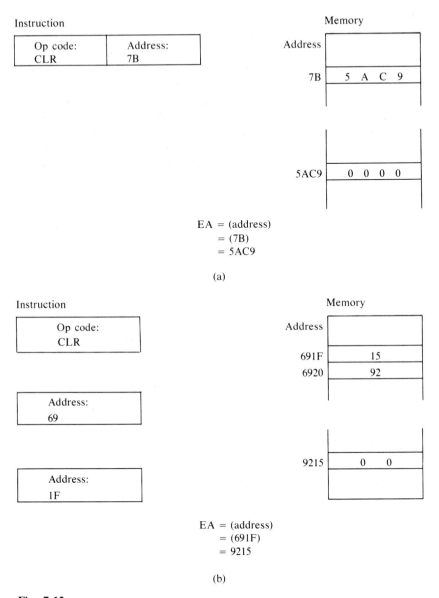

Fig. 7.12
Indirect memory addressing. (a) 16-bit computer. (b) 8-bit computer.

Some variations of indirect memory addressing are listed below.

• *Multiple levels of indirection.* In this scheme one bit—called an indirect bit—of both instruction and memory is reserved to indicate indirect addressing. Whenever that bit is 1, the given address is interpreted as an indirect address. So long as the indirect bit is 1, each address continues to point to another address. Computers may allow any number of levels of indirection.

• *Indirect pointer addressing.* One CPU register serves as a pointer to one of 16 or so scratchpad registers that act as pointers to memory. The effective address is the contents of the scratchpad register selected by the pointer register.

• *Indirect addressing with paging.* Paged addressing may be combined with indirect addressing for both page zero and the current page. Indirect addressing is helpful in reaching some page other than zero from page zero.

• *Indirect addressing with autoindexing.* A certain section of memory has the feature that when any location within it is accessed indirectly, its contents are incremented or decremented.

• *Relative indirect addressing.* Relative addressing and indirect addressing are combined. An address given relative to the program counter is considered to be an indirect address.

Illustrating these variations is left as an exercise. However, the process of combining indirect addressing with indexed addressing involves new concepts. The basic issue is which mode comes first—indexed addressing or indirect addressing.

In **pre-indexing**, indexed addressing comes before indirect addressing. The indexed address is considered to be an indirect address; it points to the effective address. The effective address thus is the contents of the memory location whose address is the sum of the contents of the index register plus the offset:

EA = ((index register) + offset).

In **post-indexing,** indirect addressing is followed by indexed addressing. First, the address given by the instruction—the base address—is handled as an indirect address; next, the contents of the memory location pointed to by the base address are added to the contents of the index register. The effective address is the sum of the contents of the memory location given by the base address and the contents of the index register:

EA = (address) + (index register).

Figure 7.13 shows pre-indexing and post-indexing.
Some examples of computers with indirect addressing are as follows.

• The PDP-8 has indirect addressing with paging. It also has autoincrementing for locations 0010_8 through 0017_8.

• The PDP-11 has several indirect modes—indirect register addressing, which may be combined with post-incrementing and pre-decrementing, and indexed addressing with post-indexing.

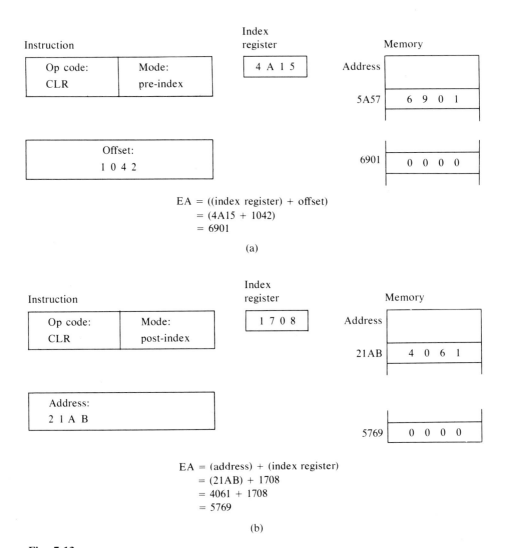

Fig. 7.13
Combining indexed and indirect addressing. (a) Pre-indexing. (b) Post-indexing.

- The MCS6500 has both pre-indexed and post-indexed indirect addressing.
- The Signetics 2650 has four indirect modes—basic, post-indexed, post-indexed with autoincrement, and post-indexed with autodecrement.

7.5 *PDP-11 Addressing Modes*

The PDP-11 has a particularly rich set of addressing modes. Its registers may be used in four ways. A register may be any of the following.

1. An accumulator; the effective address is the register.

2. A pointer; the effective address is the contents of the register.

3. A pointer that automatically steps through memory either forward (autoincrementing) or backward (autodecrementing); the effective address is the contents of the memory location pointed to, once the effect of stepping is considered.

4. An index register; the effective address is the sum of the contents of the register and the address of the word after the instruction.

We will consider each of these.

7.5.1 *Direct Addressing Modes*

As noted earlier in this chapter, addressing modes can be direct or indirect. With **direct addressing**, the addressing information yields the effective address directly. With **indirect addressing** the addressing information yields an address whose contents are the effective address. That is, the basic addressing information gives the address of the effective address. On the PDP-11 we can use either direct or indirect (called **deferred** by DEC) addressing in four different modes—register, autoincrement, autodecrement, and index. We shall first look at the four direct addressing modes, then at the four deferred modes.

To designate addressing, each operand field of a PDP-11 instruction is divided into two three-bit fields—the first for the mode and the second for the register. We will show them in octal.

Mode	Register

Register addressing uses a register as an accumulator to hold or accumulate data. The effective address is the register named. The bit pattern 0_8 in the mode field shows register addressing. For example, if an octal destination field contains 02, register 2 is being addressed with register addressing. The effective address is register 2. If R2 contains 034512_8, the operand is 034512_8. In assembly language, we show register addressing by simply writing the percent sign (%) followed by the register number. For example, to complement the contents of register 2, we can write

```
COM %2
```

If we have previously defined R2 to be %2 (by R2 = %2), we can write

```
COM R2
```

where COM is the mnemonic for COMplement.

The octal code is 0005102. As a result of this instruction, the contents of R2 become 143265_8 if before the instruction it held 034512_8. Figure 7.14 shows the effect of the instruction. As a running example of addressing modes, we will consider complementing N numbers. Table 7.1 shows a program segment for

R2

(a)   (b)

Fig. 7.14
Register addressing. (a) Register contents before COM R2. (b) Register contents after
COM R2.

Table 7.1
Complementing N numbers with register addressing

Op code	Operand	Comment
COM	%0	; COMPLEMENT R0
COM	%1	; COMPLEMENT R1
COM	%2	; COMPLEMENT R2
COM	%3	; COMPLEMENT R3
COM	%4	; COMPLEMENT R4
HALT		; STOP

complementing five numbers with register addressing. With this mode we can
complement only as many numbers as available registers.

   Autoincrement addressing uses the register named as a pointer. The effective address is the contents of the register named; the operand is the contents of
the memory location named by the effective address. After the operand is
obtained, the register is automatically incremented by 2 to advance the pointer
to the next memory location. The bit pattern 2_8 in the mode field shows
autoincrementing. For example, if a destination field contains 23, register 3 is
being addressed in autoincrement mode. Symbolically we write (%3)+ or (R3)+
if R3 has been defined as %3. (In the rest of the chapter we will assume that we
can refer to register N as RN.)

   Suppose the contents of R3 are 001122_8 and the contents of memory
location 001122_8 are 123456_8. The instruction

```
COM (R3)+
```

or

```
005123
```

results in the following actions:

1. The effective address, memory location 001122_8, is obtained from R3.
2. The operand, the contents of memory location or 123456_8, is complemented.
   The result, 054321_8, is the new contents of memory location 001122_8.
3. The contents of R3 are incremented by 2, yielding 001124_8.

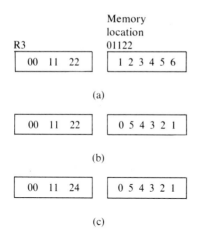

(a)

(b)

Fig. 7.15
Autoincrement addressing. (a)
Memory and register contents
before execution of COM (R3)+.
(b) Memory contents com-
plemented. (c) Register contents
(c)   incremented.

Figure 7.15 shows the effects of this instruction. Table 7.2 shows a program
segment that uses autoincrement addressing to complement the numbers located in 100 consecutive even memory locations beginning with location 2000.
With autoincrement addressing the number of locations is limited only by the
size of the memory.

Table 7.2
Complementing N numbers with autoincrement addressing

Label	Op code	Operand	Comment
COUNT	=	%1	; COUNTER IS R1
POINT	=	%2	; POINTER IS R2
	MOV	N, COUNT	; START COUNTER WITH N
	MOV	STADD, POINT	; INITIALIZE POINTER
LOOP:	COM	(POINT)+	; COMPLEMENT NUMBER SHOWN BY R2
			; AND INCREMENT POINTER
	DEC	COUNT	; DECREMENT COUNTER
	BGT	LOOP	; GO TO LOOP IF COUNTER GREATER
			; THAN ZERO
	HALT		; STOP IF COUNTER IS ZERO
N:	000144		; 100 DECIMAL
STADD:	002000		; FIRST ADDRESS IS 2000

Autodecrement addressing is similar to autoincrement addressing. However, the register contents are decremented *before* the effective address is
calculated. The symbol for autodecrement addressing shows that decrementing
occurs first by writing a minus sign for decrementing before the parentheses,
showing that the register is a pointer. Autodecrement addressing for register 3
is symbolized as −(R3); the corresponding machine code is 43. The autodecrement code is 4_8.

Suppose that R3 contains 001100_8. Suppose that memory location 001076_8 contains 000777_8. The instruction

```
COM -(R3)
```

or

```
005143
```

results in the following actions:

1. The contents of R3 are decremented by 2, yielding 001076_8 as the effective address.
2. The operand, the contents of memory location 001076_8 or 000777_8, is complemented. The result, 177000_8, is the new contents of memory location 001076_8.

Figure 7.16 shows these actions. Table 7.3 shows a program for complementing numbers located in the 100 consecutive even memory locations ending at 2616.

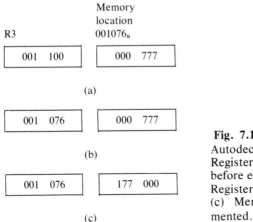

(a)

(b)

(c)

Fig. 7.16
Autodecrement addressing. (a) Register and memory contents before executing COM - (R3). (b) Register contents decremented. (c) Memory contents complemented.

Index addressing This mode differs strikingly from the preceding modes. Two machine language words are needed to specify index addressing. The first word is an instruction with a mode bit pattern of 6_8. The second word gives a value that is added to the contents of the register named to calculate the effective address. That is, the effective address is the sum of the register contents and of the number following the instruction. Let us suppose that we want the effective address to be 100_{10} locations beyond the number held in register 1. The number following the instruction would then be 000144_8. If we wished to complement the contents of that location we would write the octal code

```
005161
000144
```

Table 7.3
Complementing N numbers with autodecrement addressing

Label	Op code	Operand	Comment
COUNT	=	%1	; COUNTER IS R1
POINT	=	%2	; POINTER IS R2
	MOV	N, COUNT	; START COUNTER WITH N
	MOV	LASTAD, POINT	; PUT LAST ADDRESS IN POINTER
	INC	POINT	; INCREMENT POINTER TWICE TO
	INC	POINT	; POINT TWO AHEAD OF LAST
			; ADDRESS
LOOP:	COM	-(POINT)	; DECREMENT POINTER AND COMPLE-
			; MENT CONTENTS OF THAT LOCATION
	DEC	COUNT	; DECREMENT COUNTER
	BGT	LOOP	; GO TO LOOP IF COUNTER GREATER
			; THAN ZERO
	HALT		; STOP IF COUNTER IS ZERO
N:	000144		; 100 DECIMAL
LASTAD:	002616		; LAST ADDRESS IS 2616

Symbolically we may assign a name to the value to be added, say X, or may give the octal value. We show index addressing for register 1 by X(R1). The assembly code for the instruction above is

```
COM X(R1)
```

or

```
COM 144(R1)
```

Suppose the contents of register 1 are 000121, as shown in Fig. 7.17. When executing the instruction

```
COM 144(R1)
```

the effective address is calculated as the sum of 144 and 121, the contents of R1; thus the effective address is 265_8. If the contents of memory location 265 are 111111_8 before the instruction is executed, they will be complemented to 066666_8 afterward.

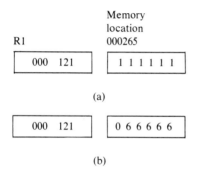

(a)

(b)

Fig. 7.17
Index addressing. (a) Register and memory contents before executing COM 144(R1). (b) Contents of memory location 00265 = 000121 + 000144 are complemented.

Table 7.4
Complementing N numbers with indexed addressing

Label	Op code	Operand	Comment
COUNT	=	%1	; COUNTER IS R1
POINT	=	%2	; POINTER IS R2
	CLR	POINT	; CLEAR POINTER
	MOV	N, COUNT	; MOVE IN TO COUNTER
LOOP:	COM	2000 (POINT)	; COMPUTE EFFECTIVE ADDRESS
			; = 2000 + CONTENTS OF POINT AND
			; COMPLEMENT THE CONTENTS OF
			; THAT LOCATION
	INC	POINT	; INCREMENT POINTER TWICE
	INC	POINT	
	DEC	COUNT	; DECREMENT COUNTER
	BGT	LOOP	; GO TO LOOP IF COUNTER GREATER
			; THAN ZERO
	HALT		; STOP IF COUNTER IS ZERO
N:	000144		; 100 DECIMAL

Table 7.4 shows a program for complementing 100 numbers starting in memory location 2000. The contents of a pointer are incremented by 2 and added to the starting address to yield the effective address. In this case index addressing requires more statements than autoincrementing does. Index addressing is better suited to problems requiring a fixed number to be added to obtain the effective address.

The four direct addressing modes are summarized in Table 7.5. Again, we follow the notation that parentheses ( ) mean "contents of." Thus (RN) means "the contents of register N."

Table 7.5
Direct addressing modes

Binary code	Assembly code	Name	Effective address	Meaning
000	RN	Register	RN	Register N holds the operand.
010	(RN)+	Autoincrement	(RN)	Register N points to the operand, and then the contents of register N are incremented.
100	−(RN)	Autodecrement	(RN) − 2	The contents of register N are decremented; register N then points to the operand.
110	X(RN)	Index	X + (RN)	The contents of register N plus the value X give the address of the operand.

Each of the four modes we have just examined—register, autoincrement, autodecrement, and index—can be used in deferred (indirect) mode as well as in direct mode. You may have noticed that the binary codes for the four direct modes all had even mode codes. Deferred addressing modes have odd mode codes. In assembly language the at sign, @, denotes deferred addressing. We will quickly look at the four deferred modes, noting their similarities to the four direct modes. We will not, however, give examples of programs using deferred addressing modes.

Register deferred addressing If we wished to use a register as a pointer but did not wish to increment or decrement it, we might choose register deferred addressing. The effective address is the contents of the register named; the register points to the operand. The code for register deferred addressing is 1_8. Suppose register 3 points to memory location 000010, containing the operand 111000, which we wish to complement. By writing the machine language instruction

005113

or the assembly language instruction

COM @R3

we complement 111000 to 066777. This process is illustrated in Fig. 7.18.

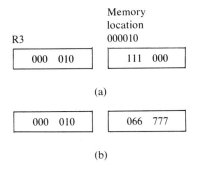

(a)

(b)

Fig. 7.18
Register deferred addressing. (a) Register memory contents before executing COM @R3. (b) Register and memory contents after executing COM @R3.

Autoincrement deferred addressing In autoincrement deferred addressing the register holds the address of the address of the operand. After the operand is acted on, the register is incremented. The effective address is the contents of the location whose address is in the register. We write the effective address as ((RN)). The double parentheses show that the effective address is the contents of the contents of the register. Alternatively, we can say that the register points to the address of the operand. In autoincrement direct addressing, by contrast, the register points to the operand. The octal code for this mode is 3; the assembly code is @(RN)+.

Memory locations

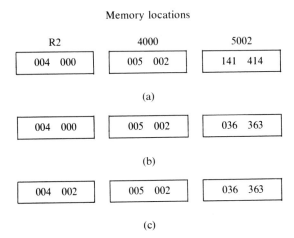

(a)

(b)

(c)

Fig. 7.19
Autoincrement deferred addressing. (a) Contents
of register and memory before executing COM
@ (R2)+. (b) Contents of register and memory after
complementing operand. (c) Contents of register
and memory after incrementing register.

Consider the example shown in Fig. 7.19. Register 2 contains 4000. Thus it
points to memory location 4000, which contains 5002. We wish to complement
the contents of memory location 5002, namely 141414. We do this with the
instruction

```
COM @(R2)+
```

or its machine code 005132. The effective address of this instruction is ((R2))
which is (4000) or 5002. When the instruction is executed, 141414 is complemented to 036363; then the contents of register 2 are incremented to become
4002. The contents of memory location 4000 are unchanged.

Autodecrement deferred addressing Autodecrement deferred addressing is much
the same except that the contents of the register are decremented before the
effective address is computed. The octal code for this mode is 5; the assembly
code is @ − (RN).

Figure 7.20 shows an example. Register 1 contains 004000. The instruction

```
COM @-(R1)
```

or its machine equivalent, 005151, first decrements the contents of R1 to
003776. The effective address of this instruction is ((R1)), the contents of the
contents of R1. We can also write the effective address as (003776), the
contents of memory location 3776, which is 001202. Thus the effective address
is 001202, and the instruction complements the contents of this location, which
are 060606 to 117171.

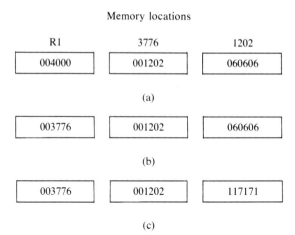

Fig. 7.20
Autodecrement deferred addressing. (a) Contents of
register and memory before executing COM
@−(R1). (b) Contents of register and memory after
decrementing register. (c) Contents of register and
memory after complementing operand.

Autoincrement deferred and autodecrement deferred addressing are rarely
used in practice. Can you see why?

Index deferred addressing Index deferred addressing calculates the address of
the effective address from the sum of a value stated in the instruction and the
contents of a register. If the value is X, the effective address is (X + (RN)), the
contents of the sum of X plus the contents of register N. As for index addressing, the binary form of this instruction takes two words, one to give the
operation code and register with mode code of 7_8 and a second to give the value
of X. The assembly code for this instruction is @X(RN).

Consider the example of Fig. 7.21. Register 4 contains 12000. Suppose we
wish to complement the contents of the memory location whose address is the
contents of 13600; X must be 1600, because 1600 + 12000 are 13600. We write
the assembly instruction as

```
COM @1600 (R4)
```

The binary form of this instruction is

```
005174
001600
```

When this instruction is executed, 1600 and the contents of R4 are added,
giving 13600. The effective address is the contents of memory location 13600,
which is 1020. Then the contents of location 1020, namely 000444, are complemented to give 177333.

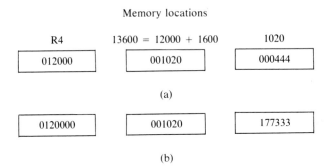

Fig. 7.21
Index deferred addressing. (a) Register and memory contents before executing COM @1600(R4). (b) Register and memory contents after executing COM @1600(R4).

The deferred addressing modes are summarized in Table 7.6. These modes are more complex than the direct addressing modes. Careful thought is needed to decide how to use them effectively.

Table 7.6
Deferred addressing modes

Binary code	Assembly code	Name	Effective address	Meaning
001	@RN	Register deferred	(RN)	Register N points to the operand.
011	@(RN)+	Autoincrement deferred	((RN))	Register N points to a pointer to the operand; then the contents of register N are incremented.
101	@−(RN)	Autodecrement deferred	((RN) − 2)	The contents of register N are decremented; register N then points to a pointer to the operand.
111	@X(RN)	Index deferred	(X + (RN))	The contents of register N plus the value X point to a pointer to the operand.

7.5.3 *Program Counter Addressing*

We have not yet exhausted the possible addressing modes of the PDP-11. We can construct four interesting modes from the basic ones by choosing the program counter, R7, for our register. The modes are immediate, absolute (or immediate deferred), relative, and relative deferred.

Immediate addressing Immediate addressing in the PDP-11 is autoincrement addressing with the program counter. Symbolically we write #N, where N is the immediate data. The pound symbol # shows immediate addressing. Thus to add 100_8 to R4 we write

```
ADD #100, R4
```

or its octal equivalent

062704
000100.

In the octal form two words are required—the first for the operation and the second for the immediate data. In the first word, 06 is the operation code for add and 27 specifies autoincrement addressing (2) with the program counter (7), thus giving immediate addressing. The 04 means register addressing with register 4. The second word gives the octal number to be added.

Figure 7.22 shows the changes in registers and memory after execution of this instruction. It assumes that the instruction is stored in location 1160, the initial value of the program counter. During execution the program counter is incremented by 2 to point to the immediate data and then by 2 again to point to the next instruction after the immediate data, 100_8, is added to R4.

Absolute addressing Absolute addressing, sometimes called immediate deferred addressing, is autoincrement deferred addressing with the program counter. The incremented program counter points to the memory location following the instruction. The effective address is the contents of the location after the instruction. This contrasts with immediate addressing, in which the operand is

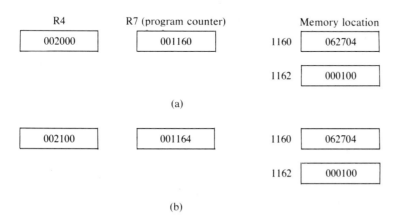

Fig. 7.22
Immediate addressing. (a) Contents of registers and memory before executing ADD #100, R4. (b) Contents of registers and memory after executing ADD #100, R4.

the contents of the location after the instruction. Like immediate addressing, absolute addressing requires two words—the first to give the operation, and the second to give the address. It is denoted by @#A, where A is the effective address.

Suppose we wish to complement the contents of memory location 14620 which now contains 022222. Using absolute addressing, we write

COM @#014620

or its octal equivalent

005137
014620

In the first word, 0051 is the op code for complement; 37 shows absolute addressing. The second word gives the address. Figure 7.23 shows changes in registers and memory. The instruction is assumed to be stored in locations 5714 and 5716.

Relative addressing Relative addressing is index addressing with the program counter. We denote it by X(R7), where X is the number to be added to the

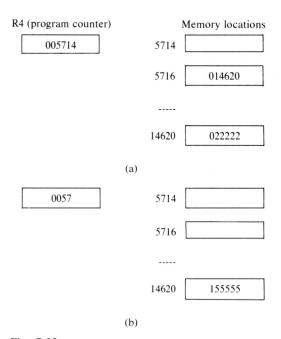

(a)

(b)

Fig. 7.23
Absolute addressing. (a) Contents of program counter and memory before executing COM/@#14620. (b) Contents of program counter and memory after executing COM/@#14620.

location following the instruction. Calculating can be a little tricky because the instruction takes two or three words. The effective address is X plus the location after the relative address word.

As an example, assume that the program counter shows 2244 and that we wish to complement the contents of memory location 2270. The complement instruction takes two words—one for the operation and one for X. Thus after the instruction is executed, the program counter will contain 2244 + 4 = 2250. Since 2270 − 2250 = 20, X must be 20. Thus we write

```
COM 20 (R7)
```

or

```
005167
000020
```

In the first word 0051 again is the op code; 67 shows relative addressing. The second word gives the offset. Figure 7.24 shows the contents of registers and memory before and after executing this instruction.

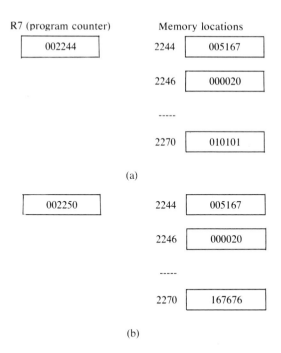

Fig. 7.24
Relative addressing. (a) Contents of program counter and memory before executing COM 20(R7); note that 2244 + 4 + 20 = 2270. (b) Contents of program counter and memory after executing COM 20(R7).

Relative deferred addressing Relative deferred addressing is denoted by @X(R7), where X is the number to be added to the location after the instruction. It is index deferred addressing with the program counter. It resembles relative addressing, but the address obtained by adding X to the location following the program counter points to the effective address. It is not the effective address itself.

Figure 7.25 shows an example of relative deferred addressing. In memory location 5102, the initial value of the program counter, and in memory location

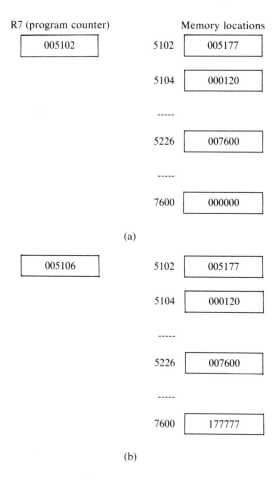

(a)

(b)

Fig. 7.25
Relative deferred addressing. (a) Contents of program counter and memory before executing COM @120(R7); note that 5102 + 4 + 120 = 5226. (b) Contents of program counter and memory after executing COM @120(R7).

5104 are stored

005177
000120

These are the octal forms of the assembly instruction

COM 120(R7).

Again, in the first word 0051 is the operation code; 77 means relative deferred addressing. The second word is the offset. As this instruction is executed, the program counter is incremented by 2 to show the value of X as 120 and incremented again by 2 to point to the next instruction. The effective address is calculated as the contents of the location whose sum is X plus the location after the instruction. Hence it is the contents of location 120 + 5106 = 5226, or 7600. The contents of 7600, originally 0, are complemented to yield 177777.

These four modes using the program counter are advantageous for writing **position independent code (PIC),** that is, code in which addresses are specified relative to the program counter.

Consider, for example, the instruction

MOV X, R2

When this instruction is translated into machine code by the assembler, two words will be written. The first will be

016702

The 01 is the MOV op code; 67 is relative addressing for source X; 02 is register addressing for register 2. The second word will give the address of X relative to the program counter. Assume that the first word of the instruction is stored in location 1240 and that X has an absolute address of 2350. Because the instruction takes two words, the address after the instruction is 1244. The address of X relative to the program counter is 2350 − 1244 = 1104. Hence the entire instruction is assembled as

016702
001104

More generally, X is assembled as PC − X, where PC is the value of the program counter after the instruction is executed and X is the actual address of the data. Other instructions are handled similarly. How would

MOV @R2, X

be assembled? How would

MOV X, Y

where both X and Y have relative addresses, be handled?

When a program is written so that it can be moved in memory without changing the relative distances between instructions and their operands, it can easily be loaded into several areas of memory for use by different users.

Instructions that use relative addressing are termed **relocatable** for this reason. Program counter addressing is also helpful in operating on unstructured data.

We should also note that the PAL-11 assembler for the PDP-11 usually uses relative addressing. The reason for using relative addressing is to make it easy to assemble the program anywhere in memory.

The eight basic addressing modes and the four program counter addressing modes are summarized in Table 7.7. Because you may use this table for quick

Table 7.7
PDP-11 addressing modes

Name	Octal code	Assembly code	Meaning
Register	ON	%N	Register N is the operand.
Autoincrement	2N	(%N)+	Register N points to the operand; then its contents are incremented.
Autodecrement	4N	−(%N)	The contents of register N are decremented; it then points to the operand.
Index	6N	X(%N)	The sum of the value X plus the contents of register N point to the operand.
Register deferred	1N	@%N	Register N points to the operand.
Autoincrement deferred	3N	@(%N)	Register N points to the effective address of the operand; then its contents are incremented.
Autodecrement deferred	5N	@−(%N)	The contents of register N are decremented; it then points to the effective address of the operand.
Index deferred	7N	@X(%N)	The sum of the value X plus the contents of register N point to the effective address of the operand.
Immediate	27	#X	The value X is the operand.
Absolute	37	@#A	A is the effective address of the operand.
Relative	67	X	The sum of X plus the address of the location after the instruction is the effective address.
Relative deferred	77	@X	The sum of X plus the address of the location after the instruction points to the effective address.

reference, we will drop the convention of referring to registers as R in the table. Instead we show the standard reference to register N as %N. We can refer to RN only if the register has been assigned this notation in the program.

Before leaving PDP-11 addressing we should consider **byte addressing.** As mentioned earlier, many PDP-11 instructions operate on bytes. Byte instructions are denoted by a B at the end of the operation code, such as MOVB, or by a 1 in the first bit of the binary code of selected instructions. Byte instructions may address odd memory locations. The program counter is always incremented or decremented by 2, however.

A byte instruction may move a byte to a 16-bit register, as in the instruction

```
MOVB CHAR, R1
```

The byte is always moved into the right half of the register, that is, into bits 7 through 0. We say the byte is **right-justified,** meaning it is as far right as it can be.

If we wish to move data from the left half of the register, we use the instruction SWAB (SWAp Byte). It exchanges the contents of the right and left halves of the register (or memory location) addressed. For example, the sequence of instructions below moves the contents of bits 15 to 8 of R2 into memory location CHAR21.

```
SWAB R2
MOVB R2, CHAR21
```

If desired, we can restore the original contents of R2 with another SWAB R2 instruction.

Addressing modes are the primary way in which computer designers provide flexibility. An instruction ordinarily supplies an address for each operand and a mode showing how the address should be changed during execution of the instruction. After the instruction is fetched and its operand address (or addresses) and mode(s) are decoded, the computer calculates an effective address for each operand and then executes the instruction.

Some addressing modes do not require calculation of an effective address. Inherent addressing involves an address, usually a register, that is inherent in the operation code for the instruction. Immediate addressing provides an operand directly.

Direct addressing modes include those in which the effective address is given directly. They include register addressing, memory addressing, paging, and indexed addressing. Paging can be done either with fixed pages or with pages that are defined relative to the current contents of the program counter. Indexed addressing requires a special index register whose contents are added to an offset supplied by the instruction. Implied addressing is a variation of indexed addressing without an offset. The address is held in a special register called a data counter; autoindexing may be used to provide a series of addresses.

Nearly all direct addressing modes can become indirect addressing modes by considering the address calculated as a pointer to the effective address. Indirect addressing modes include register addressing, memory addressing, paging, and indexed addressing. Indirect addressing can be combined with indexed addressing by either indexing first (pre-indexing) or last (post-indexing).

The PDP-11 has eight basic addressing modes—four direct modes and four deferred modes. With direct register addressing, the effective address is the register named; with direct index addressing, the effective address is the index plus the contents of the register named. The direct autoindex modes both have the effective address as the contents of the register named. For autoincrement the register is incremented by 2 after addressing; for autodecrement the register is decremented by 2 before addressing. The four deferred modes operate in a similar way except that in each case the effective address is the contents of the location whose address is given by the equivalent direct addressing instruction.

The PDP-11 has four additional modes created from the basic modes by using the program counter. Immediate addressing gives the operand in the assembly instruction and stores it in the memory location after the instruction. Absolute addressing is immediate deferred addressing; the effective address is stored in the location after the instruction. Relative addressing is index addressing using the program counter; the effective address is the index plus the location after the instruction. Similarly, in relative deferred addressing the effective address is the contents of the location whose address is the index plus the location after the instruction. The last four modes are used in position-independent coding.

Key Terms

absolute addressing	direct addressing
autodecrement addressing	direct memory addressing
autodecrement deferred addressing	direct register addressing
autodecrementing	effective address (EA)
autoincrement addressing	immediate addressing
autoincrement deferred addressing	implied addressing
autoincrementing	index addressing
autoindexing	index deferred addressing
byte addressing	indexed addressing
current page	indexed direct addressing
current-page direct addressing	index register
data counter	indirect addressing
deferred addressing	indirect memory addressing

indirect register addressing   post-indexing
inherent addressing   pre-indexing
isolated input/output   register addressing
memory-mapped input/output   register deferred addressing
paged addressing   relative addressing
page zero   relative direct addressing
page-zero direct addressing   relocatable
pointer   scratchpad register
position-independent code (PIC)

7.R *References*

All books on assembly language programming by necessity discuss addressing modes. Thus you should find it easy to obtain alternative treatments of this important topic. The programming manuals for your computer are an important reference for your programming. You may wish to compare the names of addressing modes given by the manufacturer with the ones used in this chapter. Good discussions of microcomputer addressing modes can be found in Hilburn and Julich (1976), Klingman (1977), Peatman (1977), and Korn (1977). Good material on PDP-11 addressing modes may be found in Southern (1972), Gear (1974), Stone and Sieworek (1975), Eckhouse (1975), and Cooper (1977). Addressing for other minicomputers is treated in Gruenberger and Babcock (1973), Korn (1973), and Weller (1975).

7.P *Problems*

Section 7.4

7.1 For your small computer, list the addressing modes applicable to all instructions.

7.2 Suppose Jim and Mary shake hands. We can say that they are now directly addressed or zero-level addressed with each other. If Jim now shakes hands with Jane, we can say that Jane and Mary are first-level addressed with each other. Assume that each person can and does directly address or shake hands with $2^{10} = 1024$ people in his or her lifetime. What level of addressing is required for you to shake hands (at some level) with (a) everyone in the USA? (b) everyone in the world?

7.3 Suppose you were to design a computer with four registers and two mode bits. What modes would you choose? Why?

7.4 Suppose you were to design a computer with one accumulator and two mode bits. What modes would you choose? Why?

7.5 If you could have either indexed addressing or indirect addressing but not both, which would you choose? Why?

***Section* 7.5**

7.6 Show the effective addresses of the following PDP-11 instructions.
   a) MOV (%5)+, −(%3)
   b) ADD 400 (%2), −(%1)
   c) SUB @(%0), @−(%3)
   d) ADD #123, %4
   e) MOV 200 (%7), @#100

7.7 What is wrong with the following PDP-11 instructions?
   a) MOV %2, #100
   b) ADD (%5)+, −(%5)

7.8 Write brief PDP-11 program segments to clear every location from 100 to 200 using each of the following.
   a) direct register addressing
   b) autoincrement addressing
   c) autodecrement addressing
   d) immediate addressing
   e) absolute addressing

Subroutines, Coroutines, and Macros

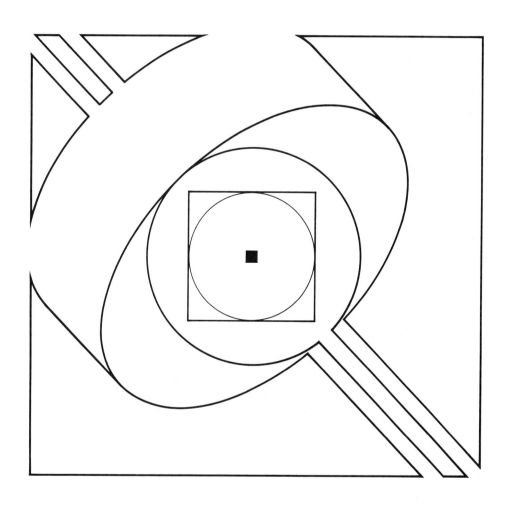

8.1 *Introduction*

Most programs, except for trivially short ones, are written as collections of subroutines and **coroutines**—a general form of subroutines. By organizing instructions into such modules and then using these to build programs, we gain several advantages:

- Modular programs are easier to understand.
- They are easier to debug because each part can be tested separately.
- The subroutines and coroutines can be used, without rewriting, as modules in any other programs where their functions are needed.
- The use of subroutines for procedures that are performed more than once in a program saves space in memory.
- Programming effort is further reduced because transfers between subroutines and a main program are handled in a standard way.

Subroutines and coroutines have one disadvantage—the required overhead of a few instructions to transfer control to them and to return control to the main program. In general, however, the benefits outweigh this cost. In this chapter we will examine subroutines, coroutines, and the hardware associated with their execution. We will also look at macros—an aid in writing programs.

As we have seen, in many cases one sequence of instructions may be needed at several places in a program. For example, we may wish to multiply several pairs of numbers on a computer that lacks multiplication instructions. Or we may wish to calculate the tangent of several angles. In such cases, it is desirable to write the sequence of instructions just once and to call it as needed from any part of the program. When we write the sequence as a subroutine, we avoid duplicating the instructions in memory. Thus we use memory more efficiently.

A subroutine is a sequence of instructions that can be entered from many places in a program. When it is called, control transfers to the first instruction of the sequence. When all subroutine instructions have been executed, control returns to the place in the main program just after the subroutine call. At the time that control transfers to the subroutine, the **return address** in the main program must be saved so that return will be made to the correct location. Because the program counter is incremented just after the instruction is fetched, the contents of the program counter during execution are the return address. Depending on the computer, the return address may be one to four bytes higher than the address of the instruction that calls the subroutine.

Two instructions are needed to use a subroutine. An instruction in the main program, commonly called a **subroutine call** instruction, transfers control to the subroutine and saves the return address. At the end of the subroutine a **subroutine return** instruction directs the transfer of control back to the main program.

Throughout this chapter we will pay attention to the special problems of microcomputers. When programs are stored in ROM, we are restricted in manipulating data. Constant data and pointers can be stored in ROM, but variable data and addresses cannot.

8.2 *Simple Handling of Subroutines*

Before looking at the way most small computers handle subroutines, we will look at a simpler way, that used by the PDP-8. Its subroutine call instruction has the form

JMS SUBRTN

where SUBRTN is the label of the starting address of the subroutine. The instruction performs two actions:

- It transfers control to the subroutine.
- It stores the return address—the address in the main program following the JMS instruction—in the first location of the subroutine (entry point).

No instruction can be stored in the first location of the subroutine because anything stored there would be destroyed by the storing of the return address. It is customary to place 0's in that location when writing the subroutine.

The last instruction of the subroutine has the form

JMP I SUBRTN

This instruction returns control to the main program. It causes an indirect jump through the first location of the subroutine, which holds the return address of the main program. An example of the use of these two instructions is shown in Table 8.1 and Fig. 8.1. Note that the flowchart of Fig. 8.1 shows the main operations only—not the detailed actions of the instructions.

The Texas Instruments TMS1000 microcomputer uses a variation of this scheme. It has two special registers—a four-bit page buffer register and a six-bit subroutine return register—that together store 10-bit return addresses. When a subroutine is called, the current values of the counterparts of these two registers—a four-bit page register and a six-bit program counter—are moved to the page buffer register and subroutine return register, respectively. A six-bit value provided by the subroutine call instruction is placed in the program counter. The contents of the page register—the current page—are replaced by the contents of the page buffer register. On return, the contents of the page buffer register and the subroutine return register are moved to the page register and the program counter, respectively.

The way that the PDP-8 and the TMS1000 handle subroutines has advantages. It is simple. It requires only one special instruction, the subroutine call instruction JMS. The subroutine return is done by the general indirect jump instruction rather than by a special return instruction. However, the method

Table 8.1
A PDP-8 program with subroutine to triple magnitudes of positive numbers

Label	Op code	Operand	Comment
			; PROGRAM TRIPLES MAGNITUDES OF
			; POSITIVE NUMBER IN LIST
	*20		; ORIGIN OF MAIN PROGRAM
	CLA		; CLEAR ACCUMULATOR
	TAD	N	; GET N
	CMA	IAC	; CALCULATE 2's COMPLEMENT
	DCA	COUNTR	; INITIALIZE COUNTER
LOOP,	TAD I	POINTR	; GET NUMBER
	SMA		; SKIP NEXT INSTRUCTION IF
			; NUMBER NEGATIVE
	JMS	TRIPLE	; JUMP TO SUBROUTINE TRIPLE
RETURN,	DCA I	POINTR	; STORE NUMBER
	ISZ	POINTR	; INCREMENT POINTER
	ISZ	COUNTR	; INCREMENT COUNTER AND CHECK
			; FOR END OF LIST
	JMP	LOOP	; NOT DONE YET, JUMP TO LOOP
	HLT		; END OF LIST, STOP
COUNTR,	0000		
POINTR,	140		; FIRST ADDRESS OF LIST
N,	57		; N IS NUMBER OF NUMBERS
TRIPLE,	0000		; FIRST ADDRESS OF SUBROUTINE
			; TRIPLE; DOES NOT CONTAIN
			; INSTRUCTION
	DCA	TEMP	; STORE CONTENTS OF ACCUMULATOR
			; IN TEMPORARY STORAGE
	TAD	TEMP	; GET NUMBER
	TAD	TEMP	; DOUBLE NUMBER
	TAD	TEMP	; TRIPLE NUMBER
	JMP I	TRIPLE	; RETURN TO LOCATION LABELED TRIPLE
			; RETURN TO MAIN PROGRAM
TEMP,	0000		; TEMPORARY STORAGE
	$		; END OF INSTRUCTIONS AND DATA

also has distinct disadvantages. Specifically, a second user cannot start using the subroutine before the first user has exited from it. An attempt to do so would result in the second user's return address replacing the first user's return address so that the first user would exit to an incorrect location. The two-user situation occurs not only when two or more people are executing programs on a computer at the same time, but also whenever a single program has several tasks executing at the same time. In addition, return addresses cannot be stored in ROM. (Why?) Hence subroutines handled by the PDP-8 method may only be stored in read-write memory (RAM), not in ROM. Nor can the PDP-8 method handle a subroutine that calls itself. For these purposes, we need a more sophisticated method such as that used by most other small computers. To

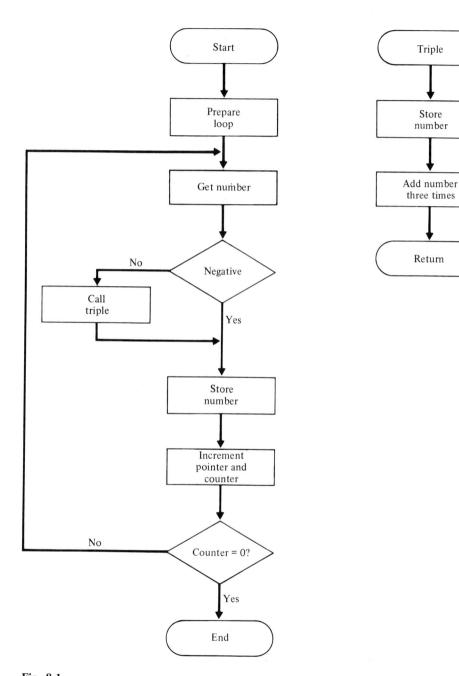

Fig. 8.1
Flowchart of program with sub-routine to triple magnitude of positive numbers.

understand its functioning, we must first learn about a hardware organization for storing return addresses.

8.3   *Stack Organizations*

A **stack** is an ordered list of numbers that operates like a spring-loaded plate holder in a cafeteria. A stack can begin at a memory address and store incoming words in preceding (lower address) memory locations, just as a plate holder stores plates above the holder surface. Storage is in **last-in, first-out** order (LIFO). Thus items can be added to the stack in sequence and retrieved in reverse order. We store an item by **pushing** it on the stack; we retrieve an item by **popping** it from the stack. A **stack pointer** points to the most recent addition to the stack. Figure 8.2 shows an example of the contents of a stack after a few transactions.

Several variations of this organization are possible. There is nothing magic about pushing items in memory locations with decreasing addresses so that the stack grows from high addresses to low addresses. Instead, a stack can be organized so that items are pushed into memory locations with increasing addresses; then the stack grows from low addresses to high addresses. Similarly, the stack pointer does not need to point to the last item pushed on the stack; it can just as well point to the next location into which data can be pushed—the first empty location. Thus the term **top of the stack (TOS)** is used only loosely to refer to the location shown by the stack pointer. Ordinarily a computer designer will choose a stack organization, and we, as programmers, will live with that choice. The computer's basic stack instructions will be designed to work with the stack as designed. If we wish to expend some effort, we can write instruction sequences to create and use a different stack organization.

Most of the computers that we describe in this book have the stack growing from high addresses to low addresses. The Rockwell PPS-8 has a stack growing in the opposite way. The PDP-11 and the 8085 have stack pointers that point to the last item pushed on the stack. The M6800 has a stack pointer that points to the location into which the next item can be pushed. Check this detail for your computer.

Another difference between stack organizations is whether they are intended for 8-bit or 16-bit data. The M6800 has a byte stack for pushing or popping one 8-bit byte at a time. The 8085 has a stack that handles two 8-bit bytes at a time; we will illustrate this in the next section. The PDP-11 can handle stacks with either 16-bit words or 8-bit bytes, using any of its general purpose registers as a stack pointer. Register 6 is a hardware stack pointer that operates with 16-bit words only.

The stacks we have just discussed are held in memory—in RAM rather than ROM for microcomputers. (Why?) When a stack is held in memory, we can usually choose its first address by initializing the stack pointer. Our objec-

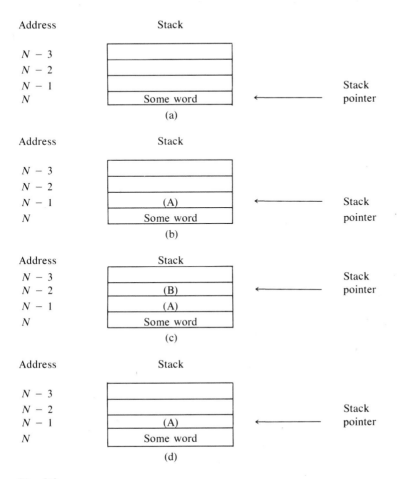

Fig. 8.2
Organization of stacks. (a) Initial stack. (b) Stack after PUSH A command. (c) Stack after PUSH B command. (d) Stack after POP B command.

tive here is to manage memory so that the stack will not encroach on other data or instructions as it grows. **Stack depth** (number of storage locations) is basically limited by our assignment of memory for other uses. This limit is not automatic. Thus, if we are not careful, a stack can overwrite and hence destroy other memory contents. We must also watch the balance of push and pop instructions so that we do not try to pop more data than we have pushed.

Some relatively primitive microcomputers as well as some pocket calculators have stacks located in registers on the CPU chip rather than in RAM. The number of registers for stack use and hence the maximum stack length are permanently fixed. No stack pointer is needed because data pushed on the stack can always be moved into the top register. The contents of all the other registers ripple down one, and the contents of the bottom register are lost. Figure 8.3 illustrates this organization for a stack of depth 4.

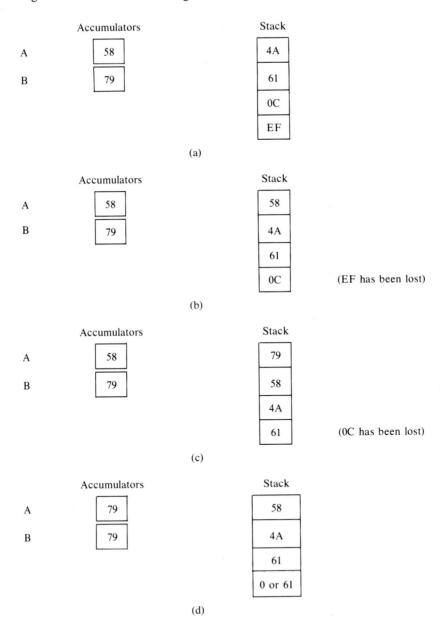

Fig. 8.3
Organization of a CPU stack. (a) Before PUSH A command. (b) After PUSH A command. (c) After PUSH B command. (d) After POP A command.

Some examples of microcomputers with stacks implemented as CPU registers include the four-bit Intel 4004 and 4040, with stack depths of 3 and 7,
respectively. The Intel 8008 has a stack depth of 7. The Rockwell PPS-8 has a
stack of 32—ample for most practical purposes.

8.3.1 *Stack Instructions*

Most microcomputers and many minicomputers have push and pop instructions. The stack instructions of the M6800 are particularly simple. For pushing
data, the command PSH A or PSH B is used. As a result the byte held in the
accumulator named is stored in the location shown by the stack pointer. The
stack pointer (SP) is then decremented to point to the next available location.
For popping data, the command PUL A or PUL B is given. This command first
increments the stack pointer and then moves the contents of the indicated
memory location into the accumulator named. Figure 8.4 shows examples of
the execution of these instructions.

The stack instructions of the 8080/8085 are more complex. Its stack pointer
(SP) always points to the top two bytes of memory in the stack; more exactly,
the top two bytes are in the memory location addressed by the stack pointer
and the memory location whose address is one more than that given by the
stack pointer. Data is popped from these two locations. Data pushed on the
stack goes into the locations with addresses one and two less than the contents
of SP. The register pair (rp) designated may be B, D, H, or PSW. The register
contents are stored in the stack with the high-order byte in the higher numbered
memory location. When the register pair is PSW, the contents of A are stored in
the higher numbered location and cancelation codes are stored in the lower
numbered location.

PUSH rp   PUSH contents of rp onto stack
POP rp   POP contents of top of stack to rp

After a PUSH, the stack pointer is decremented by 2. After a POP, it is
incremented by 2.

A brief example, repeated from the discussion of stack operations in
Chapter 5, may clarify these instructions. Suppose SP holds the address 4A5C
hexadecimal. Suppose B holds A0 hex and C holds B1 hex. (See Fig. 8.5a.) The
instruction

PUSH B

loads B1 into location 4A5B and A0 into 4A5A. SP is decremented by 2 to
4A5A; the contents of B and C are not changed. (See Fig. 8.5b.) After this
move, the instruction

POP D

moves the contents of 4A5A, namely B1, to E and the contents of 4A5B,
namely A0, to D. These two instructions have thus moved the contents of
register pair B to pair D. (See Fig. 8.5c.)

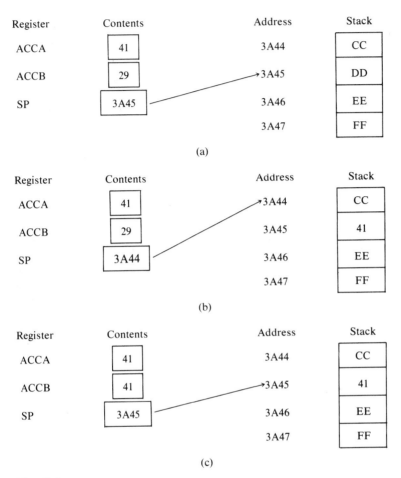

Fig. 8.4
Stack instructions of the M6800. (a) Before PSH A command. (b) After PSH A command. (c) After PUL B command.

Suppose the next instruction is

PUSH PSW

We recall that register pair PSW consists of A and the five condition codes. Specifically, the 8-bit register for the condition codes has the following form.

7	6	5	4	3	2	1	0
S	Z	0	AC	0	P	1	C

Suppose the accumulator holds E7, and the parity and carry condition codes are 1 while all others are 0, resulting in 07 hex. Then the result of the instruction is to move E7 into 4A5B and 07 into 4A5A; the contents of the accumulator and the condition codes are not changed. (See Fig. 8.5d.)

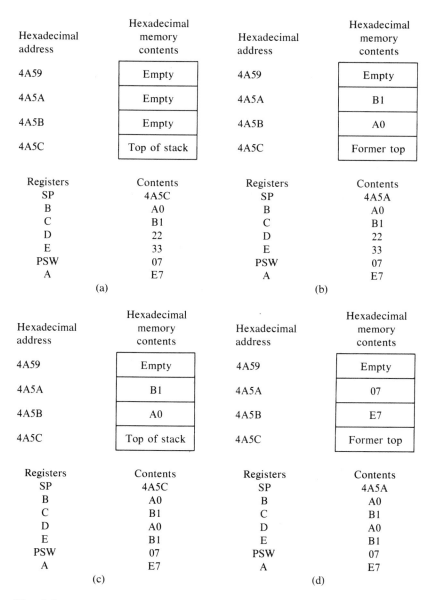

Hexadecimal address	Hexadecimal memory contents
4A59	Empty
4A5A	Empty
4A5B	Empty
4A5C	Top of stack

Registers	Contents
SP	4A5C
B	A0
C	B1
D	22
E	33
PSW	07
A	E7

(a)

Hexadecimal address	Hexadecimal memory contents
4A59	Empty
4A5A	B1
4A5B	A0
4A5C	Former top

Registers	Contents
SP	4A5A
B	A0
C	B1
D	22
E	33
PSW	07
A	E7

(b)

Hexadecimal address	Hexadecimal memory contents
4A59	Empty
4A5A	B1
4A5B	A0
4A5C	Top of stack

Registers	Contents
SP	4A5C
B	A0
C	B1
D	A0
E	B1
PSW	07
A	E7

(c)

Hexadecimal address	Hexadecimal memory contents
4A59	Empty
4A5A	07
4A5B	E7
4A5C	Former top

Registers	Contents
SP	4A5A
B	A0
C	B1
D	A0
E	B1
PSW	07
A	E7

(d)

Fig. 8.5
Results of PUSH and POP operations. (a) Before PUSH B. (b) After PUSH B.
(c) After POP D. (d) After PUSH PSW.

A somewhat unusual single-byte instruction of the Intel 8080/8085 exchanges the contents on the top two bytes of the stack with the contents of register pair HL.

XTHL   eXchange Top of stack with HL

Two 16-bit values are exchanged—the contents of the memory locations at the top of the stack and the contents of the H and L registers. The contents of L and the byte addressed by the stack pointer are exchanged. The contents of H and the byte whose address is one greater than the stack pointer are exchanged.

The PDP-11 does not provide special push and pull instructions. We must develop them from its MOV instruction. Any register of the PDP-11 except register 7, the program counter, can be a stack pointer. The PDP-11 instructions treat register 6 as a hardware stack pointer for subroutine and interrupt service. To push data from a source location (src) onto the stack, we write a move instruction in autodecrement mode:

MOV src, −(SP)

First the stack pointer is decremented by 2 to point to the next available location. Then the source data is pushed on the stack. To pop data from the stack to a destination (dst), we use a move instruction in autoincrement mode:

MOV (SP)+, dst

First the contents of the location addressed by the stack pointer are moved to the destination; then the stack pointer is incremented by 2 to point to the top of the stack.

Before using a stack for the first time, we initialize the stack pointer by loading it with the desired address of the base of the stack. Microcomputers often have specialized instructions for initializing the stack pointer. For example, the 8080/8085 has the special instruction

SPHL   load Stack Pointer from H and L

which requires first initializing H and L. The stack pointer can also be initialized with the more general instruction

LXI SP, xxxx   Load register pair with immediate data

The M6800 has a special instruction for loading the stack pointer from the index register

TXS   Transfer from indeX register to Stack pointer

which decrements the contents of the index register by 1 before the transfer. It also has an instruction for initializing the stack pointer from the contents of two memory locations or from immediate data,

LDS M   LoaD Stack pointer

This instruction loads the more significant byte of the stack pointer from the memory location named in the instruction and loads the less significant byte from the next higher byte of memory.

The PDP-11, in contrast, can load the stack pointer, register 6, with any addressing mode applied to its basic MOV instruction. See Fig. 8.6.

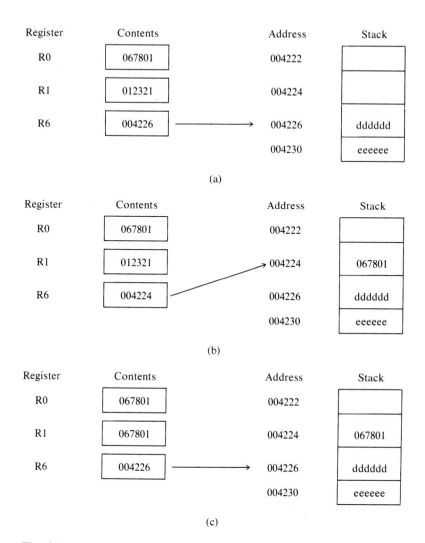

Fig. 8.6
PDP-11 stack instructions. (a) Before MOV R0, –(SP). (b) After MOV R0,
–(SP). (c) After MOV (SP)+, R1.

8.4   *Subroutine Linkage via Stacks*

A small computer that has a stack will ordinarily use the stack for transfers
between a main program and a subroutine. The procedure is simple. Typically
the subroutine call instruction performs these functions:

- The return address—the location of the next instruction after the subroutine call instruction—is pushed on the stack.

- The address of the subroutine is placed in the program counter.
- The stack pointer is incremented or decremented appropriately to point to the new top of the stack.

The subroutine return instruction performs complementary functions:

- The contents of the top of the stack—the return address—are popped into the program counter.
- The stack pointer is incremented or decremented appropriately.

The Intel 8080/8085 handles subroutines in just this way. Its one unconditional and eight conditional subroutine call instructions each take three bytes, including a 16-bit address. The M6800 is more complicated, with two unconditional subroutine call instructions, offering an 8-bit address, a 16-bit address, or an address relative to the program counter.

The PDP-11 has a more complicated method of subroutine transfer that involves a **linkage register**—a register chosen by the programmer to hold the return address. It calls a subroutine with an instruction of the form

JSR REG, SUBRTN

Where REG is the linkage register. This instruction performs four functions:

- It stores the contents of the linkage register on the stack controlled by R6.
- It decrements the contents of R6 by 2 to point to the new top of the stack.
- It stores the address of the next instruction in the main program (the contents of the incremented program counter) in the linkage register.
- It places the first address of the subroutine in the program counter.

The JSR instruction takes one or two words, depending on the address of the subroutine. Figure 8.7(a and b) shows the contents of registers and the stack before and after instruction JSR %4, MULT is executed.

The PDP-11 executes a RTS instruction to return from a subroutine. The form of the instruction is

RTS REG

where REG is the linkage register. For example, the instruction

RTS %4

can be used to return from the subroutine MULT of the preceding example. This instruction jumps to the next instruction of the main program and restores the contents of register 4. (See Fig. 8.7c.)

The Intel 4040 varies this scheme in an interesting way. It calls a subroutine with a two-word JMS instruction that transfers control to a 12-bit address and pushes the return address on the stack. The return instruction BBL (Branch Back and Load data in accumulator) not only returns control to the main program but also loads four bits of data into the accumulator.

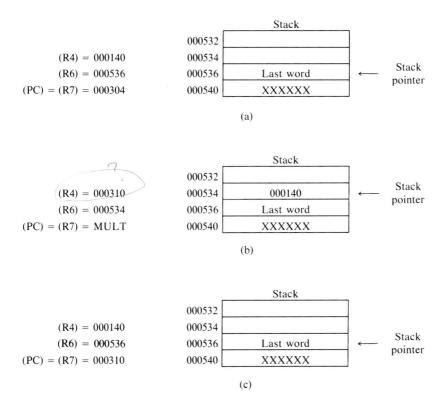

Fig. 8.7
Contents of relevant PD8-11 registers and stack for subroutine call. (a) Conditions before JSR %4, MULT is executed. (b) Conditions after JSR %4, MULT is executed. (c) Conditions after RTS %4 is executed.

Subroutines present problems of register management. We must ensure that our subroutines do not inadvertently use registers whose contents must later be used in the main program. We should try to use whatever registers the CPU provides as effectively as possible. Sometimes there are not many. The M6800 has so few registers, with its two 8-bit accumulators and one index register, that our subroutines must usually use the accumulators, which are holding values that are still needed by the main program. The Intel 8080/8085, with its seven 8-bit registers, including an accumulator, allows a little more leeway. So does the PDP-11, with its eight registers, although after we allocate R7 as a program counter, R6 as a stack pointer, and another for a linkage register, we have only five left for calculations.

It is best to have the subroutine—not the main program—save registers because only the registers used by the subroutine need to be saved. We will consider two ways to save registers. The first stores the contents of any registers used by the subroutine on the stack. For example, suppose an Intel 8080/8085 subroutine uses registers A, B, and C. The first instructions of the subroutine could then be

```
PUSH PSW      ;SAVE CONTENTS OF A AND FLAGS ON STACK
PUSH B        ;SAVE CONTENTS OF B AND C ON STACK
```

The subroutine could then use these registers for its calculations. The last three instructions of the subroutine would then be

```
POP B        ;RESTORE THE PREVIOUS CONTENTS OF B AND C
POP PSW      ;RESTORE THE PREVIOUS CONTENTS OF A AND FLAGS
RET          ;RETURN TO MAIN PROGRAM
```

Note that the register contents are restored in reverse order.

Similarly, suppose we wished to use R1 and R2 in a PDP-11 program that used R5 as a linkage register. The first instructions of the subroutine might be

```
MOV %1, -(%6)     ;SAVE CONTENTS OF R1 ON STACK
MOV %2, -(%6)     ;SAVE CONTENTS OF R2 ON STACK
```

The last three instructions might then be

```
MOV (%6)+, %2     ;RESTORE CONTENTS OF R2
MOV (%6)+, %1     ;RESTORE CONTENTS OF R1
RTS %5            ;RETURN
```

There is nothing sacred about having the instructions that save register contents appear first in a subroutine and the instructions that restore register contents appear last. We could save register contents just before the subroutine uses the registers, wherever that might be, and restore them just afterward. However, if we form the habit of always saving register contents at the beginning of a subroutine and restoring them at the end, we will always know where to find these statements. Thus we can check our subroutines more quickly and easily.

You'll note that up to this point we have been careful to speak about saving and restoring the *contents* of registers, rather than the registers themselves. We will drop this convention now and speak of saving and restoring registers. This shorter jargon should cause no problems, since we must be concerned with saving register contents, not the physical registers.

The second method of saving registers involves designating an area of memory for temporary storage. We will illustrate this for the PDP-11, because the method is applicable to minicomputer programs that are stored in main memory, rather than to microcomputer subroutines, which are usually stored in ROM. (Why?) An area of memory must be saved with the .WORD pseudoinstruction, such as

```
STORE:    .WORD    0,0    ;SAVE TWO WORDS OF MEMORY
```

Registers are saved by the subroutine with the following two instructions:

```
MOV %1,    STORE;     ;SAVE R1 IN LOCATION STORE
MOV %2,    STORE+2    ;SAVE R2 IN THE WORD FOLLOWING STORE
```

Then they are restored, and return from the subroutine is accomplished by

```
MOV        STORE+2, %2;        ;RESTORE R2
MOV        STORE, %1;          ;RESTORE R1
RTS                            ;RETURN
```

A disadvantage of this method is that memory must be dedicated to the storage of registers. Saving registers on a stack, in contrast, ties up memory only temporarily.

8.5   *Reentrant Programs*

We can now compare two methods of storing return addresses—the PDP-8 method of storing the return address in the first location of the subroutine and the more desirable method of storing the return address and the addresses of any needed registers in a stack. The storing of a return address in the sub-routine modifies the subroutine; a program that modifies itself is called a **self-modifying program**.

A program that does not modify itself is called a **reentrant program**. A reentrant routine can be used simultaneously by many programs. It can be entered by one program while it is still being used by another program, and many tasks can be in various stages of processing in the routine at any time. From a programmer's viewpoint the main feature of a reentrant routine is that it consists only of "pure code." That is, it contains only instructions and con-stants. It has no information that will be changed when the program is exe-cuted. More specifically, a reentrant subroutine is designed to access only the following.

- Data stored in CPU registers.
- Data directly addressed in RAM or ROM in a read-only mode.
- Data addressed indirectly via a pointer in a CPU register that was in-itialized in the main program.

An important feature of reentrant subroutines is that they can be inter-rupted by an external device that needs to use the same subroutine. We will have more to say about this when we discuss input/output in Chapter 10.

A current trend in computer architecture is to separate instructions and data in memory and to avoid self-modifying programs. Reentrant programs have four advantages:

- They are easy to debug.
- They can be stored in read-only memory.
- They save memory because they primarily use registers for data storage.
- They can be interrupted and restarted without errors.

8.6   *Coroutines*

Coroutines are a general form of subroutines. The interaction between a main program and a subroutine resembles a boss directing a worker; the main program calls the subroutine, which completes a task and reports back. In contrast, the interaction between two coroutines resembles the activities of two colleagues. Each coroutine performs a task and then calls on the other for another task. The interaction is symmetric. Coroutine A pauses while coroutine B executes instructions; then coroutine B pauses while coroutine A executes instructions. When one coroutine has completed a segment of instructions, it passes control back to the return address in the other coroutine. The return address in a coroutine immediately follows the address of its call coroutine instruction. Thus calculation in each coroutine resumes where it left off—not at the beginning of the coroutine. Figure 8.8 shows the interaction between two coroutines.

As we will see in Chapter 10, coroutines are well suited to input-output programs. They are also ideal for programs that are naturally structured as two or more mutually dependent processes, especially highly interactive processes.

Coroutines can easily be implemented on the PDP-11 with its hardware stack. A special form of the JSR instruction is used to switch from one coroutine to another, using the program counter (R7, here called PC) and the

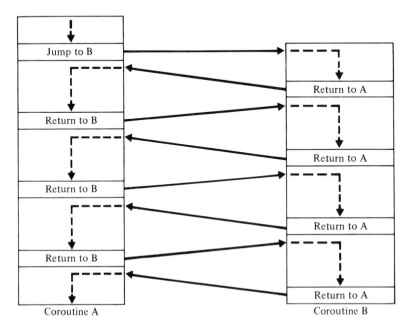

Fig. 8.8
Two coroutines.

hardware stack pointer, R6. The form is

JSR PC, @(%6)+

A call from coroutine A to coroutine B must:

1. Save the contents of the program counter as the return address for A.
2. Enter B at its last return address.

The special form of the JSR instruction accomplishes both. It first transfers control to the destination address (the return address for B), which the com-

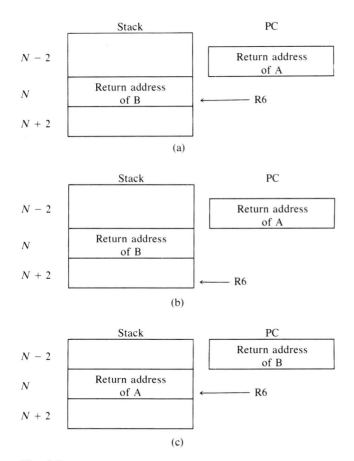

Fig. 8.9
Calling coroutines. (a) Coroutine A calls coroutine B with the instruction JSR PC, (%6)+. (b) The return address of B is popped and the stack pointer is autoincremented. (c) The stack pointer is autodecremented and the contents of the program counter (return address of A) are pushed on the stack. Coroutine B is entered.

puter finds by popping it from the stack associated with R6 as controlled by the @(%6)+ for deferred autoincrement mode. Because the linkage register is also the program counter, PC holds the return address of A, which is pushed on the stack, after B's return address has been popped from the stack. Then the return address of B, the coroutine being called, is placed in the program counter to transfer control to B. The instruction switches the contents of the program counter and the contents of the top of the stack. Thus the return address of coroutine A replaces the old return address of coroutine B. Figure 8.9 illustrates this process as implemented for the PDP-11.

The 8080/8085 has the instruction

XTHL

which exchanges the top two bytes of the stack with the contents of the HL register pair. This instruction is useful for coroutines.

8.7 *Parameter Passing*

Most subroutine and coroutine calls and returns involve parameters. For example, a call to a multiplication subroutine must include the two numbers to be multiplied, and the subroutine must return their product to the calling program. The multiplier, multiplicand, and product are all parameters that must be passed between the calling and called programs. If we consider the return address as a parameter to be passed, all subroutine and coroutine calls transfer at least one parameter.

We use the word **parameter** in two senses. One meaning is that of a dummy variable. For example, consider a multiplication subroutine MULT that multiplies together a multiplicand MPLCN and a multiplier MLPLR to give a product PRDCT. This subroutine, thus, is

MULT(MPLCN, MLPLR, PRDCT)

The parameters MPLCN, MLPLR, and PRDCT are dummy variables for the subroutine MULT. Dummy variables are **formal parameters**. The subroutine processing is described in terms of them, but when the subroutine is executed, they will be replaced by other variables. For example, we might call

MULT (X, Y, ANSWR)

The values of X, Y, and ANSWR replace those of MPLCN, MLPLR, and PRDCT, respectively. Quantities that replace formal parameters during the execution of a subroutine are called **actual parameters**. X is an actual parameter that replaces the formal parameter MPLCN.

There are many ways to pass parameters between two programs. Not all are applicable to every computer; some require many registers, a second stack pointer, program storage in RAM, or other special features. We will consider five methods by which parameters are passed during subroutine calls. In each case we will ask two questions:

1. What information—the values or the addresses of parameters—is transferred during a subroutine call?
2. Where is the information placed for the transfer?

8.7.1 *Common Data*

The first method uses **common data**, also called **global data**. This means data stored in memory locations that can be accessed by both the calling program and the subroutine. For example, we might use the PDP-11 instructions below.

```
        MOV    X, MPLCN     ;STORE X IN MPLCN
        MOV    Y, MLPLR     ;STORE Y IN MLPLR
        JSR    %4, MULT     ;JUMP TO SUBROUTINE MULT
        ⋮
MULT:   MOV    MPLCN, %0    ;BRING MULTIPLICAND TO R0
        MOV    MLPLR, %1    ;BRING MULTIPLIER TO R1
        ...    ...          ;MULTIPLY
```

Similar instructions can be written for the Intel 8085. Locations for MPLCN and MLPLR must be in RAM:

```
        MOV       MPLCN, X    ;STORE X IN MPLCN
        MOV       MLPLR, Y    ;STORE Y IN MLPLR
        CALL MULT
        ⋮
MULT:   MOV       B, MPLCN    ;PUT MPLCN IN B
        MOV       C, MLPLR    ;PUT MLPLR IN C
```

These instructions use the same symbolic names in the calling program and the subroutine MULT; thus the values are stored in the same memory locations. The product is passed in the same way on the return. When the programs are assembled together, they can both refer to the same names. If the programs are assembled separately, MPLCN and MLPLR must be treated as **external symbols**, as explained in Chapter 6.

This method has two disadvantages. First, having many references to external symbols can be inconvenient and confusing. Second, computers have a relatively small amount of memory available for common data. We should avoid using it for permanent storage of parameters for a large number of programs.

8.7.2 *Registers*

A second method is to place parameters in the CPU registers, where they can be accessed by both the main program and the subroutine. For example, we can use the following PDP-11 instructions:

```
MOV    X, %0     ;MULTIPLICAND
MOV    Y, %1     ;MULTIPLIER
JSR    %4, MULT  ;JUMP TO SUBROUTINE
```

For the 8085:

```
MOV       B, X        ;MULTIPLICAND
MOV       C, Y        ;MULTIPLIER
CALL MULT
```

We can even do the same thing for the M6800, with its limited registers, but we would have trouble coping with more parameters:

```
LDA       A, X        ;MULTIPLICAND
LDA       B, Y        ;MULTIPLIER
JSR MULT
```

The main disadvantage of this method is that it severely restricts the number of parameters that can be passed. When some registers are reserved for the program counter, stack pointer, and return address, only a few are available for passing parameters. In addition, we may need to store the previous contents of those registers before we can use them for parameter passing. Saving and restoring the contents of registers adds to the execution time for subroutine calls and returns. Register storage is even more limited than common area storage. However, register storage is temporary. It is better for parameter passing than dedicating part of memory to long-term storage of parameters.

8.7.3 *Parameter Areas*

A third method involves storing parameters in special areas of memory called **parameter areas**. The parameters are stored in successive positions in a parameter area by autoincrementing a register before the subroutine is called. Then the base address of the parameter area is given to the subroutine in a register. The following PDP-11 instructions show the procedure.

```
            MOV   PARAM, %3   ;R3 HOLDS THE ADDRESS OF THE
                              ;PARAMETER AREA
            MOV   X, (%3)+     ;STORE MULTIPLICAND
            MOV   Y, (%3)+     ;STORE MULTIPLIER
            JSR   %4, MULT     ;JUMP TO SUBROUTINE
            ⋮
PARAM:            AREA
AREA:,      =     .+4          ;PARAMETER AREA
```

A similar procedure for the 8085 uses the HL register pair as a pointer to memory.

```
            LHLD   PARAM   ;LOAD HL FROM LOCATION
                           ;PARAM
            MOV    M, X    ;STORE X
            INX    H       ;INCREMENT HL
            CALL   MULT

PARAM:  DW     AREA    ;PARAM HOLDS ADDRESS AREA
AREA:   DS     2       ;ALLOW TWO BYTES OF STORAGE
```

8.7.4   *In-Line Parameter Areas*

A variation of this method uses **in-line parameter areas**. The parameter area immediately follows the JSR instruction. Therefore, the program does not need to pass the base address of the parameter to the subroutine in an extra register. The subroutine linkage register automatically holds the address of the first parameter. Autoincrementing gives the other parameter. When this method is used, the program is self-modifying. Return from the subroutine goes to the location just after the parameter area. The following PDP-11 program segment illustrates this method.

```
        JSR %4, MULT        ;CALL SUBROUTINE
        .WORD X, Y          ;VALUES OF X AND Y TAKE
                            ;TWO WORDS
NEXT:   SOME INSTRUCTION    ;FIRST INSTRUCTION AFTER
                            ;RETURN FROM SUBROUTINE
MULT:   MOV (%4)+, %1       ;MOVE MPLCND TO R1
        MOV (%4)+, %2       ;MOVE MLPLR TO R2
                            ;RETURN ADDRESS HAS BEEN
                            ;ADVANCED TO POINT TO NEXT
        RTS %4              ;RETURN TO NEXT
```

This method is not appropriate for microcomputer programs stored in ROM.

8.7.5   *Stack*

The last method that we will consider holds the parameters in a stack we construct in memory. This stack will use a register other than the usual hardware stack pointer. We push parameters on the stack before entering the subroutine. The subroutine can access the top locations of the stack for the parameters by indexing relative to the stack pointer. The following set of PDP-11 instructions illustrates this method. Note the reverse order of storing parameters and the autodecrement addressing.

```
        MOV #100, %3        ;INITIALIZE STACK POINTER
        MOV Y, -(%3)        ;PUSH MULTIPLIER
        MOV X, -(%3)        ;PUSH MULTIPLICAND
        JSR %4, MULT        ;JUMP TO SUBROUTINE
        :
MULT:   MOV (%3)+, %1       ;PLACE MULTIPLICAND IN R1
        MOV (%3)+, %2       ;PLACE MULTIPLIER IN R2
        :
        RTS %4              ;RETURN TO MAIN PROGRAM
```

For the 8085 the procedure might be:

```
        LXI SP, 2000H       ;INITIALIZE STACK POINTER
        MOV B, X            ;MULTIPLICAND
        MOV C, Y            ;MULTIPLIER
        PUSH B              ;PUSH BOTH ON STACK
```

```
        CALL MULT
        ⋮
MULT:   POP B           ;MULTIPLICAND IS IN B, MULTIPLIER
                        ;IS IN C
        RET
```

A major advantage of using a stack for parameter passing where possible is that it requires little memory. Stacks for parameter passing within a nested sequence of subroutines can be constructed so that each stack disappears on return to the calling routine. Thus the maximum area needed is the maximum number of parameters occurring in one subroutine. By contrast, the methods that use parameter areas require saving the total of all parameter areas.

The following characteristics are desirable for parameter passing:

- Few registers are needed.
- Little memory is needed.
- Many parameters can be passed.
- The linkage method is simple.

The stack method looks good by all these criteria. How do you think the other methods compare on these points?

8.8 Macroinstructions

8.8.1 Macro Definitions and Calls

Sometimes we need to repeat a sequence of assembly language instructions at several places in a program. For example, we might want to decrement register REG on some computer four times. We can do this by writing the decrement instruction DEC four times.

```
DEC REG     ;DECREMENT CONTENTS OF REG BY 1
DEC REG
DEC REG
DEC REG
```

But repeating this sequence several times in a program is tiresome. We could write it just once and duplicate it on paper tape or some other medium; then we could insert a copy anywhere in the program as needed. Even better, we could write this sequence just once and have the assembler repeat it when needed. We could, of course, define this sequence as a subroutine. However, we have another choice, which is often useful for short sequences of instructions. We can define and call a **macroinstruction**, or **macro**, that will cause the assembler to generate the series of instructions for us. A macro is an open subroutine, as contrasted with the **closed subroutines** discussed earlier in this chapter. A macro or open subroutine requires memory for each instruction each time it is called, just as though we had copied the instructions on paper tape and inserted them in the program, whereas a closed subroutine has the instructions written in memory only once. Thus macros are used only for relatively short sequences of instructions; otherwise, the demands on memory would be too much. Their advantage is that they execute more rapidly than closed subroutines, because no time is needed for subroutine call and return instructions. Another distinction between macros and closed subroutines is that a special assembler, called a macro assembler, is needed for macros, whereas virtually all assemblers can deal with closed subroutines.

Assuming that we have the PDP-11 macro assembler MACRO-11, let us define a macro called DCRFR for the preceding example. We write

```
.MACRO    DCRFR, X    ;MACRO DEFINITION BEGINS WITH
          DEC X       ;MACRO NAME DCRFR AND ONE
          DEC X       ;ARGUMENT X
          DEC X
          DEC X
          .ENDM       ;END OF MACRO DEFINITION
```

We call this macro to decrement A four times by writing

```
DCRFR A
```

The assembler replaces this instruction by the definition of DCRFR. In the definition X was given as an argument; now X is replaced by A every time it occurs, a procedure called **macro expansion**. Thus the DCRFR A instruction produces four DEC A instructions. Similarly, the instruction

```
DCRFR REG 1
```

produces four DEC REG 1 instructions.

A similar macro for the 8085 would be defined as follows.

```
DCRFR     MACRO       RPAIR
          DCX         RPAIR
          DCX         RPAIR
          DCX         RPAIR
          DCX         RPAIR
          ENDM
```

Each time DCRFR is called for a given register pair, the 8085 macroassembler substitutes four DCX instructions operating on the register pair named. Hence DCRFR B produces four DCX B instructions.

More generally, MACRO-11 has the definition format

```
.MACRO    NAME        ARG1, ARG2,...,ARGN
          INSTR1
          INSTR2
          ⋮
          INSTRL
          .ENDM
```

After the command .MACRO, the name of the macro is followed by arguments separated by commas. Because the arguments are dummy variables not defined outside the macro, they cannot be referred to outside the macro. The body of the macro contains the instructions that define the macro. The macro ends with

.ENDM. If desired, the last statement can be

```
.ENDM NAME
```

Including the name of the macro is a checking feature. It helps both the programmer and the assembler to verify that the .MACRO and .ENDM statements are paired as they should be.

The 8085 has a similar but not identical format for defining macros. It is

```
NAME        MACRO       ARG1, ARG2,..., ARGN
            INSTR1
            INSTR2
            ⋮
            INSTRL
            ENDM
```

For both of these computers—and most others—the macro is called or referenced by giving its name, followed by a list of the actual arguments.

Suppose we write an 8085 macro CLEAR to clear two registers.

```
CLEAR       MACRO       REG1, REG2
            MVI         REG1, 0
            MVI         REG2, 0
            ENDM
```

Then we might call the macro with B and D as arguments.

```
CLEAR       B,D
```

The resulting macro expansion is

```
MVI         B, 0
MVI         D, 0
```

Macro assemblers can deal with situations in which the macro call supplies either fewer or more arguments than the macro definition. The 8080 macro assembler is a case in point. If the macro call supplies fewer arguments than the macro definition, nulls are substituted for the missing arguments. Thus

```
CLEAR       C
```

would result only in clearing register C. If the macro call supplies more arguments than the macro definition, the extra arguments are ignored. Hence

```
CLEAR       B, C, D, E
```

results in clearing registers B and C only.

8.8.2 *Local Symbols*

Suppose we want to define a macro ORDER to put two variables in nondecreasing order. The macro will compare the two variables. If the first is greater than the second, it will interchange them. We will need a third location as temporary storage. If we choose to use a register for the interchange for some reason, we will need to save the contents of that register during the macro. As a result the

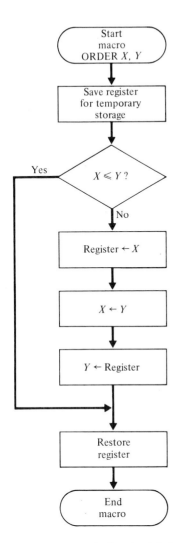

Fig. 8.10
Flowchart of macro ORDER X,Y.

macro ORDER for the PDP-11 will look like this. (See Fig. 8.10 for a flowchart of this procedure.)

```
.MACRO    ORDER X, Y    ;DEFINE MACRO ORDER TO PUT TWO
                        ;VARIABLES IN NONDECREASING ORDER
          MOV %0, TEMP  ;SAVE CONTENTS OF R0 IN TEMP
          CMP X, Y      ;COMPARE X WITH Y
          BLT FINISH    ;IF X LESS THAN OR EQUAL TO Y,
                        ;BRANCH TO FINISH
          MOV X, %0     ;X IS GREATER THAN Y,
          MOV Y, X      ;INTERCHANGE X AND Y
          MOV %0, Y
FINISH:   MOV TEMP, %0  ;RESTORE CONTENTS OF R0
          BR +2         ;BRANCH OVER TEMP
TEMP:     .WORD 0       ;TEMPORARY STORAGE
          .ENDM
```

Each time this macro is called, TEMP and FINISH will be redefined. As a result the assembler will give an error message. We can solve this problem in two ways. We can put TEMP and FINISH as arguments in the macro so that the macro call becomes

```
.MACRO ORDER X, Y, TEMP, FINISH
```

Then the programmer must define these locations before calling the macro.

A better solution is to use **local symbols** that are provided by the PDP-11 assembler. They are symbolic addresses with a restricted range. Local symbols have the form *n*$ for any decimal integer *n* between 1 and 127. The programmer can use any of these addresses. The assembler can create local symbols between 64$ and 127$ in numerical order. The range of a local symbol goes from the preceding instruction to the next instruction with a label. Any local symbol defined within that range can be called within that range. Outside that range we can reuse the symbol. However, we should be careful, since there will be a conflict if we forget to place a label between two different uses of the same local symbol. The macro segment below shows an example using the same symbol within two different ranges, delimited by the label HERE. The first branch is to the first line labeled 2$; the second branch is to the second such line.

```
            MOV %0, %;
2$:         ADD X, %1
            BVC 2$
HERE:       ADD Y, %1
2$:         SUB Z, %1
            BPL 2$
```

We can use local symbols for branches within macros. To do so, we write $ARG in the macro definition. If the argument ARG is not specified in the macro call, the assembler creates the next local symbol. Thus we can rewrite macro ORDER as follows.

```
.MACRO      ORDER X, Y, $A, $B
            MOV %0, A
            CMP X, Y
            BLT B
            MOV X, %0
            MOV Y, X
            MOV %0, Y
B:          MOV A, %0
A:          .WORD 0
            .ENDM ORDER
```

Then calling

```
ORDER M, N
```

is equivalent to the following:

```
          MOV %0, 64$
          CMP M, N
          BLT 65$
          MOV M, %0
          MOV N, M
          MOV %0, N
          MOV M, %0
          BR +4
65$
64$
```

The 8085 macro assembler has different ways of providing local symbols. Labels that appear in the body of a macro are considered to be local symbols. Otherwise they would be written every time the macro is called, causing multiple-label errors. For example, consider the macro DCTEN

```
DCTEN     MACRO RPAIR
          MVI A, OAH
LOOP:     DCX RPAIR
          DCR A
          JNZ LOOP
          ENDM
```

It uses a counter (the accumulator) and a loop to decrement a register pair ten times. Every time this macro is called, the label LOOP will be copied. This could cause confusion unless it is understood that LOOP is a local label, valid only within each macro expansion.

If we want to define a global label within a macro, we must follow the label in the macro definition with two colons, for example,

```
LOOP::
```

Then if the macro is called more than once, the second and succeeding references will be identified as errors.

The 8085 pseudoinstruction EQU (equate) always defines local symbols within a macro. Thus a given name can be equated with one value within a macro definition and another later, outside the macro. Hence the following sets of instructions correctly assign different values to the variable case. First we have the macro definition:

```
NEW       MACRO
CASE      EQU 2
          DB CASE
          ENDM
```

then the call and expansion:

```
CASE      EQU 4
          DB CASE
          NEW
CASE      EQU 2
          DB CASE
```

In contrast, the 8085 pseudoinstruction SET defines local values if used only within a macro. If SET statements for the same variable are used both inside and outside a macro, the definitions are global. Each time a SET statement is encountered, the value of the variable is changed to the value given by the SET statement.

8.8.3 *Nesting of Macros*

Macros may be nested much as subroutines may be nested. That is, macros may be defined inside other macros. Macros may also be called within other macros, a situation that we will discuss in a moment. We can therefore speak of levels of macros. The first macro defined can be considered a first-level macro. A macro defined inside a first-level macro is a second-level macro, and so on. The following example, written in the format of the PDP-11, shows three levels of nesting.

```
.MACRO    LEVEL1, X, Y    ;FIRST-LEVEL MACRO BEGINS
          ADD X, Y
.MACRO    LEVEL2, A, B    ;SECOND-LEVEL MACRO BEGINS
          ADD A, B
.MACRO    LEVEL3, C, D    ;THIRD-LEVEL MACRO BEGINS
          ADD C, D
          .ENDM LEVEL3    ;THIRD-LEVEL MACRO ENDS
          INC A
          .ENDM LEVEL2    ;SECOND-LEVEL MACRO ENDS
          DEC X
          .ENDM LEVEL1    ;FIRST-LEVEL MACRO ENDS
```

At the beginning of assembly only first-level macros are defined; they may be called in the usual way. Once a first-level macro is called, any second-level macros inside it are defined, and hence ready to be called, and so on. Any higher-level macro is not defined until the lower-level macro containing it has been called. The sequence of calls shown below results in the following actions.

Macro call	Equivalent instructions	Comment
LEVEL1, I, J	ADD I, J	Enables level 2 macro.
	DEC I	
LEVEL2, M, N	ADD M, N	Enables level 3 macro.
	INC M	
LEVEL3, U, V	ADD U, V	

If instead we called LEVEL1 and then LEVEL3, we would receive an error message, because LEVEL2 must be called to define LEVEL3.

The body of a macro definition may call other macros. These macros must be defined before a call is made to the macro that contains calls to them. For example, the macro definition of MAX below calls macro ORDER, which we have already seen. Any program that defines MAX must define ORDER before calling MAX.

```
.MACRO        MAX A, B, C
              ORDER A, B
              ORDER B, C
              .ENDM MAX
```

A macro may call itself—a procedure called **recursion**. When this occurs, steps should be taken to make sure that the expansion of the macro will end within a reasonable amount of time.

Now that we know how to define and call macros, we might think about their advantages and disadvantages.

- Both macros and subroutines facilitate developing standard segments of code that can be used repeatedly either within a program or in several programs.

- Subroutines require extra time for execution of the call and return instructions.

- Macros may require more memory because the macro expansion is stored in memory every time it is called. (However, short macros may not take more space than that needed for the call and return instructions.)

- Macros can simulate new instructions or instructions of other small computers. Thus they can be helpful in translating programs from one computer to another.

8.8.4 *Conditional Assembly*

Sometimes we want parts of a program to be executed on an optional basis. If some condition occurs, we wish to execute a block of statements; otherwise we don't. The block of statements may be a macro; it may be inside a macro; or it may be elsewhere in the program. We use a conditional assembly directive that takes the following general form for the PDP-11.

```
.IF COND, ARGUMENT(S)
:                            Block of code
.ENDC
```

COND is a conditional operator that tests the arguments. It may do any of the following:

1. Test the value of an argument.
2. Test the presence or absence of an argument.
3. Determine whether an argument symbol is defined.
4. Compare two arguments to see whether they are identical.

Table 8.2 shows conditional directives for the PDP-11. Some deal with arguments enclosed in angle brackets, $\langle \, \rangle$. If the condition is satisfied, the block of

Table 8.2
PDP-11 conditional assembly directions

Instruction	Condition
.IF EQ	Argument = 0
.IF NE	Argument ≠ 0
.IF GT	Argument > 0
.IF GE	Argument ≥ 0
.IF LT	Argument < 0
.IF LE	Argument ≤ 0
.IF B	Argument is blank (missing).
.IF NB	Argument is not blank (present).
.IF DF	Argument symbol is defined.
.IF NDF	Argument symbol is not defined.
.IF IDN	Two arguments are identical.
.IF DIF	Two arguments are different.

statements from the .IF statement to the .ENDC statement are assembled. Otherwise they are skipped.

Conditional statements may be nested. For each .IF statement there must be a corresponding .ENDC statement. If the outermost .IF condition is not satisfied, the entire group of nested statements is skipped. If the first .IF is satisfied, the code of its block is assembled until an inner .IF is encountered. Then the condition of the inner .IF is tested, and the code corresponding to it is assembled only if its condition is satisfied.

Using the .IF GT instruction, we could call macro ORDER only when both A and B are positive.

```
.IF GT A
.IF GT B
ORDER A, B
.ENDC
.ENDC
```

The 8085 conditional assembly statements are more limited. Their form is

```
IF EXPRESSION
⋮
ENDIF
```

The value of the expression is tested to see whether it is 0. If 0, the statements between IF and ENDIF are ignored. Otherwise they are assembled just as though IF and ENDIF were not present.

8.8.5 *Repeat Blocks and System Variables*

If we want to repeat a single block of PDP-11 code several times, we can use a **repeat block.** It has the following format:

.REPT N   Repeat the following block *n* times.
:   Block to be repeated.
.ENDR   End repeat block.

For example, the following block repeats the instruction INC %4 nine times.

```
.REPT 9
INC %4
.ENDR
```

A related instruction is the PDP-11 indefinite repeat instruction. By writing

```
.IRP X,   ⟨A⟩
:
.ENDM
```

we can repeat the instructions between .IRP and .ENDM any number of times, as determined by X and the list ⟨A⟩. Each time the block is repeated, X takes on each value from list ⟨A⟩ in turn.

8.S *Summary*

A subroutine is a sequence of instructions that can be executed several times in a program. When it is called, control transfers to the first instruction of the subroutine. After all instructions have been executed, control is transferred back to the next instruction in the calling program. Although the address of that next instruction—called the return address—can be stored in registers or in the subroutine, it most commonly is saved in a stack.

A stack stores information in a last-in, first-out manner. The item most recently pushed on the stack is located at the top of the stack. A stack pointer shows the top of the stack. Data is retrieved from the stack by popping the data to a register or memory location.

When a stack is used for subroutine calls and returns, the return address is pushed on the stack during the subroutine call. On return the address is popped into the program counter. A linkage register may also be used during subroutine transfers. The PDP-11 stores the return address in a linkage register while saving the previous contents of that register on the stack.

Subroutine calculations often require using registers that are also needed for the main program. In that case the subroutine should save the contents of all registers needed for the subroutine before beginning calculations. Afterward the subroutine should restore the previous contents of registers before transferring control to the main program. Register contents may be saved on a stack or in a temporary storage area of memory.

Programs or routines that do not modify themselves are called reentrant programs or routines. They contain only instructions and constants, not data that will be changed during execution.

Coroutines are a general form of subroutines. Each of two coroutines may perform a task and then call the other. Calculation in each coroutine resumes where it left off the previous time, rather than at the beginning of the coroutine.

Most subroutine and coroutine transfers involve parameters. A formal parameter is a dummy variable specified in a subroutine or coroutine. During execution of a subroutine formal parameters are replaced by actual parameters—the quantities used in the calculations. Methods for passing parameters include storing them in memory common to both the program and the subroutine, placing them in registers, storing them in special parameter areas, and placing them in stacks.

Macros are an alternative to subroutines, especially for short sequences of instructions. A macro definition assigns a name to a set of instructions. Thereafter, when a macro is called, it is expanded into the defined instruction sequence. Macros can require more storage than subroutines, but they do not require time for execution of call and return instructions.

Key Terms

actual parameter	parameter area
closed subroutine	pop
common data	push
conditional assembly	recursion
coroutine	reentrant program
external symbols	repeat block
formal parameters	restoring registers
global data	return address
in-line parameter area	saving registers
last-in, first-out (LIFO)	self-modifying program
linkage register	stack
local symbol	stack depth
macro assembler	stack pointer (SP)
macro expansion	subroutine
macroinstruction	subroutine call
nesting	subroutine return
parameter	top of the stack (TOS)

8.R *References*

Several of the books referenced in earlier chapters have good discussions of subroutines, coroutines, and macros. Eckhouse (1975), Gear (1974), Stone and Sieworek (1975), Korn (1973), and Cooper (1977) have good discussions of subroutines for minicomputers. Osborne (1978), Peatman (1977), and Korn (1977) describe the special problems of implementing subroutines for microcomputers.

8.1   What are some of the advantages of building programs from subprograms?

8.2   What are the advantages and disadvantages of storing return addresses in a register or in the subroutine?

8.3   How is a stack organized?

8.4   What problems may occur in working with stacks?

8.5   How is a stack used for subroutine calls and returns?

8.6   How can a linkage register be used for transfers between main programs and subroutines?

8.7   When and how should registers be saved?

8.8   What are the characteristics of reentrant routines?

8.9   Explain the interaction of coroutines.

8.10 Describe several methods of passing parameters.

8.11 Compare macros with subroutines.

8.12 How are local symbols used in macros?

8.P   *Problems*

Section 8.3

8.1 Assume the stack pointer of a hypothetical computer initially points to the top of an empty stack at FA40. Describe the effect of the following instructions.

```
PUSH R1
PUSH R2
PUSH R3
POP   R4
POP   R3
POP   R2
POP   R1
```

Section 8.4

8.2 Write the necessary segments of code to save the contents of two registers of your computer at the beginning of a subroutine and to restore them at the end.

Section 8.7

8.3 Write the code for two different methods of passing parameters for the subroutine MULT for your computer. The main program should pass the multiplier and multiplicand; the subroutine should pass back the product.

Section 8.8

8.4 Write a macro to clear all registers of your computer except the program counter. Then write a subroutine to accomplish the same actions. Assuming that the macro or subroutine will be called four times during your main program, calculate the storage needed for the two methods. Recalculate assuming that the macro or subroutine will be called ten times.

8.5 Write a macro to exchange the contents of all working registers of your computer in some logical pattern, such as moving them around in a circle.

Arithmetic and Logical Operations

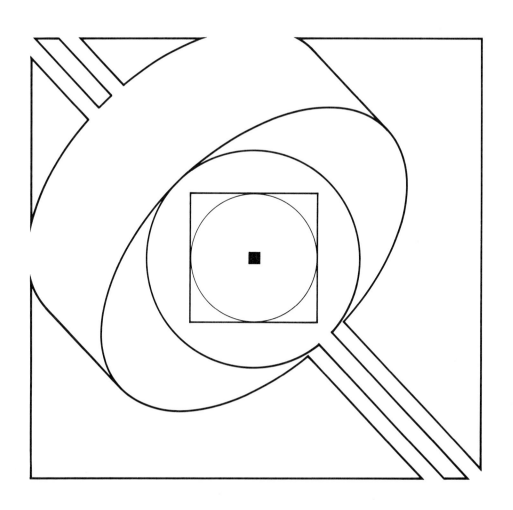

9.1 *Introduction*

Chapter 2 explained the principles of 2's complement arithmetic, the basic system for minicomputers and microcomputers. Subsequent chapters showed examples of simple programs for addition—programs that added numbers without checking whether the sum was in range. Now we wish to program more advanced arithmetic operations. In this chapter we will consider overflow in addition and subtraction, methods for multiplication and division, multiple-precision arithmetic, and decimal arithmetic.

Not all programs require arithmetic calculations. Often we wish to manipulate parts of data. For example, we may wish to examine just one or a few bits of a word. Having done so, we may wish to extract these useful bits from several words and combine them together either to reduce storage requirements or to produce new data. In the latter part of this chapter we will study the logical functions that allow us to carry out these operations.

9.2 *Addition and Subtraction*

Let's begin our discussion of addition and subtraction by briefly reviewing 2's complement addition, as presented in Chapter 2. The rules for binary addition are $0 + 0 = 0$; $0 + 1 = 1 + 0 = 1$; $1 + 1 = 10$ (sum of 0 with carry of 1). To see whether the sum is correct, we examine carries into and out of the sign bit. If there are two carries or no carries, the sum is correct. If there is just one carry (either into or out of the sign bit), we know that the sum is incorrect, that is, that its magnitude is too large to be represented correctly. This condition is called **overflow**. (It is sometimes called **underflow** in the case of negative numbers; however, we will refer to both conditions as overflow.)

In the simple addition programs of Chapters 4 and 5, we did not test for overflow. We just assumed the sum was correct. A much better procedure is to check for overflow after every addition even if we think that the sum is correct. Many small computers have an overflow flag that we can test. For example, both the PDP-11 and the M6800 have a V flag that shows overflow. It is set or cleared according to the results of several instructions, including all arithmetic operations. (See your programmer's manual for details.) Thus the flag can be checked after each addition. If it is set ($V = 1$), the program can branch to take an appropriate action, such as printing an error message. If it is cleared ($V = 0$), the addition can be assumed to be correct.

Suppose, for example, that we wish to add the contents of the M6800 accumulator B to those of accumulator A. If overflow occurs, we wish to branch to location ERROR. If the sum is correct, we will continue in sequence. The code is

```
          ABA                      ;ADD ACCB TO ACCA AND
                                   ;SET V FLAG IF OVERFLOW OCCURS
          BVS ERROR                ;GO TO ERROR IF OVERFLOW
          [next instruction]       ;OTHERWISE CONTINUE
          ⋮
ERROR:    [some instruction]       ;BEGIN ERROR PROCEDURE
```

Similar PDP-11 instructions for adding R2 to R1 and testing for overflow are almost identical:

```
        ADD %2, %1              ;ADD R2 to R1 AND
                                ;SET V IF OVERFLOW OCCURS
        BVS ERROR               ;GO TO ERROR IF OVERFLOW
        [next instruction]      ;OTHERWISE CONTINUE
        ⋮
ERROR:  [some instruction]      ;BEGIN ERROR PROCEDURE
```

Working with computers that lack an overflow flag, such as the 8080/8085, requires more effort from the programmer. We note that overflow in addition occurs only when two operands of the same sign are added and when the sum has the opposite sign. That is, either the addition of two positive numbers results in a sum with a negative sign or the addition of two negative numbers results in a sum with a positive sign. The four-bit examples below illustrate the two possibilities.

```
  +4        0 100
  +5       +0 101
            1 001       Carry into but not out of sign bit; overflow.
                        Operands have the same sign; sum has the opposite
                        sign.


   -4        1 100      Carry out of but not into sign bit; overflow.
 + -6       +1 010      Operands have the same sign; sum has the opposite
            10 110      sign.
               ↑
            Carry
```

To test for overflow we could either observe carries into and out of the sign bit or we could compare the signs of the operands with the sign of the result. Which should we do? The computers that we have described have carry flags that correspond to a carry out of the sign bit. They lack a flag for a carry into the sign bit. However, these computers all have sign flags; hence checking the signs of the operands and the sum is a simple procedure. Figure 9.1 shows a flowchart for testing overflow in addition. The operands are referred to as the addend (the first number) and the augend (the second number). We check their signs to see if they are negative (sign flag = 1). If the augend and addend have different signs, the sum is correct. If they have the same sign, we must check to see whether the sum also has that same sign. If so, the sum is correct. If not, overflow has occurred. We can code this procedure for any computer, including those that have overflow flags. (See Problem 9.1.)

Subtraction presents similar problems. You'll probably remember from elementary school that subtraction is

Minuend − subtrahend = difference

Most but not all computers provide instructions for 2's complement subtrac-

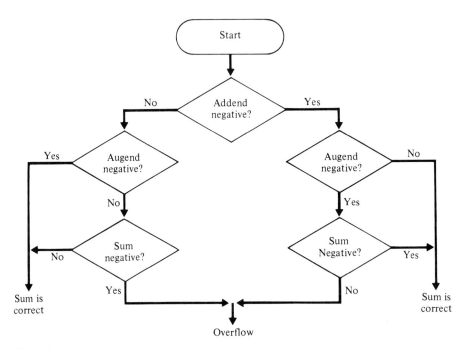

Fig. 9.1
Flowchart of test for overflow in addition.

tion. For computers that lack subtraction instructions, we must change the subtraction into an addition by 2's complementing the subtrahend and adding it to the minuend. For example, we could write the following code for the PDP-8 or the IM6100 to subtract the contents of memory location SUBTR from those of location MINU.

```
CLA             ;CLEAR ACCUMULATOR
TAD     SUBTR   ;BRING SUBTRAHEND TO ACCUMULATOR
CMA             ;COMPLEMENT CONTENTS OF ACC
IAC             ;ADD 1 TO YIELD 2'S COMPLEMENT
TAD     MINU    ;ADD MINUEND, GIVING DIFFERENCE
```

Overflow must be considered in subtraction. It occurs when operands of different signs are subtracted and the difference has the same sign as the subtrahend. The example below, in which we have converted subtraction to addition of the 2's complement of the minuend, illustrates this.

$$
\begin{array}{rrr}
+3 & 0011 & 0011 \\
-\ -6 & -1010 & +0110 \\
\hline
& & 1001
\end{array}
$$

Carry into but not out of the sign bit; overflow. Difference and subtrahend have the same sign; the minuend has the opposite sign.

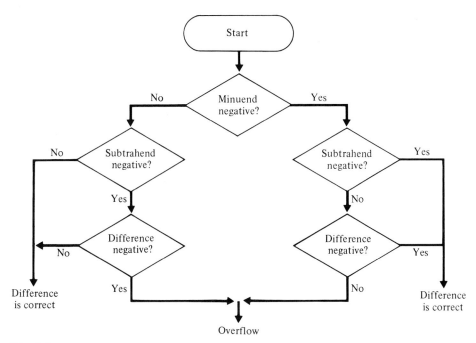

Fig. 9.2
Flowchart of test for overflow in subtraction.

Those computers that have overflow bits set them when overflow occurs in subtraction, as explained above, and clear them otherwise. For a computer that lacks an overflow flag, we must program an overflow test ourselves as flowcharted in Fig. 9.2.

9.3 *Multiple-Precision Arithmetic*

The short word lengths of mini- and microcomputers are adequate only for adding or subtracting small numbers. If we wish to work with larger numbers, each number will take two or more bytes of storage and require two or more repetitions of any arithmetic operation. **Multiple-precision arithmetic** deals with multibyte (or multiword) numbers.

9.3.1 *Multiple-Precision Addition*

Consider adding the two unsigned hexadecimal numbers shown below on an 8-bit microcomputer. Each number has 8 hexadecimal digits that we can think of as being grouped into four pairs.

```
  427 09B8 A
+ 21B21ACF
```

We begin the addition with the two least significant digits of each operand. A single ADD instruction on any 8-bit microcomputer will add these two 8-bit numbers, yielding a sum and a carry.

```
  8 A              10001010
 +CF             +11001111
 1 5 9          1  01011001
```
Carry

Here the sum is 59 and the carry is 1. This carry must be included in the addition of the next two pairs of hexadecimal digits—9B and 1A. Fortunately, the designers of most 8-bit microcomputers anticipated this situation and provided an addition-with-carry instruction. It automatically adds the value of the carry flag to the sum of the two operands. That is, if the carry is 1, it adds to the sum of the operands; otherwise, the add-with-carry instruction just adds the two operands in the same way as the basic add instruction. Hence the next addition in our example proceeds as follows.

```
   1                   1
   9 B              10011011
  +1 A             +00011010
   B6               10110110
```

This time the carry is 0. Again using the add-with-carry instruction for addition of the next two pairs of hexadecimal digits, we have

```
  7 0              01110000
 +B2              +10110010
 12 2             100100010
```

The carry of 1 from this addition must be added to the sum of the most significant pair of hexadecimal digits.

```
   1                   1
   42               01000010
  +21              +00100001
   64               01100100
```

The total result is

```
  427 09B8 A
 +21B21ACF
  642 2B6 5 9
```

An 8085 program to perform this calculation is shown in Table 9.1. Its flowchart is shown in Fig. 9.3. The program assumes that the addend is stored in four successive locations beginning at address ADDND, with the least significant byte stored first. Register pair D points to the addend. The augend is

Table 9.1
Intel 8080/8085 program for adding two unsigned 32-bit numbers

Label	Op code	Operand	Comment
ADDND:	DB	8AH	; INSTRUCTIONS ADD TWO 4-BYTE NUMBERS
	DB	9BH	; ADDEND STORED LEAST
	DB	70H	; SIGNIFICANT BYTE FIRST
	DB	42H	; STARTING AT ADDRESS ADDND
AUGND:	DB	0CFH	; AUGEND STORED LEAST
	DB	1AH	; SIGNIFICANT BYTE FIRST
	DB	0B2H	; STARTING AT ADDRESS AUGND
	DB	21H	; SUM REPLACES AUGEND
	MVI	C,4	; INITIALIZE COUNTER AT 4
	XRA	A	; CLEAR A AND CARRY
	LXI	D, ADDND	; LOAD D WITH ADDRESS
			; OF LEAST SIG BITS OF ADDEND
	LXI	H, AUGND	; LOAD H WITH ADDRESS
			; OF LEAST SIG BYTES OF AUGEND
LOOP:	LDAX	D	; LOAD A WITH BYTE OF ADDEND
	ADC	M	; ADD BYTE OF AUGEND WITH CARRY
	STAX	D	; STORE RESULT AT SUM
	INX	H	; INCREMENT D
	INX	D	; INCREMENT H
	DCR	C	; DECREMENT COUNTER
	JNZ	LOOP	; ADD NEXT BYTES IF C NOT 0
	HLT		; STOP

stored in four successive locations beginning at address AUGND, with its least significant byte first. Register pair H points to the augend. The sum will replace the addend and will also be stored with the least significant byte first.

The program is based on a loop. Before the loop is entered for the first time, the pointers are initialized to their starting addresses and the counter is set to 4. The accumulator and carry register are cleared by the XRA A instruction. The 8085 does not have a separate instruction to clear the carry flag. The carry flag can be cleared by any XRA register instruction. Within the loop the accumulator is first loaded with a byte of the addend. Then the augend is added to it with the carry from the previous addition. The sum is stored, the pointers are incremented, the counter is decremented and tested for completion.

A similar program for the M6800 using indexed addressing is shown in Table 9.2. The flowchart of Fig. 9.3 basically applies, although just one pointer is needed and the accumulator does not have to be cleared.

Some computers lack add-with-carry instructions. When we program such a computer, we must test for a carry after each addition. If the carry is 1, we must add 1 to the next addition. The PDP-11 is an example of a computer that has no add-with-carry instruction. Table 9.3 shows a PDP-11 program to add two unsigned 64-bit numbers by the procedure of the flowchart in Fig. 9.4. Basic PDP-11 instructions operate on 16-bit words. We assume that each 64-bit

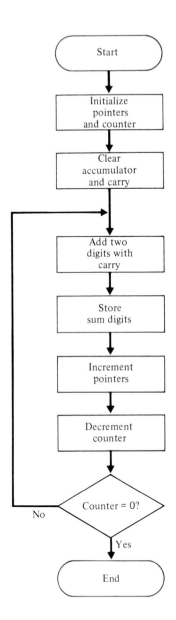

Fig. 9.3
Flowchart for microcomputer addition of several pairs of digits.

number is stored as four 16-bit words with the least significant word first. Note that the addition of 1, if there was a carry from the previous addition, must be done before adding the augend to the addend. (Why?)

These examples dealt with addition of unsigned numbers. Adding 2's complement numbers isn't much harder. Just add the tests for overflow from the previous section to the multiple-precision procedures outlined in this section.

Table 9.2
M6800 program for adding two unsigned 8-byte numbers

Label	Op code	Operand	Comment
			; PROGRAM TO ADD TWO 4-BYTE NUMBERS
			; ADDEND STORED LEAST SIGNIFICANT LOCATION
			; HELD IN INDEX REGISTER
			; AUGEND STORED LEAST SIGNIFICANT
			; BYTE FIRST STARTING AT ADDND + 4
			; SUM REPLACES ADDEND
	CLC		; CLEAR CARRY
	LDA B	#4	; INITIALIZE ACCB WITH 4
LOOP:	LDA A	X	; LOAD A WITH BYTE OF ADDEND D
	ADC A	4, X	; ADD BYTE OF AUGEND WITH CARRY
	STA A	X	; STORE BYTE OF SUM
	INX		; INCREMENT INDEX REGISTER
	DEC	B	; DECREMENT COUNTER
	BNE	LOOP	; IF NOT DONE, ADD NEXT BYTE
	SWI		; SOFTWARE INTERRUPT
ADDND:	FCB	8AH	; DEFINE DATA
	FCB	9BH	
	FCB	70H	
	FCB	42H	
	FCB	0CFH	
	FCB	1AH	
	FCB	0B2H	
	FCB	21H	

Table 9.3
PDP-11 program for adding two unsigned 64-bit numbers

Label	Op code	Operand	Comment
			; ADDEND STORED LEAST SIGNIFICANT
			; BYTE FIRST STARTING AT ADDRESS IN R0
			; AUGEND STORED LEAST SIGNIFICANT
			; BYTE FIRST STARTING AT ADDRESS IN R1
			; SUM STORED LEAST SIGNIFICANT
			; BYTE FIRST STARTING AT ADDRESS IN R0
	CLR	%3	; CLEAR R3 AND CARRY
	MOV	#4, %4	; INITIALIZE R4 WITH COUNT OF 4
LOOP:	MOV	@%0, %3	; LOAD WORD OF ADDEND INTO R3
	BCC	NOCAR	; IF NO CARRY, BRANCH DOWN
	ADD	#1, %3	; IF CARRY, ADD 1
NOCAR:	ADD	@(%1)+, %3	; ADD WORD OF AUGEND
	MOV	%3, (%0)+	
	DEC	%4	; DECREMENT COUNTER
	BNE	LOOP	; IF COUNTER NOT ZERO, ADD NEXT BYTE
	HALT		

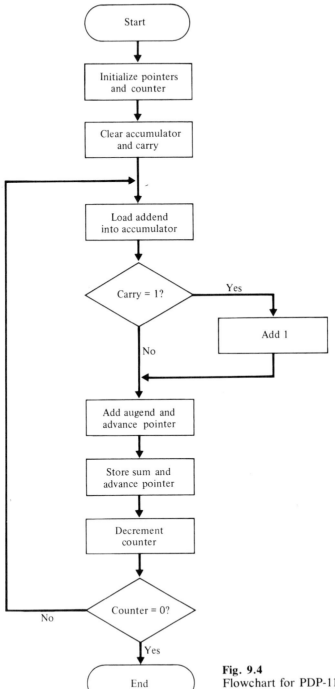

Fig. 9.4
Flowchart for PDP-11 addition of two 64-bit numbers.

Be careful when writing programs involving add-with-carry instructions or tests of the carry flag. Computers differ with regard to which instructions affect the carry flag. In general, arithmetic operations affect the carry flag while move instructions and conditional branch instructions do not. Read your programmer's manual carefully. Many programs err because the carry flag isn't affected when the programmer thinks it is or, conversely, because a carry flag is unintentionally cleared by an instruction before the programmer tests it for a conditional branch.

9.3.2 *Multiple-Precision Subtraction*

The carry flag may be thought of as a borrow bit in subtraction. Most computers that provide an add-with-carry instruction also provide a subtract-with-borrow instruction for multibyte subtraction. The 8085 has SBB (SuBtract with Borrow); the M6800 has SBC (SuBtract with Carry). The PDP-11 lacks a subtract-with-borrow instruction. Let's see how this works. Suppose we wish to subtract

$$6907_{16}$$
$$\underline{-4519_{16}}$$

First we must subtract the least significant bytes. We take the 2's complement of the minuend and add to the subtrahend.

$$
\begin{array}{rcr}
0\,7_{16} & = & 00000111_2 \\
\underline{-1\,9_{16}} & & \underline{+11100111_2} \\
\text{EE}_{16} & & 11101110_2
\end{array}
$$

No carry occurred out of the sign bit, yet we know that to perform this subtraction we must borrow from the more significant byte. Hence we interpret a carry out of the sign bit of 0 as a borrow of 1. Whenever the magnitude of the subtrahend is larger than the magnitude of the minuend, the carry flag of the computer will be set to show a borrow of 1 for the next subtraction. Otherwise it is cleared to show a borrow of 0. The role of the carry flag in subtraction thus is just opposite to its role in addition.

We accomplish the subtraction of the most significant byte with the subtract-with-borrow instruction. It adds 1 to the subtrahend, which is the same as subtracting 1 from the minuend. Hence this subtraction becomes

$$
\begin{array}{rcr}
69_{16} & = & 01101001_2 \\
\underline{-(45\,+\,1)_{16}} & & \underline{+\,10111010_2} \\
23_{16} & & 1\,00100011_2
\end{array}
$$

In this subtraction there was a carry out of the sign bit, showing that no borrow is needed. The carry flag is reset to 0 to show a borrow of 0. The complete result is 23EE_{16}.

Programming multibyte subtraction differs little from programming multibyte addition. It is left as an exercise.

9.4 *Multiplication*

Many small computers have so-called hardware multiplication and division—instructions for these operations already implemented on the computer. Be thankful if yours does, because you won't need to learn how to program these two operations. An example of hardware or preprogrammed multiplication is the multiplication instruction available on some versions of the PDP-11. It has the form

MUL dst, src

where dst is a general notation for a destination register and src is a general notation for the contents of a source register that may be addressed in any mode. The values of both the source and destination are considered to be 16-bit 2's complement integers. If the destination register has an even number, the signed 32-bit product will have its most significant bits stored in the destination register and its least significant bits stored in the register whose number is one higher than the destination register. If the destination register has an odd number, the least significant 16 bits of the product will be stored in the destination and the most significant bits will be lost.

For example, suppose R1 contains 001000_8 ($+512_{10}$) and R2 contains 010002_8 ($+4098_{10}$). The command

MUL %2, %1

results in a product of $253,952_{10}$ stored as 002000_8 in R3 and 00040_8 in R2.

If we lack special multiplication instructions, we must write our own multiplication routines. Recall from Chapter 2 that multiplication is just repeated addition. Binary multiplication is especially easy because each bit of our multiplier can be only 1 or 0. If it is 1, the partial product to be added equals the multiplicand. If it is 0, the partial product is 0.

Just as in decimal multiplication, we start multiplying with the least significant bit, multiply it by the multiplicand, write down the partial product, and shift to the next more significant bit. If the bit is 0, the partial product is 0. If it is 1, the partial product is the multiplicand. When we program binary multiplication, we will add partial products after each bit multiplication rather than summing them at the end as we usually do in decimal multiplication. Hence our procedure amounts to testing each multiplier bit, adding the multiplicand to the product if the bit is 1, shifting the result one position to the right, and repeating until all bits of the multiplier have been completed.

Consider the binary multiplication of 9_{16} by 6_{16}.

```
  1001
  1110
  ────
  0000   Multiplier bit is 0, partial product is 0.
  1001   Multiplier bit is 1, shifted partial product is multiplicand.
  1001   Multiplier bit is 1, shifted partial product is multiplicand.
 0000    Multiplier bit is 0, shifted partial product is 0.
 ──────
 110110  Product is sum of partial products.
```

Intel 8080/8085 instructions and a M6800 subroutine to multiply two unsigned 8-bit numbers according to this procedure are shown in Tables 9.4 and 9.5 respectively. A flowchart for the 8080/8085 program is given in Fig. 9.5.

Table 9.4
Intel 8080/8085 programs for multiplying two unsigned 8-bit numbers

Label	Op code	Operand	Comment
			; MULTIPLICAND IS IN B
			; MULTIPLIER IS IN E
			; 16-BIT PRODUCT WILL BE IN RP D
	MVI	D, 0	; SET MOST SIG BYTE OF PRODUCT TO 0
	MVI	C, 8	; SET COUNTER TO 8
LOOP:	MOV	A, E	; MOVE MULTIPLIER TO A
	RAR		; ROTATE RIGHT INTO CARRY
	MOV	E, A	; RESTORE LEAST SIG BYTE OF PRODUCT
	JNC	NOCAR	; IF CARRY = 0, SKIP
	MOV	A, D	; GET MOST SIG BYTE OF PRODUCT
	ADD	B	; ADD MULTIPLICAND
NOCAR:	RAR		; SHIFT RIGHT
	MOV	D, A	; RESTORE MOST SIG BYTE
	DCR	C	; DECREMENT COUNTER
V	JNZ	LOOP	; REPEAT IF NOT DONE
	HLT		

Table 9.5
M6800 subroutine for multiplying two unsigned 8-bit numbers

Label	Op code	Operand	Comment
			; MULTIPLICAND IN A
			; MULTIPLIER IN B
			; PRODUCT WILL BE IN A (MOST
			; SIGNIFICANT BYTE) AND B (LEAST
			; SIGNIFICANT BYTE)
MULT:	PSH	A	; PUSH MULTIPLICAND ON STACK
	LDA	A, #8	; INITIALIZE COUNT
	PSH	A	; PUSH COUNT ON STACK
	TSX		; LOAD INDEX REGISTER FROM STACK POINTER
	CLR	A	; CLEAR A
	ROR	B	; ROTATE MULTIPLIER INTO CARRY
LOOP:	BCC	NOCAR	; IF CARRY = 0, SKIP
	ADD	A 1, X	; IF CARRY = 1, ADD MULTIPLICAND
NOCAR:	ROR	A	; ROTATE PRODUCT
	ROR	B	; ROTATE PRODUCT
	DEC	0, X	; DECREMENT COUNTER
	BNE	LOOP	; IF COUNTER NOT ZERO, REPEAT
	INS		; RESTORE STACK
	INS		
	RTS		; RETURN

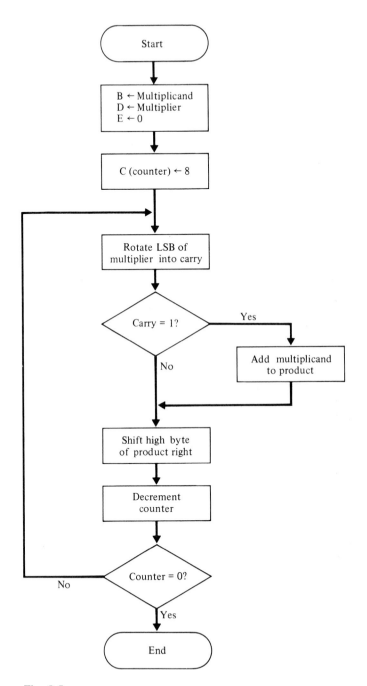

Fig. 9.5
Flowchart of microcomputer program for multiplying two bytes.

Note the differences in the two program modules. The 8085 takes advantage of its large number of registers to perform the multiplication in scratchpad registers. The M6800 instead uses indexed addressing to maintain the product and counter in memory.

9.5 *Division*

Some small computers have division instructions. The PDP-11, for example, has a DIV (DIVide) instruction that divides a 32-bit dividend by a 16-bit divisor to produce a 16-bit quotient and a 16-bit remainder. All operands are interpreted as 2's complement integers. The remainder is calculated to have the same sign as the dividend. A test is made to see whether the divisor is 0; if so, the carry and overflow flags are set. The instruction is aborted if the quotient would exceed 15 bits.

The quotient must be placed in two adjacent registers with its most significant word in an even-numbered register and its least significant word in the next higher odd-numbered register. Suppose, for example, that R2 contains 000040_8 and R3 holds 002003_8. The instruction

```
DIV #4, %0
```

results in a quotient of 010002_8 in R2 and a remainder of 001400_8 in R3.

If our computer lacks division instructions, we must program it. We can think of binary division as a series of trial subtractions. We start the division by trying to subtract the divisor from the dividend. If we can accomplish the subtraction without needing a borrow, then we write a 1 in the quotient. Otherwise we write a 0 and omit the subtraction. (We say we restore the dividend.) Then we shift the divisor right one position and again try to subtract.

The procedure is the same as for decimal division except that it is simpler. In decimal division, we must estimate a quotient digit and multiply. In binary division, we know the quotient bit can only be 0 or 1, so multiplication is not necessary. Consider the following division of 65_{16} by 4_{16}.

```
           11001
0100 |01100101
       -0100          Try to subtract divisor.
        0100          No borrow, quotient bit is 1.
       -0100          Shift divisor and try to subtract.
        0001          No borrow, quotient bit is 1.
       -0100          Shift divisor and try to subtract.
         0010         Borrow needed, omit subtraction, quotient bit is 0.
        -0100         Shift divisor and try to subtract.
          0101        Borrow needed, omit subtraction, quotient bit is 0.
         -0100        Shift divisor and try to subtract.
             1        No borrow, quotient bit is 1.
                      Remainder is 1.
```

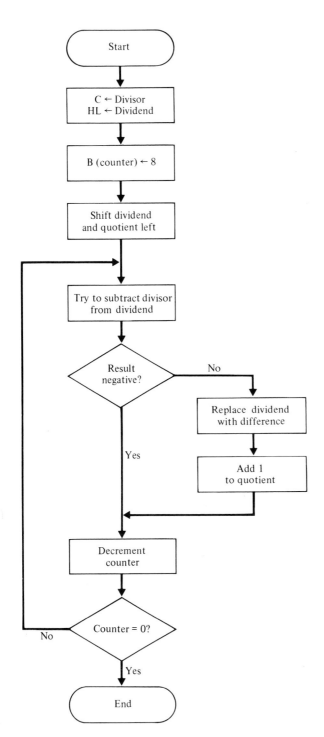

Fig. 9.6
Flowchart of 8080 division.

Table 9.6
8080/8085 subroutine for dividing an unsigned 16-bit dividend by an unsigned 8-bit divisor

Label	Op code	Operand	Comment
			; DIVISOR IS IN C
			; DIVIDEND IS ORIGINALLY IN HL
			; QUOTIENT WILL BE IN L
			; REMAINDER WILL BE IN H
	MVI	B, 8	; INITIALIZE COUNTER B WITH 8
LOOP:	DAD	H	; SHIFT DIVIDEND AND QUOTIENT LEFT
	MOV	A, H	; PLACE HIGH PART OF DIVIDEND IN A
	SUB	C	; TRY TO SUBTRACT DIVISOR
	MOV	H, A	; SUBTRACTION IS POSSIBLE
	INR	L	; ADD 1 TO QUOTIENT
NEXT:	DCR	B	; DECREMENT COUNTER
	JNZ	LOOP	; IF NOT 0, CONTINUE DIVISION
	RET		; OTHERWISE RETURN

We can easily program this for any small computer. An 8080/8085 subroutine to divide an unsigned 16-bit integer by an unsigned 8-bit integer is shown in Table 9.6; the flowchart is given in Fig. 9.6. We can accumulate the quotient and remainder in the 16-bit register pair that originally holds the dividend. Instead of shifting the divisor to the right, we shift the dividend to the left, gradually replacing it by the quotient and remainder.

An M6800 subroutine to divide an unsigned 16-bit integer by an unsigned 16-bit divisor, yielding an unsigned 16-bit quotient, in shown in Table 9.7. Because of the shortage of registers, the dividend, divisor, and counter are held in a stack. During division the quotient replaces the dividend. Figure 9.7 shows the stack contents before division begins and after it has finished.

Counter
Divisor MSB
Divisor LSB
Dividend MSB
Dividend LSB
Return address MSB
Return address LSB

(a)

0
Divisor MSB
Divisor LSB
Quotient MSB
Quotient LSB
Return address MSB
Return address LSB

(b)

Fig. 9.7
Stack contents before and after division. (a) Before division. (b) After division.

Table 9.7
M6800 subroutine for dividing an unsigned 16-bit dividend by an unsigned 16-bit divisor

Label	Op code	Operand	Comment
			; DIVIDEND IS IN
			; ACCA (MS BYTE) AND ACCB (LS BYTE)
			; MS BYTE OF DIVISOR IS IN (X)
			; LS BYTE OF DIVISOR IS IN (X + 1)
			; QUOTIENT WILL BE IN ACCA AND ACCB
DIVID:	PSH	B	; PUSH MSB OF DIVIDEND
	PSH	A	; PUSH MSB OF DIVIDEND
	LDA	A X	; GET DIVISOR
	LDA	B 1, X	
	PSH	B	; PUSH LSB OF DIVISOR
	PSH	A	; PUSH MSB OF DIVISOR COUNT
	DES		; DECREMENT SP TO LEAVE SPACE FOR
	TSX		; LOAD INDEX REG FROM SP
	LDA	A #1	
	TST	1, X	; COMPARE WITH MS BYTE OF DIVISOR
	BMI	LOAD	; IF MINUS, BRANCH TO
CHECK:	INC	A	; INCREMENT A
	ASL	2, X	; SHIFT DIVISOR LEFT
	ROL	1, X	
	BMI	LOAD	
	CMP	A #17	; CHECK COUNT
	BNE	CHECK	; IF NOT DONE, REPEAT CHECK
LOAD:	STA	A X, X	; STORE COUNT
	LDA	A 3, X	; LOAD DIVIDEND
	LDA	B 4, X	
	CLR	3, X	; CLEAR SPACE
	CLR	4, X	
TRIAL:	SUB B	2, X	; SUBTRACT DIVISOR
	SBC A	1, X	
	BCC	NOBOR	; BRANCH IF NO BORROW
	ADD B	2, X	; OTHERWISE RESTORE
	ADC C	1, X	
	CLC		; CLEAR BORROW
	BRA	SHIFT	; GO TO SHIFT
NOBOR:	SEC		; SET BORROW
SHIFT:	ROL	4, X	; SHIFT DIVIDEND
	ROL	3, X	
	LSR	1, X	; SHIFT DIVISOR
	ROR	2, X	
	DEC	0, X	; DECREMENT COUNTER
	BNE	TRIAL	; IF NOT DONE, REPEAT
	INS		; CLEAR STACK
	INS		
	INS		
	PUL A		; POP QUOTIENT
	PUL B		
	RTS		; RETURN

9.6   Decimal Arithmetic

Many microcomputers are designed for decimal arithmetic on binary coded decimal (BCD) numbers. In a typical 8-bit microcomputer, each 8-bit cycle can represent two BCD digits because, as you will recall, each digit is represented by its four-bit binary equivalent. The bit patterns for the hexadecimal digits A through F are not used.

Decimal digit	BCD representation	Decimal digit	BCD representation
0	0000	5	0101
1	0001	6	0110
2	0010	7	0111
3	0011	8	1000
4	0100	9	1001

Most microcomputers do not have special instructions for decimal addition or subtraction. Instead, addition and subtraction are done in binary. The result is then corrected to account for the missing six bit patterns.

9.6.1   BCD Addition

For BCD addition, 6 must be added to the binary sum (to account for the six unused bit patterns) whenever the sum exceeds 10_{10} or when a carry occurs in the addition of two digits. The correction is accomplished by a decimal adjustment instruction with the help of the carry and **auxiliary carry** flags. The latter, sometimes called a **half carry**, shows a carry from the four least significant bits to the four most significant bits.

The procedure for BCD addition is the following. First, two 8-bit numbers are added in the accumulator with ordinary binary addition. If a carry out of the four least significant bits occurs during this addition, the auxiliary carry flag is set to 1; otherwise it is cleared to 0. Similarly, if a carry out of the four most significant bits of A occurs during this addition, the carry flag is set; otherwise it is cleared. Then the decimal adjustment is made. This takes two steps.

1. If the four least significant bits of the accumulator represent 10 through 15, or if the auxiliary carry is 1, 6 is added to the four least significant bits of the accumulator. Otherwise no adjustment is made to these four bits.

2. Next, if the four most significant bits of the accumulator represent 10 through 15, or if the carry bit is 1, 6 is added to four most significant bits. Otherwise they are left as is.

Suppose register B holds 59_{16} and A (the accumulator) holds 62_{16}. The command

```
ADD B
```

is executed in binary as follows.

Contents of B	0101	1001	59_{16}
Contents of A	0100	0010	42_{16}
Binary sum in A	1001	1011	$9B_{16}$

The result 9B requires decimal adjustment in two steps that are executed automatically by the command

DAA

1. The sum of the four least significant bits is 10 or more. Thus 6 must be added.

Contents of A	1001	1011	$9B_{16}$
+6		0110	$+6_{16}$
	1010	0001	$A1_{16}$

The auxiliary carry is 1.

2. The sum of the four most significant bits is 10. Hence 6 must be added.

Contents of A		1010	0001	A1
+60		0110		+6 0
	1	0000	0001	1 0 1

The carry is 1.

Thus A holds 1 and the carry is 1 to represent the sum 101. Remember that the decimal adjustment command carries out these operations. We show the details so that you can see what happens.

We can use decimal adjustment to add multidigit numbers. Suppose we wish to add two 10-digit numbers. Each number will take five bytes. We will assume that the first number is stored in the five bytes of memory beginning at address ADDND, and that the second number is stored in the five bytes beginning at AUGND. Both numbers are stored with their least significant

Table 9.8
8080/8085 program for decimal addition of two 10-digit numbers

Label	Op code	Operand	Comment
	LXI	B, ADDND	; SET ADDRESS OF NUM1 TO BC
	LXI	H, AUGND	; SET ADDRESS OF NUM2 TO HL
	MVI	E, 5	; LOAD COUNTER E WITH 5
	XRA		; CLEAR CARRY
LOOP:	LDAX	B	; PUT VALUE OF NUM1 IN A
	ADC	M	; ADD VALUE OF NUM2
	DAA		; DECIMAL ADJUST
	STAX	B	; STORE SUM IN BC
	INX	H	; INCREMENT HL
	INX	B	; INCREMENT BC
	DCR	E	; DECREMENT COUNTER E
	JNZ	LOOP	; IF NOT DONE, GET NEXT TWO DIGITS
	HLT		; STOP

bytes first. The 8080/8085 instructions needed to add the two numbers and to store their sum in the space originally occupied by the first number are shown in Table 9.8. Register E is a byte counter; it counts the 10 digits as five two-digit bytes. Register pairs B and H serve as pointers to the numbers to be added and the sum.

9.6.2   *BCD Subtraction*

BCD subtraction requires generating the **10's complement** of the subtrahend and adding it to the minuend. The 10's complement of a decimal number resembles the 2's complement of a binary number. We can obtain the 10's complement of a digit in either of two ways.

- Subtract N from 10.
- Subtract N from 9 (take the **9's complement** of N) and add 1.

When operating 8-bit computers, we may choose to work with two digits at a time. We may form the **100's complement** or the **99's complement**. The 100's complement of a two-digit number MN is $100 - MN$. The 99's complement is $99 - MN$.

BCD subtraction of two-digit numbers proceeds as follows.

1. Set carry flag to 1, showing borrow = 0.
2. Load accumulator with 99.
3. Add 0 to the accumulator with carry, producing $9A_{16}$ and a carry of 0.
4. Subtract the subtrahend from the accumulator, forming the 100's complement.
5. Add the minuend to the accumulator.
6. Decimal adjust, yielding the decimal difference.

Suppose we wish to subtract 29_{10} from 41_{10}. The results of each step are as follows.

1. Set carry:
   Carry = 1, Borrow = 0.
2. Place 99 in accumulator:
   ACC holds $99_{16} = 10011001_2$, Carry = 1.
3. Add 0 to accumulator with carry:
   ACC holds $9A_{16} = 10011010_2$, Carry = 0.
4. Subtract subtrahend:

ACC	9A	10011010	10011010	
$-$SUBTR	-29	-00101001	$=11010111$	
	71_{16}		01110001	Carry = 0

5. Add minuend:

ACC	7 1	01110001	
$+$MINU	$+4\,1$	01000001	Carry = 0
	$B2_{16}$	10110010	Auxiliary carry = 0

6. Decimal adjust:
   No adjustment to least significant digits; 6 must be added to most significant digits.

ACC	10110010
+60	01100000
	1 00010000 Carry = 1 means Borrow = 0

Result is 12 with no borrow.

Table 9.9 shows 8080/8085 instructions for subtracting two two-digit BCD numbers.

Table 9.9
8080/8085 program for subtracting two two-digit BCD numbers

Op code	Operand	Comment
		; SUBTRAHEND IS IN LOCATION SUBTR
		; MINUEND IS IN LOCATION MINU
		; DIFFERENCE WILL BE IN A
STC		; SET CARRY FOR BORROW OF 0
MVI	A, 99H	; LOAD A WITH 99
ACI	0	; ADD 0 TO A WITH CARRY
MVI	B, SUBTR	; PUT SUBTRAHEND IN B
SUB	B	; SUBTRACT
ADI	MINU	; ADD MINUEND
DAA		; DECIMAL ADJUST

The procedure for subtracting multibyte BCD numbers varies only slightly. Steps 2 through 6 are repeated as many times as needed. The carry formed in step 6 is brought forward to step 2. The result of adding 0 to the accumulator in step 3 yields either 99 or 9A depending on the carry brought from step 6. Similarly, in step 4 either the 99's complement of the 100's complement is formed. See the flowchart of Fig. 9.8.

9.6.3 *Decimal Mode Operations*

Many recent microcomputers offer a choice of binary or decimal modes. When we select **decimal mode**, the computer automatically makes decimal adjustments whenever they are needed. We do not have to concern ourselves with them. When we have finished all decimal calculations, we can clear the decimal mode and return to binary operation. The Mostek 6500 microprocessor offers this feature.

9.6.4 *Calculation of Elapsed Time*

An application of decimal arithmetic that illustrates effective use of subroutines is shown in Table 9.10. The problem is the calculation of elapsed time in hours,

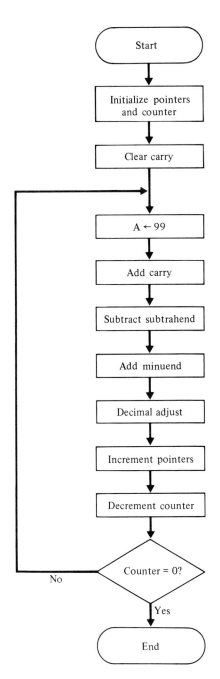

Fig. 9.8
Flowchart of multiple-byte BCD subtraction.

Table 9.10
8080/8085 program for computing elapsed time in hours, minutes, seconds, and hundredths of seconds

Label	Op code	Operand	Comment
	ORG	1200H	
	LXI	H, 1000H	; H POINTS TO STARTING TIME
	LXI	D, 1004H	; D POINTS TO FINAL TIME
	LXI	B, 1008H	; B POINTS TO ELAPSED TIME
	STC		; SET CARRY FOR NO BORROW
	CALL	SUBTR	; SUBTRACT HUNDREDTHS OF SECONDS
	CALL	INCPT	; STORE HUNDREDTHS AND INCREMENT
			; POINTERS TO SECONDS
	CALL	SUBTR	; SUBTRACT SECONDS
	CNC	ADJ60	; IF BORROW OCCURS, ADJUST
	CALL	INCPT	; STORE SECONDS AND INCREMENT
			; POINTERS TO MINUTES
	CALL	SUBTR	; SUBTRACT MINUTES
	CNC	ADJ60	; IF BORROW OCCURS, ADJUST
	CALL	INCPT	; STORE MINUTES AND INCREMENT
			; POINTERS TO HOURS
	CALL	SUBTR	; SUBTRACT HOURS
	STAX	B	; STORE HOURS
	HLT		; STOP
SUBTR:	MVI	A, 99H	; INITIALIZE A WITH 99
	ACI	0	; ADD CARRY
	SUB	M	; SUBTRACT STARTING TIME
	XCHG		; POINT H TO FINAL TIME
	ADD	M	; ADD FINAL TIME
	DAA		; DECIMAL ADJUST
	XCHG		; POINT H TO STARTING TIME
	RET		; RETURN
ADJ60:	ADI	60H	; ADD 60 TO ADJUST FOR SECONDS AND
			; MINUTES
	DAA		; DECIMAL ADJUST
	ORA		; CLEAR CARRY
	RET		; RETURN
INCPT:	STAX	B	; STORE ANSWER IN ELAPSED TIME
	INX	B	; INCREMENT ELAPSED TIME
	INX	H	; INCREMENT STARTING TIME
	INX	D	; INCREMENT FINAL TIME
	RET		; RETURN
	END		

minutes, seconds, and hundredths of seconds. Elapsed time is the difference between starting time and final time. We will assume that both starting and final time are stored in memory locations 1000H through 1007H as shown in Fig. 9.9. Elapsed time when calculated will be stored in the next four locations. Each time is stored with hundredths of seconds in the first location and hours in the fourth location. Hours are given in military or European time, that is, hours are based on a 24-hour clock. Each location holds two decimal digits.

Memory
location

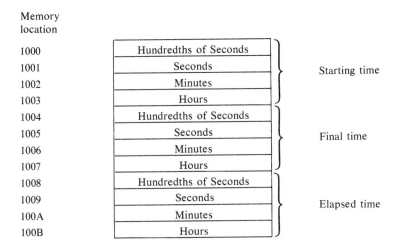

Fig. 9.9
Memory storage for calculation of elapsed time.

The program begins by initializing register pairs H, D, and B to point to
starting, final, and elapsed time. The carry is set to 1 to show that the borrow is
0. The main part of the program consists of calls to three subroutines, which (1)
subtract, (2) adjust if necessary, and (3) store the answer and increment pointers. Memory space and a programmer's effort have been saved by writing each
of these routines just once. We will consider each of them separately below.
The program ends with storage of the hours of elapsed time and a halt.

The SUBTR routine performs subtraction and decimal adjustment. It begins by putting 99H (representing 99 decimal) into the accumulator and adding
the carry (complement of the borrow) from the preceding subtraction. Then the
starting time (the subtrahend) is subtracted. The register pair H is exchanged
with pair D so that H now points to the final time (the minuend), which is
added. This exchange is needed because in the 8080, the main gateway to
memory is register pair H. The commands ADD M and SUB M refer to the
location to which H points. The result is decimal adjusted, yielding the true
subtraction of starting time from final time with borrow. Then register pairs H
and B are switched again so that they again point to starting time and final time,
respectively.

The ADJ60 routine adjusts the subtractions of seconds and minutes to a
base of 60. (The hours do not need to be adjusted, assuming the starting and
final times occur on the same day.) The adjustment is relatively simple. It must
be done only if the subtraction resulted in a borrow. (Why?) The number 60 is
added to the seconds or minutes, and the result is decimal adjusted. The carry
is cleared to show a borrow.

The INCPT subroutine stores the answer and increments the three pointers. It requires the fewest bytes of any of these subroutines—five bytes,

including one for the return instruction—because all instructions are single bytes. Calling the subroutine takes three. Because the subroutine was called only three times, more memory was needed to implement the instructions in a subroutine than if we had written them each time in the main program. Furthermore, more time was required to execute the program because of the time required to call and return from the subroutine. Nonetheless, a programmer's time was saved, and the tradeoff was probably justified; the extra time should not matter in a program like this, and the memory needed is small. Alternatively, we could write this routine as a macro. What advantages would be gained by doing so?

9.7 Floating-Point Operations

In our discussion of arithmetic functions thus far we have assumed that we were working with integers only. Sometimes, especially in scientific calculations, we want the greater flexibility of floating-point numbers. Some small computers—notably the more powerful minicomputers—offer instructions for performing floating-point arithmetic. Alternatively, we can program floating-point arithmetic for any small computer, but that is beyond the scope of this text. We will limit our discussion to an example of floating-point operations on the PDP-11. If you are rusty on floating-point operations, you may want to review the discussion in Chapter 2 before reading this section.

The PDP-11 offers a floating-point option with instructions for floating-point addition, subtraction, multiplication, and division. Each floating-point number takes two 16-bit words. The bits are assigned as follows:

- 1 bit for the sign of the mantissa (0 for positive, 1 for negative)
- 8 bits for the exponent
- 23 bits plus one **hidden bit** that is always 1 for the magnitude of the mantissa

The 8-bit exponent allows representing exponents between -128_{10} and $+127_{10}$. The number system that represents the exponent is called **excess-128**. This simply means that 128_{10} is added to the usual binary representation of the number. The following examples show how this works. You will notice that excess-128 just changes the sign bit.

Decimal exponent	Octal representation	Binary representation	Octal excess-128 representation	Binary excess-128 representation
0	000	00 000 000	200	10 000 000
+1	001	00 000 001	201	10 000 001
+127	177	01 111 111	377	11 111 111
−1	377	11 111 111	177	01 111 111
−128	200	10 000 000	000	00 000 000

The mantissa is represented as a sign-and-magnitude fraction. The magnitude of the fraction is always normalized to be between ½ and 1. Hence the first bit of the fraction is always 1. Because it is always 1, this bit can be understood and not represented directly. Thus one extra bit of precision can be obtained. This first bit of the magnitude that is always 1 is called the hidden bit.

The format of a floating-point number for the PDP-11 is shown below.

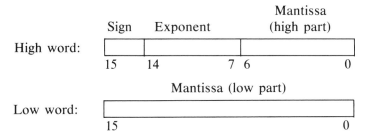

Consider the representation of -75_{10} in this format.

$$-75_{10} = -1000011_2$$
$$= -(2^7)_{10} \times .1000011_2$$

Sign   Exponent   Mantissa

| 1 | 1 0 0 0 1 1 1 | 0 0 0 0 1 1 0 |

↑

Hidden bit is 1.

Mantissa

| 0 0 0 0 | 0 0 0 0 | 0 0 0 0 | 0 0 0 0 |

For all floating-point operations one register, chosen by the programmer, serves as a pointer to stack containing the operands and result. If the operands are A and B, the selected register R holds stack addresses as follows.

(R)	High operand B
(R)+2	High operand B
(R)+4	High operand A
(R)+6	Low operand A

The result of the floating-point operation is stored on the stack in the following locations.

(R)+4	Low result
(R)+6	High result

The four floating-point instructions have the format of OPCODE R, where R is the register just described. They are:

FADD	Add A and B
FSUB	Subtract B from A
FMUL	Multiply A by B
FDIV	Divide A by B

9.8 *Logic Operations*

When dealing with data that comprise only part of a word, we need to do operations besides the usual add, clear, move, and so forth. These other operations are called logic operations because they use the same mathematical logic as does the computer's hardware. This is not surprising since the hardware must implement the operations we program. Logic operations include a variety of shifts to move data around, mainly within a word. They also include a number of combinational logic operations.

9.8.1 *Shifts*

We often want to move information within a computer word. For example, we may want to move one field to the right end so that we can operate on it. Or, in working with floating-point numbers, we may want to move one number so that the binary points are aligned. The operation of moving numbers to the left or right is called **shifting**.

Figure 9.10 shows several common types of shifts. For simplicity they are shown on an 8-bit register, such as one in a microcomputer. We can categorize shifts in four ways.

1. Shifts may occur to the left or the right.
2. Shifts may be logical, cyclic, or arithmetic, as explained below.
3. Shifts may move data one, two, four, eight, or some other number of bits.
4. Shifts may or may not involve a special one-bit register, called a carry, link, or extend register.

Any given shift will combine all four of these options. A very large number of shifts can occur. Generally, any computer will directly implement a few of these possible shifts with its basic shift instructions.

Figure 9.10(a) shows a **logical shift** of one bit to the right without a carry. (Carries are usually omitted in logical shifts.) Each bit is shifted one place to the right; the low-order bit is lost; the high-order bit is replaced by a 0. Figure 9.10(b) shows a logical shift of two bits to the left. Logical shifts can isolate a field within a word. The 0's are shifted out the other end. How would you use logical shifts to isolate a field in the middle of a word?

A **cyclic shift** or rotation moves bits around in a circle. Figure 9.10(c) shows a rotation of one bit to the right without a carry. No information is lost. This rotation of one bit to the right is exactly the same as a rotation of seven bits to the left. More generally, for a computer with an n-bit word, a rotation of m bits to the right is the same as a rotation of $n-m$ bits to the left. Hence computers do not need both left and right cyclic shifts, though they usually have both. Cyclic shifts are often made with carries.

Figure 9.10(d) shows a rotation of one bit to the left with a carry; the one-bit carry is in a condition code register designated C. It acts as bit 16. The

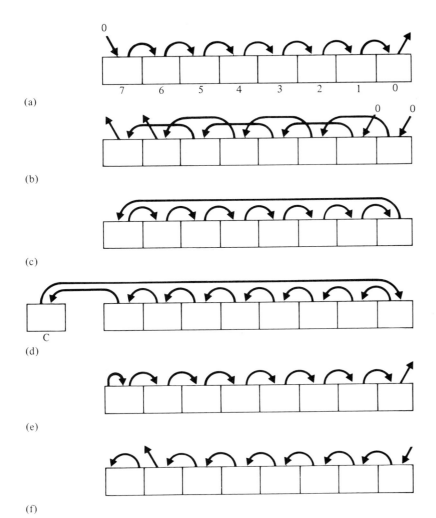

(a)

(b)

(c)

(d)

(e)

(f)

Fig. 9.10
Shifts. (a) Logical right one bit. (b) Logical left two bits. (c) Rotate right. (d) Rotate left
with carry. (e) Arithmetic right. (f) Arithmetic left.

high-order bit is moved into the condition code register; the contents of the
condition code register are moved into the low-order bit; and all other bits shift
one position to the left.

Arithmetic shifts, shown in Figures 9.10(e and f), leave the sign bit unchanged. The arithmetic right shift copies the sign bit and moves the sign bit
and all other bits one to the right; the low-order bit is lost. The arithmetic right
shift is 2's complement multiplication by 2. Similarly, the arithmetic left shift is
a 2's complement division by 2.

In Chapters 4 and 5 we examined the shift instructions of the PDP-11, the

8080/8085, and the M6800. Now you should be able to classify them into the categories described here. If the computer you are using lacks one of the standard shifts, you can probably program it. Some shifts are easier to program with the combinational logic functions described in the next section.

9.8.2 *Combinational Logic Operations*

We often wish to perform identical operations on each bit of a computer word. At other times we wish to treat some bits differently from others. To do this we need bit-oriented instructions that operate independently on each bit of a word.

The simplest of these operations is the NOT operation. It is a unary (one-variable) operation whose result is the logical complement of the operand. Its table is shown below.

X	NOT X
0	1
1	0

The PDP-11 implements NOT with the COM instruction discussed earlier. That is, it COMplements each bit of a word. The 8080/8085 can complement data only in the accumulator with the CMA (CoMplement Accumulator) instruction. The 6800 can complement data in either accumulator with its NEG (NEGate) instruction.

Suppose that we wish to deal with the information in only part of a word. For example, we might wish to extract the octal digit from the ASCII representation of a character. ASCII represents the octal digit n as $26n_8$. Assume that the character is in the right half of a byte. The number 5 then would appear in binary as

$$10110101_2 = 265_8$$

We want to extract the final 101. To do this we wish to **mask** the rest of the number. We introduce the AND operation. It yields a 1 only if both operands are 1; otherwise it yields a 0. The table below summarizes the AND operation on any two binary operands.

X	Y	X AND Y
0	0	0
0	1	0
1	0	0
1	1	1

If we construct a mask that has 1's in the three lowest-order bits and 0's elsewhere, we can AND the mask with the ASCII character. Thus we can

extract the desired number while masking the undesired information. The operation works as follows.

ASCII character	10110101
Mask	00000111
ASCII character	00000101
(Octal number)	

Most microcomputers have AND instructions. The 8080/8085 has two AND instructions—one for ANDing the contents of a register or memory with those of the accumulator (ANA) and a second for ANDing the accumulator with immediate data (ANI). The latter is more useful for masking. For example, to extract the octal number, we might write

```
ANI  07H
```

The M6800 has a flexible AND instruction—with op code AND—that can be used with immediate, direct, extended, and indirect addressing for either accumulator.

The PDP-11 has no AND instruction that does exactly this, but it does have a form of the AND. In the PDP-11 an ANDing of source and destination is done with a BIT test (BIT) instruction. It does not change either the source or destination operands. Instead, the condition code Z (for Zero) is set to 1 if the result is 0; that is, if the source and destination have no 1's in the same bits. The M6800 has a similar instruction, BIT. We do not find this instruction useful in masking, even though it is the AND operation.

For PDP-11 programs we can use a BIC (BIt Clear) instruction to do the masking. This somewhat unusual instruction replaces the destination by the logical AND of the destination with the complement of the source. That is, it computes NOT SOURCE AND DESTINATION and places the result in the destination. Suppose R3 contains 100200_8, and R4 contains 111333_8. The instruction

```
BIC  %3,%4
```

first calculates the complement of the contents of R3 and then ANDs it with the contents of R4, as shown below. The overbar denotes NOT, or complement.

$$
\begin{aligned}
(R3) &= 100200_8 = 1000000010000000_2 \\
(\overline{R3}) &= 077577_8 = 0111111101111111_2 \\
(R4) &= 111333_8 = 1001001011011011_2 \\
\overline{R3} \text{ AND } (R4) &= 011133_8 = 0001001001011011_2
\end{aligned}
$$

Because the BIC instruction complements the source, we must first complement the source to get a true AND of source with destination. We can simulate an AND by the two general instructions

```
COM  src
BIC  src, dst
```

Suppose an ASCII-coded octal digit that we wish to extract is in register 2. We can extract it with one instruction by using the complement of the mask 000007_8, namely 177770_8. We write

```
BIC #177770,%2.
```

The reverse of the mask or extract operation is a **merge**. Suppose we have an octal number and wish to convert it to its ASCII representation. We need to resupply the leading bits. To do this we use the logical OR operation. It yields a 1 whenever either or both of its operands are 1; it is 0 only when both operands are 9. The table below shows the OR operation on any two binary operands.

X	Y	X OR Y
0	0	0
0	1	1
1	0	1
1	1	1

To produce the ASCII byte representation of any octal number we OR the number with the pattern 260_8 or B0H. This operation merges the octal number with the correct leading bits. The operation looks as follows.

Octal number 5	00000101
Pattern	10110000
Number OR Pattern	10110101

Most microcomputers have OR instructions. Those of the 8080/8085 work in much the same way as their AND instructions. They are ORA for ORing contents of a register or memory with the accumulator and ORI for ORing the accumulator with immediate data. Hence the merge to produce an ASCII representation could be done with

```
ORI B0H
```

The M6800 has the instruction ORA for ORing with either accumulator using immediate, direct, extended, or indirect addressing.

The PDP-11 implements an OR with a BIt Set (BIS) instruction. It calculates the OR of the source and destination operands and leaves the result in the destination. Suppose the octal number 5 is in register 1. We can form its ASCII representation with the single instruction

```
BIS #000260,%1
```

We might also like to check a word to see whether it matches a pattern precisely. Suppose we want to search a list of ASCII characters stored with two characters per word to see whether any word contains HI. In ASCII, HI is

$$1100100011001001_2 = 144311_8.$$

The simplest way to check whether a word has a particular value is to use the EXCLUSIVE OR (XOR) operation. It gives the result 1 whenever the two operands differ; it gives the result 0 whenever the two operands agree. The table below shows the XOR operation.

X	Y	X XOR Y
0	0	0
0	1	1
1	0	1
1	1	0

Using the XOR operation we can check any word by XORing it with the ASCII cord for HI. If the words match in every bit, the result will be all 0's. Examples of unsuccessful and successful checks are shown below.

Test	1010101010000111
HI	1100100011001001

Test XOR HI	0110001001001110

(Test is not HI.)

Test	1100100011001001
HI	1100100011001001

XOR HI	0000000000000000

(Test = HI.)

The PDP-11 has an XOR instruction. It allows us to compare the EXCLUSIVE OR of a register with the destination and store the result in the destination. Thus we could implement the check for HI by placing the ASCII word for HI in a register and comparing it with desired test words. Because the result of the XOR operation replaces the original contents of the destination, we would probably want to copy the words to be tested before executing the XOR instruction.

Most microcomputers have EXCLUSIVE OR instructions. The 8080/8085 has XRA, which operates on the contents of registers or memory and the accumulator, and XRI, which operates on immediate data and the accumulator. The M6800 has EOR, which can be used with the same addressing modes as the other logic instructions.

EXCLUSIVE OR instructions can be used for other purposes. One simple application is clearing the accumulator. The 8080/8085 instruction

```
XRA A
```

clears the accumulator by XORing each bit of A with itself. This works because the XOR operating on two identical bits yields a 0.

We can complement the contents of any register by XORing it with all 1's. For example, the 8080/8085 command

```
XRI E, OFFH
```

results in complementing every bit of register E. (Why?)

Table 9.11
8085 program illustrating macros for masking and packing

Label	Op code	Operand	Comment
			; 8085 PROGRAM TO TAKE
			; 60 SIX-DIGIT
			; NUMBERS STORED IN ASCII
			; STARTING IN LOCATION
			; 4000, CONVERTING TO BCD,
			; PACKING
			; INTO TWO DIGITS PER
			; LOCATION, AND
			; STORING STARTING IN
			; LOCATION 4300
SHIFT	MACRO		; MACRO TO SHIFT LEFT FOUR
			; PLACES
	RLC		
	RLC		
	RLC		
	RLC		
	ENDM		
MASK	MACRO		
	ANI	OFH	
	ENDM		
PACK	MACRO		; MACRO TO PACK TWO BCD
			; DIGITS INTO ONE BYTE
	MOV	A, M	; GET FIRST ASCII CHARACTER
	MASK		; EXTRACT BCD DIGIT
	SHIFT		
	MOV	B, A	; STORE FIRST DIGIT TEMPORARILY
	INX	H	; ADVANCE POINTER
	MOV	A, M	; GET SECOND ASCII CHARACTER

Another application of XOR is to compare two bytes to identify differences in their bits. For example, the 8080/8085 instruction

XRA B

results in 0's in A for each bit in which A and B agreed and 1's for each bit in which A and B differed.

As an example of logic operations, consider that we have a list of 60 six-digit numbers—perhaps student numbers or parts numbers. They are stored in their ASCII representations, most significant digit first, in 360 consecutive memory locations. We recognize that we can save memory if we pack two digits per byte. Each ASCII character must first be masked with $0F_{16}$ to extract the decimal digit. The first such number for each byte must be shifted left four positions. The second number can be merged with it by adding or by ORing.

An 8085 program to pack these numbers is given in Table 9.11. This program makes liberal use of macros. Five macros are defined:

• SHIFT—for shifting left four positions

Table 9.11 (cont.)

Label	Op code	Operand	Comment
PACK	MASK		
	ADD	B	; COMBINE TWO DIGITS
	INX	H	
	ENDM		
STORE	MACRO		; MACRO TO STORE TWO BCD
			; DIGITS
	XCHG		
	MOV	M, A	
	XCHG		
	INX	D	
	ENDM		
CRAM	MACRO		; MACRO TO CONVERT SIX-
			; DIGIT NUMBER
	MVI	B, 3	; INITIALIZE COUNTER
LOOPC:	PACK		
	STORE		
	DCR	B	
	JNZ	LOOPC	
	ENDM		
	LXI	H,4000H	; BEGIN PROGRAM BY
			; INITIALIZING
	LXI	D,4300H	; POINTERS AND COUNTER
	MVI	C,50	
LOOP:	CRAM		; CALL CRAM
	DCR	C	
	JNZ	LOOP	; REPEAT 60 TIMES
	HLT		

- MASK—for masking with $0F_{16}$
- PACK—for merging two BCD digits into one byte
- STORE—for storing the two digits
- CRAM—for handling a six-digit number

Macro PACK calls macros MASK and SHIFT, both of which must be defined beforehand. Similarly, macro CRAM calls macros PACK and STORE. This program thus illustrates nesting of macros. It may not represent optimal use of macros; you may be able to improve on it. Remember that macros consume more memory, while subroutines consume more time.

9.9 Delay Routines

Commonly, when working with microcomputers (and occasionally when working with minicomputers), we will want to produce a precise timing interval. We may, for example, wish to synchronize with a teleprinter that sends one bit every 9.1 ms. Or we may want to ignore irregularities that occur soon after a switch is closed by not examining the switch until it has been closed for 20 ms. Or we may want to sample the output of a device every 5 seconds. In each of these cases we want to program a **delay routine**—a series of instructions that require a specific time interval for execution.

The timing of microcomputer instructions is based on clock cycles. Hence the first thing we must know before we can write a delay routine is the frequency of our clock. Suppose it operates at 2.0 MHz; then a **clock cycle** is the reciprocal of this or 0.5 μsec (0.5×10^{-6} sec).

Next, we must know the number of clock cycles needed to execute each instruction. Table 9.12 shows the clock cycles required for 8080 instructions, which we will use as an example for this discussion. Timing for the 8085 differs for some instructions. Timing for the M6800 depends on the addressing mode used and hence is somewhat more complicated.

Table 9.12
Clock cycles of 8080 instructions

Instruction	Clock Cycles
ADD reg, ADC reg, SUB reg,	4
SBB reg, ANA reg, XRA reg,	4
ORA reg, CMP reg	4
RLC, RRC, RAL, RAR	4
CMA, STC, CMC, DAA	4
EI, DI, NOP, XCHG	4
MOV reg, reg; INR reg, DCR reg	5
SPHL, PCHL	5
INX, DCX	5
MOV M, reg; MOV reg, M	7
MVI reg	7
ADD M, ADC M, SUB M, SBB M	7
ANA M, XRA M, ORA M, CMP M	7
ADI, ACI, SUI, SBI	7
ANI, XRI, ORI, CPI	7
STAX, LDAX	7
MVI M, INR M, DCR M	10
JMP, JC, JNC, JZ, JNZ, JP, JM, JPE, JPO	10
RET, DAD	10
IN, OUT	10
LXI, POP	10
PUSH, RST	11
STA, LDA	13
SHLD, LHLD	16
CALL	17
XTHL	18
RC, RNC, RZ, RNZ, RP, RM, RPE, RPO	5/11*
CC, CNC, CZ, CNZ, CP, CM, CPE, CPO	11/17*

* Smaller number if condition false, larger number if condition true—for example, CC takes 11 cycles if the carry is 0 and control passes to the next instruction, but 17 cycles if the carry is 1 and the subroutine must be called.

Now we are ready to write a delay routine. The simplest possibility might be just to write repeated NOP (no operation) instructions; each one takes four clock cycles, equivalent to 2 μsec for a 2-MHz clock. However, if we want to use more than a few microseconds, the best solution is to have one or more **delay loops**—a series of repeated instructions that consume time without doing anything else. A basic delay loop consists of repeatedly decrementing a register.

A simple delay loop is:

```
TIME1: DCR E
       JNZ TIME1
```

These two instructions are executed repeatedly until the contents of register E are 0. DCR E takes 5 cycles; JNZ TIME1 takes 10 cycles. Hence, each execution of both instructions takes 15 cycles, or 7.5 μsec. We can control the number of times the instructions are executed by initializing the E register. For example, suppose we write

```
       MVI E, 200
TIME1: DCR E
       JNZ TIME1
```

The loop of DCR E and JNZ TIME1 will be executed 200 times and will consume 200×7.5 μsec. = 1.5 msec. For precise timing, we should add the time required to initialize the loop, which is 7 cycles or 3.5 μsec.

We now have a basic delay loop with these steps.

1. Initialize a register.
2. Decrement the contents of the register.
3. If the register contents are not 0, repeat step 2.

The maximum delay obtained from this basic loop occurs when E is initialized to 0 so that the loop instructions are executed 256 times. Then the delay, exclusive of the time for initialization, is 256×7.5 μsec. = 1.92 msec. If we want longer delays, we can nest loops. Ignoring problems of initialization for the moment, suppose we write:

```
TIME1: DCR E
       JNZ TIME1
       DCR D
       JNZ TIME1
```

This segment has two loops—an inner loop, composed of DCR E and JNZ TIME1, and an outer loop, composed of DCR D and JNZ TIME1. If the contents of both registers are initially 0, the outer loop instructions will be executed 256 times, requiring 7.5 μsec for each execution of its two instructions—DCR D and JNZ TIME1. For each execution of the outer loop instructions, the inner loop instructions will be executed 256 times. We can calculate the delay as follows.

Delay = 256 × (7.5 μsec + 256 × 7.5 μsec)
    = 256 × (7.5 μsec + 1.92 msec)
    = .49344 sec

For delays of several seconds, we can add a third, outermost loop:

```
TIME1: DCR E
       JNZ TIME1
       DCR D
       JNZ TIME1
       DCR C
       JNZ TIME1
```

If the contents of all three registers are initially 0, we can calculate the delay. Again we ignore the time required to initialize the registers.

Delay = 256 × [7.5 μsec + 256 × (7.5 μsec + 256 × 7.5 μsec)]
    = 256 × (7.5 μsec + .49344 sec)
    = 126.32 sec

Thus with three loops we can obtain a delay of a little more than two minutes. Initializing the registers with MVI instructions will add 3 × 3.5 μsec = 10.5 μsec, an insignificant addition. Naturally, we can vary the delay by changing the initial contents of the registers. We have options here. We can initialize all three registers before entering the outermost timing loop. Then the initialization affects each loop just once; on the second and following executions the inner loop instructions are executed 256 times whenever the loop is entered. Alternatively, we can initialize the loop register just before entering the loop each time. Suppose we write

```
       MVI C, 80
TIME3: MVI D, 100
TIME2: MVI E, 200
TIME1: DCR E
       JNZ TIME1
       DCR D
       JNZ TIME2
       DCR C
       JNZ TIME3
```

Now we should consider the time to initialize at least the D and E registers. (Why?)

Delay = 3.5 μsec + 80 × [7.5 μsec + 3.5 μsec + 100
                    × (7.5 μsec + 3.5 μsec + 200 × 7.5 μsec)]
    = 3.5 μsec + 80 × (10.5 μsec + 100 × 1.5105 msec)
    = 3.5 μsec + 80 × (151.05 msec)
    = 12.084 sec

Note that the time required to initialize the outermost loop register C is insignificant compared to the total. However, the time required to initialize the innermost loop register E is more important; initializing the E register 8000 times takes 28 msec.

We can also use register pairs in delay loops. The procedure is, however, more complicated because DCX instructions do not set the zero flag. Hence CMP or ORA instructions are needed to test both registers of the pair for 0. Because one register pair loop can be executed up to 65,536 times, longer delays can be written with fewer loops nested.

To avoid losing register contents we may wish to save the contents of any registers used on the stack before starting a delay routine. We can do this most easily by pushing the registers on the stack before entering the delay routine and then popping them when leaving the delay routine. For accurate timing we must then count the time required to execute the PUSH and POP instructions.

9.S *Summary*

Programs for the four basic arithmetic operations can be written following the procedures described in Chapter 2. Most small computers provide both addition and subtraction commands. For a computer that lacks subtraction commands, we can form the 2's complement of the subtrahend and add it to the minuend. The carry bit is interpreted as a borrow for subtraction. Many small computers provide overflow flags. For those that do not, we can determine overflow by comparing the signs of the operands with the sign of the result.

Multiple-precision addition and subtraction requires bringing along a carry or borrow bit from a low-order byte or word to the next higher byte or word. Most small computers provide add-with-carry and subtract-with-borrow commands expressly for multiple-precision arithmetic.

Some small computers, especially the more powerful minicomputers, provide multiplication and division commands. For those computers that lack such instructions we can program multiplication with repeated additions and division with trial subtractions.

BCD arithmetic involves representing decimal numbers as their four-bit binary equivalents, operating on the binary numbers, and adjusting to give a correct decimal result. A single decimal adjustment instruction works for both addition and subtraction. Decimal subtrahends are assigned their 100's or 99's complements for subtraction. Some computers allow selecting a decimal mode in which all decimal adjustments are made automatically.

Logic operations include several types of shifts. Cyclic shifts or rotations move bits around in a circle, with or without a carry bit. Logical shifts move bits in one direction with bits lost off one end and replaced by 0's at the other end. Arithmetic shifts involve repeating the sign bit and are used for arithmetic calculations.

Combinational logic functions are usually found on mini- and microcomputers. The simplest is the NOT operation or logical complement. The AND operation provides a 1 output only when both inputs are 1. It is helpful in masking one field of a word while extracting another field. The OR operation provides a 1 output when either input is 1. It allows merging two patterns together. The EXCLUSIVE OR or XOR operation yields a 1 output when exactly one of two inputs is 1. It can be used in searching for a target pattern, in comparing two words, or in clearing registers.

Delay routines are intended to give precise timing intervals. They are implemented as delay loops that can be nested to result in delays of from a few microseconds to many seconds.

Key Terms

arithmetic shift	100's complement
auxiliary carry	logical shift
clock cycle	mask
cyclic shift	merge
decimal mode	9's complement
delay loop	99's complement
delay routine	overflow
excess-128	rotation
extract	shift
half carry	10's complement
hidden bit	underflow

9.R References

Most of the books mentioned earlier provide some examples of programming arithmetic and logic operations. User's manuals for any small computer usually present examples of arithmetic calculations. Leventhal (1978b) has detailed examples for the 8080/8085. Peatman (1977) has examples of arithmetic and logic operations for a number of microcomputers. Gear (1974), Eckhouse (1975), and Stone and Sieworek (1975) have applications for the PDP-11.

9.Q Questions

9.1 Which arithmetic operations are most likely to be found as commands?

9.2 How can a computer subtract without a subtract command?

9.3 Explain one procedure for multiplying two binary numbers.

9.4 Explain one procedure for dividing two unsigned binary numbers.

9.5 When and how are decimal adjustments made?

9.6 What is the advantage of operating in decimal mode?

9.7 What is the purpose of a hidden bit in floating-point operations?

9.8 Distinguish between cyclic, logical, and arithmetic shifts.

9.9 Explain the uses of AND, OR, and NOT operations.

9.10 Explain the operation of a delay routine.

9.P *Problems*

Section 9.2

9.1 Write a program for your computer to test for overflow in addition without using the overflow flag.

9.2 Write a program for your computer to test for overflow in subtraction without using the overflow flag.

Section 9.3

9.3 Write a program to add two 6-byte numbers.

9.4 Write a program to subtract two 8-byte numbers.

Section 9.4

9.5 Write a program to multiply a 16-bit number by an 8-bit number.

Section 9.6

9.6 Write a program to multiply two pairs of two-digit BCD numbers.

Section 9.9

9.7 Write delay routines for your computer that as accurately as possible executes in the following times exactly.
a) 1 ms   b) 10 ms   c) 100 ms   d) 1 s   e) 10 s

Input/Output Programming

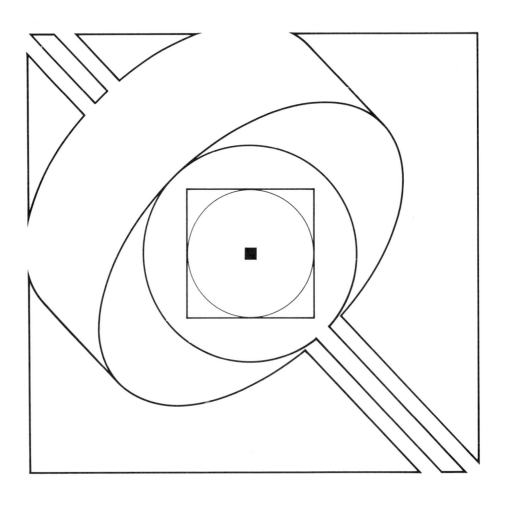

10.1   *Introduction*

In earlier chapters we learned how to write fairly complex programs. Still, we have not yet learned how to exchange information with the outside world. Our programs until now have been limited to manipulating information that is already stored in computer memory. In this chapter we will learn how to program transfers of information between various input/output devices and the computer so that we will be able to deal with events in the outside world. In a later chapter we will consider **interfacing**—handling the hardware connections between the CPU and external devices.

Input/output programming presents us with several difficulties. Timing of inputs and outputs can be tricky. We must transfer information when both the device and the computer are ready for the transfer. We must check the status of each device and consider the importance of the information it holds. If more than one input/output operation can occur, we must be sure that these operations can interact without mistakes. Most small computers treat each type of input/output device differently, so that we must write different programs for each one.

10.2   *Input/Output Devices*

Input/output transfers involve three kinds of signals, as shown in Fig. 10.1. (Address lines, not shown, select the device.) These are:

- Data signals between the computer and the device
- Control signals from the CPU to the device
- Status signals from the device to the CPU

A data transfer from the computer to an external device is considered an output transfer. A data transfer from a device to the computer is similarly considered an input transfer. Note that control and status signals flow in one direction only and that the CPU is always directly involved. Data may be transferred via the CPU or may go directly to memory, as we will see later in the chapter.

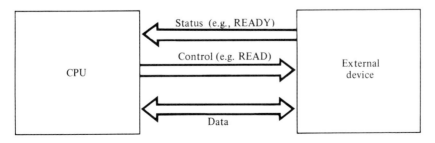

Fig. 10.1
Signals between CPU and external device.

An **input/output** or **peripheral device** transfers information between the computer and the outside world. In the process it usually must convert the form of energy in which the information is represented. An input device may receive information in mechanical form, such as pressure on keys, in thermal form, such as temperature, or in optical form, such as light shining through holes. It must convert information from its original form to electrical signals before it transfers the information to the computer. Similarly, an output device that receives electrical signals from the computer may need to convert them to an optical output, such as display lights, to a mechanical form, such as holes punched in a paper tape, or to a thermal form, such as the heating of print on a page.

The types of devices that we might wish to connect to a computer vary greatly. One way to classify them is by data rate. We can roughly recognize three speeds of devices:

- **Slow devices**—Data rates of less than one per second with data held constant for several milliseconds; examples are switches, displays, mechanical sensing devices, and thermometers.

- **Medium-speed devices**—Data rates of 1 to 10,000 per second; examples are keyboards, Teletypes, cassette recorders, communications lines, and instrumentation systems.

- **High-speed devices**—Data rates of over 10,000 per second; examples are magnetic tapes, magnetic discs, and high-speed communications lines.

Dealing with slow devices requires special circuits called latches to hold data output from the computer constant until the output device is ready to accept it. Slow devices are usually combined together in a procedure called multiplexing so that several slow devices can share one output port. We will defer further discussion of slow devices to Chapter 13; in this chapter we will primarily consider programming for medium-speed and high-speed devices. The main problem we will encounter is that of synchronizing their operation with the computer.

The part of a typical medium- or high-speed peripheral device that converts information between electrical energy and some other form is a **transducer.** It is connected to a **data register** or **buffer register** that stores the electrical signals representing the information. Each input/output device also has a **control** or **status register** that accepts control signals from the computer and sends status signals to the computer, as shown in Fig. 10.2. The organization of this register varies from device to device, but it may contain the following kinds of information.

- One or more bits to show the state of the device—a BUSY bit shows the device is busy; a READY or DONE bit shows that it is ready for operation. These bits can be set or cleared by hardware or by the program; they can be examined by the program to determine the availability of the device.

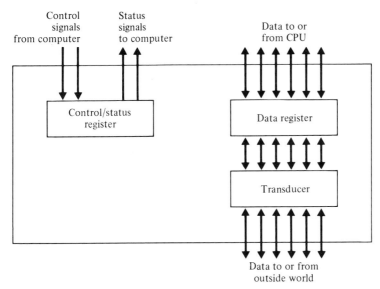

Fig. 10.2
Input/output device register and signals.

- An ENABLE bit that when set allows the device to transfer information.
- An INTERRUPT ENABLE that when set allows the device to interrupt the computer when it is ready to transfer information or when an error has occurred.
- Device function bits to select the specific operation a device should perform, such as reading one bit or eight bits.
- ERROR bits to show device malfunctions.
- Unit-select bits to select the proper unit or channel on a device.
- Memory extension bits to specify longer addresses.

Of these we will be most concerned with the ENABLE, BUSY, and READY or DONE bits. Suppose the computer wishes to send information to a peripheral device—an output operation. The transfer may not begin until the READY bit is 1, meaning that the device is ready for the transfer. The computer then loads data into the device data register; while this action occurs, the READY bit is 0. When the transfer is completed, the READY bit is set to 1.

Input operations occur in a similar manner. When the computer is ready for information to be transferred to it from an input device, it requests the transfer by setting an ENABLE bit in the control and status register of the device to 1. Until the input device is ready to transfer information, its BUSY bit is set to 1. When the information is ready in the data register for transfer, the BUSY bit is reset to 0 and the READY bit is set to 1. Then the computer can read information from the buffer register of the device; the ENABLE bit is reset to 0.

The computer can sense the READY/DONE bit to determine whether the device is ready for a transfer. The PDP-11 uses two instructions to do this

```
WAIT: TSTB DEVICE
      BPL WAIT
```

The TSTB instruction (TeST Byte) tests the 8 low-order bits of the device control and status register, named DEVICE. It sets the N condition code when bit 7 (the byte sign bit) is 1. Because the READY/DONE bit is bit 7 of the control and status register, the instruction sets N as soon as bit 7 becomes 1. Until N is set, the BPL (Branch if PLus) instruction returns control to WAIT to retest DEVICE. When N becomes 1, control passes out of the loop to the following instruction. This kind of loop is called a **wait loop.**

You may have noticed that we wrote this sequence with the same PDP-11 instructions as we have used before. The PDP-11 and the M6800 do not have a special class of input/output instructions; instead, they treat input/output transfers just like memory transfers. This scheme is called **memory-mapped input/output.** Other small computers may have special input/output instructions—a scheme called **isolated input/output.** They generally have the form shown below.

I/O instruction	I/O op code	Device

One or more bits show that the instruction is an input/output instruction. Other bits denote the input/output operation code, such as TEST READY, SET READY, READ DATA REGISTER, and the like. The remaining bits show the code of the device addressed. The 8085 may use isolated input/output or may be specially interfaced for memory-mapped input/output. The 8080 has only isolated input/output.

The 8080 might test the READY/DONE bit as follows:

```
WAIT: IN DEVICE
      ORA A  ; SET FLAGS
      JP WAIT
```

To facilitate treating input/output operations like memory operations, the PDP-11 assigns two "memory locations" to each input/output device. These locations have addresses greater than 170000_8; they are not used as real memory locations, which must have addresses between 000000 and 157777. Each device is assigned one location for its data register and one for its control and status register. In effect, then, the PDP-11 treats these registers as shown in Fig. 10.3.

For most memory-mapped microcomputers we select "memory locations" for devices through interfacing.

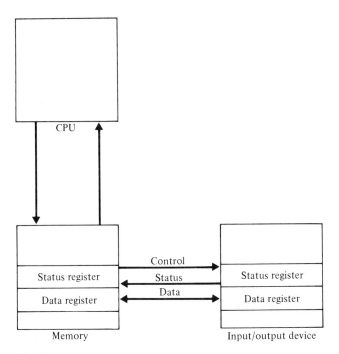

Fig. 10.3
PDP-11 signals for one input/output device.

The input/output programs that we have just discussed are examples of **programmed input/output operations.** Transfers of information between external devices and the CPU occur under the control of the program. When the program needs information transferred, the CPU determines whether the external device is ready. As we have seen, the CPU may need to waste time in a wait loop until the device is ready. Then the transfer proceeds under program control. Later in the chapter we will explore other methods of input/output operations that waste less CPU time. First, however, we will turn our attention to some typical input/output devices.

10.3 *Typical Devices*

10.3.1 *Teletype*

Perhaps the most common peripheral device used with most small computers is the **Teletype.** It is both an input and output device. The input unit is a **keyboard/reader;** the output unit is a **printer/punch.** The keyboard resembles a typewriter but it is not mechanically coupled with the print mechanism, as it is on a typewriter. The reader is a paper-tape reader, and the punch is a paper-tape punch; we will discuss their operation in more detail in the next section.

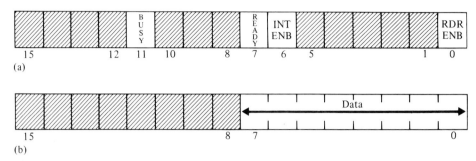

Fig. 10.4
Teletype keyboard/reader. (a) Status register. (b) Data register.

The Teletype keyboard/reader has an 8-bit buffer register, which we call TYKRB. It puts together and stores the code of the last character struck on the keyboard or read from the paper tape. The bits of each Teletype character are sent serially (one bit at a time) to TYKRB; from there they may be transferred in parallel (all 8 bits at once) to any register or memory location. Figure 10.4 shows this register and the Teletype keyboard/reader status register, which we call TYKRS. All shaded bits are not used. The status register has four important bits:

1. The BUSY bit shows that keyboard/reader is busy assembling information in the buffer register.

2. The READY bit shows that a character is available in the buffer register.

3. The INT ENB (interrupt enable) bit allows an error or READY signal to cause an interrupt.

4. The RDR ENB (reader enable) bit lets the reader read one character.

The Teletype printer/punch also has an 8-bit buffer register, which we call TYPPB. It holds a character that is transferred in parallel to it from the computer at the normal Teletype rate of 100 milliseconds. The printer/punch status register, called TYPPS, has three important bits, as shown in Fig. 10.5.

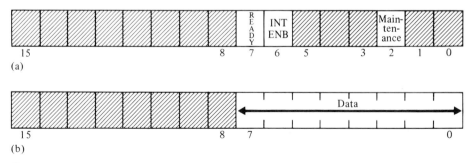

Fig. 10.5
Teletype printer/punch. (a) Status register. (b) Data register.

1. The READY bit shows that the punch is ready to receive a character.
2. The INT ENB (interrupt enable) bit lets a READY signal cause an interrupt.
3. The MAINTENANCE bit is a maintenance function in which the output of the punch is connected to the reader buffer register.

The PDP-11 address assignments for these four registers are

TYKRS   177560   TKS
TYKRB   177562   TKB
TYPPS   177564   TPS
TYPPB   177566   TPB

We usually assign these registers with the direct assignment statement (e.g., TYKRS = 177560) so that we can refer to them symbolically. For microcomputers we can assign these registers as we like.

Assuming that these assignments have been made, we can write a few PDP-11 instructions to read a character from the keyboard and send it to a register. We do not have to enable the keyboard to read a character because the person at the keyboard presses keys on the keyboard to send characters.

```
WAIT1:TSTB TYKRS      ;TEST READY BIT OF KEYBOARD
      BPL WAIT1       ;WAIT IF READY IS 0
      MOVB TYKRB, %1  ;MOVE BYTE TO R1 WHEN READY
```

Similarly, we can write instructions to output a character from a CPU register to the teletype printer/punch.

```
WAIT2:TSTB TYPPS      ;TEST READY BIT OF PRINTER
      BPL WAIT2       ;WAIT IF NOT READY
      MOVB %2, TYPPB  ;MOVE BYTE TO PRINTER WHEN READY
```

We can make the Teletype act like a typewriter by writing a program that will read the keyboard and **echo** it (print the incoming character) to the printer as shown in Table 10.1. Note that we use all four registers of the Teletype—the buffer register and control/status register of both the input and output units. The enabling of the keyboard/reader is unnecessary for the keyboard but is needed if input may come from the reader.

This program can cause characters to be lost if characters are entered via the keyboard more rapidly than the printer can respond. If the program is in WAIT2, waiting a chance to echo a character, while a new character enters the keyboard buffer, one character will be lost. Because the keyboard and printer operate at comparable speeds this failure will not often occur. However, it illustrates a general problem of input/output programming. If the input device can operate more rapidly than the computer can process incoming information, the input data should be stored until the computer can process them. Later, when the input rate has slowed or stopped, the computer can process the stored data without losing information, assuming the computer has enough space to store the data. The critical timing in this case is the interval between successive

Table 10.1
PDP-11 program to echo on printer a character typed on keyboard

Label	Op code	Operand	Comment
TYKRS	=	177560	; ASSIGN KEYBOARD/READER STATUS REGISTER
TYKRB	=	177562	; ASSIGN KEYBOARD/READER BUFFER
TYPPS	=	177564	; ASSIGN PRINTER/PUNCH STATUS REGISTER
TYPPB	=	177566	; ASSIGN PRINTER/PUNCH BUFFER
	.=	2000	; BEGIN AT 2000
ECHO:	INC	TYKRS	; ENABLE KEYBOARD/READER
WAIT1:	TSTB	TYKRS	; TEST READY BIT OF KEYBOARD/READER
	BPL	WAIT1	; CONTINUE TESTING UNTIL READY BIT = 1
WAIT2:	TSTB	TYPPB	; TEST READY BIT OF PRINTER/PUNCH
	BPL	WAIT2	; CONTINUE TESTING UNTIL READY BIT = 1
	MOVB	TYKRS, TYPPB	; MOVE CHARACTER FROM KEYBOARD/
			; READER TO PRINTER/PUNCH
	BR	ECHO	; RETURN TO ECHO FOR NEXT CHARACTER
	.END	ECHO	

executions of the MOVB TYKRS, TYPPB instructions. For any given computer, this time can be calculated. Then, instead of using a simple wait loop, we can write a delay routine for the calculated interval. More difficult timing problems occur when the interval between critical instructions is unpredictable. Later in the chapter we consider methods of handling timing problems.

10.3.2 *Paper-Tape Reader/Punch*

The Teletype paper-tape reader and punch work slowly—at 10 characters per second. We often prefer to purchase higher-speed devices that can read tape at 300 to 2000 characters per second and punch tape at 60 characters per second. Standard paper tape uses the presence or absence of 8 holes to represent a character. The tape has 8 channels and a line of sprocket holes that run along the length of the tape, as shown in Fig. 10.6. Each character takes one column that runs across the width of the tape.

The registers of the paper-tape reader have almost the same format as the corresponding registers of the Teletype keyboard/reader. The buffer registers are identical, with the 8 low-order bits for data. The status register of the paper-tape reader differs from that of the Teletype keyboard/reader by having an extra bit. It uses bit 15 for an error signal that is set when the reader runs out of tape. The registers of the paper-tape punch are similar. Its buffer register is just like the buffer register of the Teletype printer/punch. Its status register has bit 15 as an error bit to show that the punch is out of tape.

To read a character from the paper-tape reader, we should first test the reader READY bit, unless we are sure the reader is not busy. When the reader is ready, we must enable it with the PDP-11 instruction

INC READER

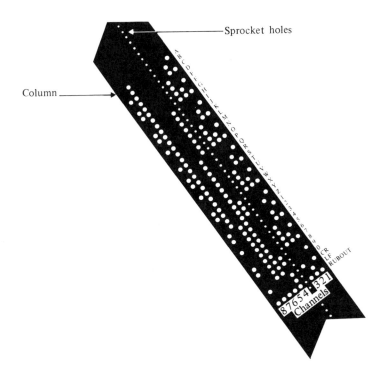

Sprocket holes

Column

Fig. 10.6
Paper tape.

This instruction sets bit 0, the reader enable bit, to 1. Setting the enable bit causes the BUSY bit to be set to 1, the READY bit to be reset to 0, and a character to be read from the paper tape into the buffer register. When the character has been read, the BUSY bit is reset to 0, the READY bit is set to 1, and the reader enable bit is reset to 0.

The complete series of instructions needed to read a character and transfer it to register 0 of the PDP-11 follow. READSR is the paper-tape reader status register (assigned 177554); READBR is the corresponding buffer register (177556).

```
WAIT1: TSTB READSR      ;TEST READY BIT
       BPL WAIT1        ;TEST AGAIN IF NOT READY
       INC READSR       ;ENABLE READER
WAIT2: TSTB READSR      ;TEST TO SEE IF READ COMPLETE
       BPL WAIT2        ;TRY AGAIN IF NOT DONE
       MOVB READBR,%0   ;MOVE CHARACTER TO RO
```

To improve efficiency we should try to overlap the relatively slow reading operation with faster CPU computations. (A high-speed reader can read 300 characters per second, but this is more than 33 milliseconds per character, and during that time the CPU can process more than 10,000 instructions.) Suppose we have a program that performs calculations on characters read from a paper tape, and that the paper-tape reading is done in a subroutine. The subroutine should enable the reader just before the return-from-subroutine instruction. Then the time-consuming step of enabling the reader to read the next character will take place while the main program performs calculations on the character just read. We say the two operations occur in parallel. Using parallel operations whenever possible makes programs run faster. The subroutine can begin by testing the ready bit to continue reading the next character. You may have noticed that the reader will not be enabled until after the first pass through the subroutine. Hence we must enable the reader early in the main program so that it will be ready to read the first character.

A more complicated program using the paper-tape reader is given in Table 10.2. This program is loaded by hand, using the bit switches and deposit switch as discussed in Chapter 4, into the top 14 words of the first 4K of memory. It can load a short paper tape written in a special format into successive bytes beginning at the lower limit, LOW = 17400, and extending no farther than 17744. (Why?) This program is an example of a simple loader; Chapter 6

Table 10.2
PDP-11 program to read paper tape into memory

Octal location	Contents	Label	Op code	Operand	Comment
	017400	LOW	=	17400	; LOWER
					; LIMIT FOR DATA
	177440		.=	177440	; STARTING ADDRESS
017740	016700	START:	MOV	READER, %0	; PUT READER ADDRESS
					; IN R0
017742	000032				; INPUT DEVICE ADDRESS
					; IS 017776
017744	012701		MOV	#0,%1	; PUT DISPLACEMENT IN
					; R1
017746	000000				
017750	005210	READ:	INC	(%0)	; ENABLE PAPER TAPE
					; READER
017752	105710	WAIT:	TSTB	(%0)	; IS READER READY?
017754	100376		BPL	WAIT	; IF NO, TEST AGAIN
017756	116061		MOVB	2(%0), LOW(%1)	; STORE CHARACTER IN
					; BUFFER
017760	000002				
017762	017400				
017764	005201		INC	%1	; INCREMENT OFFSET
017766	022701		CMP	#10, %1	; CHECK FOR 8
					; CHARACTERS
017770	000010				
017772	001366		BNE	READ	; READ ANOTHER
					; CHARACTER
017774	104400		TRAP		; RETURN TO MONITOR
017776	177560	READER:	.WORD	177560	; ADDRESS OF READER
	000000		.END	START	

discusses loaders in more detail. You should trace through the program to be sure that you understand the paper-tape operations and the addressing modes used. To punch a character, we must first be sure that the device is ready for transfer. Then moving a character into the punch buffer register, PUNCHB = 177556, starts the punch. When the punch has finished punching a character, it sets the READY bit in its status register, PUNCHS = 177554, to 1. The instructions needed to punch a character are shown below.

```
WAIT: TSTB PUNCHS     ;IS PUNCH READY?
      BPL WAIT        ;IF NOT, TEST AGAIN
      MOVB %1, PUNCHB ;WHEN READY, MOVE CHARACTER
                      ;INTO PUNCH BUFFER REGISTER
```

To overlap punch operations with main program calculations, a punch subroutine should move the character to the punch just before return to the main program. The first steps of the punch subroutine should be the wait loop. The punch does not have an enable operation that can be done while the main program calculates.

10.4 *Interrupts*

The programs in the last section all had wait loops. As a result, the computer was forced to spend time waiting when it could have been doing other things. Because input/output devices operate much more slowly than the CPU, the computer could have executed several hundred or several thousand instructions during the time required for a single wait loop. Obviously, the computer can operate more efficiently if, instead of waiting, it can go about its business and let peripheral devices tell it when they are ready. An **interrupt system** permits an input/output device to interrupt the computer when the device is ready; it permits the computer to perform other useful activities until the device is ready. We say that the device **requests** an interrupt when it is ready for service. The computer responds to the interrupt request by going to an **interrupt service routine.**

An **interrupt** is a subroutine call executed by the computer hardware; that is, it does not require the programmer to write a subroutine call instruction. An interrupt can occur only after the complete execution of an instruction and before the fetch of the next instruction. As with a subroutine call, the return address and the status of the condition codes must be saved. For example, if an interrupt occurs just after the computer has executed a comparison instruction and before it fetches a conditional branch instruction, condition codes must be saved. Then, when the computer has finished servicing the interrupt, it can continue processing the main program and branch to the appropriate location as determined by the results of the comparison.

Small computers vary considerably in their handling of interrupts. The main differences concern their ability to identify a number of devices via hardware and their determination of the relative importance or priority of different interrupts. The simplest interrupt systems, called **polled interrupts,** treat all interrupts in the same way. They may jump to a fixed interrupt location, such as memory location 0, and begin an interrupt service routine to take care of the interrupt. Alternatively, the address of the interrupt service routine might be stored in a fixed location in ROM (the M6800 uses addresses F8 and F9 on page FF) or in a special CPU register (a scheme used in the RCA COSMAC). If such a simple computer needs to identify the interrupting device so that it can treat a Teletype differently from a paper-tape reader, the interrupt service routine must identify the device. Identification requires polling or testing each device until the interrupting device is found. It must also determine the priority of the device, especially if another interrupt occurs.

More powerful computers have hardware to identify the device; each peripheral device may be given its own device code. When an interrupt occurs, the device code may be sent to a device code register in the CPU. Then the CPU can branch to a special interrupt service routine for that device. A variation of this scheme has the interrupting device present the CPU with the address of its interrupt service routine. Such schemes, in which the interrupting device causes execution of the appropriate interrupt service routine, are called **vectored interrupts.** Depending on the computer, the interrupting device may be able to present one of a wide or a limited range of addresses. Devices connected to the Intel 8080, for example, must present one of eight addresses on page 0—00, 08, 10, 18, 20, 28, 30, or 38. The computer may also have several levels of priority built into the hardware. Then, if two interrupts occur at once, the hardware can decide which one to service first.

The PDP-11 has a versatile priority interrupt system. Each input/output device is assigned a priority level between 4 and 7. The highest priority level is 7. The Teletype, paper-tape reader, and punch all have priority 4—the lowest priority. These priorities are characteristics of each device and cannot be changed by the programmer. (The LSI-11, in contrast, has only the single priority level 4.) However, a device can be prevented from interrupting the computer by resetting the interrupt enable (INT ENB) bit in its device status register. Any pending interrupt by the device will be held until the interrupt enable bit is set to 1.

A program that is being executed has a priority level from 0 to 7 as determined by bits 7 to 5 of the processor status register. Any device that has its interrupt enable bit set and that has a priority higher than the priority of the program being executed can interrupt the CPU. Thus the Teletype can interrupt the CPU when its interrupt is enabled and when the current program has a priority lower than 4. When an interrupt occurs, the processor status word (PSW) and the contents of the program counter (PC) are pushed on the stack based on register 6. The effect is the same as the execution of the two instructions:

```
MOV PSW, -(%6) ;PUSH PROCESSOR STATUS WORD
MOV %7,  -(%6) ;PUSH PROGRAM COUNTER
```

As a result the condition codes and priority of the current program and its return address are saved while the interrupt is serviced. The CPU loads the program counter and processor status register from two consecutive locations whose address is determined by the interrupting device. These locations are called an **interrupt vector**. For the Teletype keyboard/reader and printer/punch these addresses are 60 and 64, respectively. Table 10.3 shows common device priorities and interrupt vectors for the PDP-11. The program counter then contains the address of the interrupt service routine for that device; the processor status register holds the processor status word for the routine. Usually the interrupt service routine has the same priority as the interrupting device; thus the Teletype interrupt service usually has priority 4. The reason for giving the service routine the same priority is to prevent a device from interrupting again before it has been completely serviced.

An interrupt service routine for any computer typically saves on the stack the contents of any registers it will use. Then it services the device. For example, it might move a character from the keyboard/reader buffer to a register or memory location. Finally it restores from the stack the contents of any registers it saved. It must return the stack pointer to the position it had just after the interrupt occurred. Control returns to the main program with a return-from-interrupt instruction. The return address is popped from the stack to the program counter. The main program can then continue execution in its original condition from the point where it was interrupted.

Computers vary in the power of their interrupts and their interrupt return instructions. As we have seen, the PDP-11 interrupt automatically saves the processor status word as well as the return address on the stack. Similarly, the PDP-11 return instruction (RTI) restores the processor status word and returns control to the point of interruption. The M6800 has an even more powerful interrupt system that automatically saves all CPU registers on interrupt and restores them with the return instruction RTI. Computers with less powerful interrupt systems, such as the 8080/8085, require us to write instructions to save and restore any registers disrupted by the interrupt service routine.

Table 10.3
PDP-11 device priorities and interrupt vectors

Device	Interrupt vector	Priority level
Teletype keyboard/reader	60	4
Teletype printer/punch	64	4
Paper-tape reader	70	4
Paper-tape punch	74	4
Line clock	100	6
Real-time clock	104	6
Line printer	200	4
Disk (256K)	204	4
Disk cartridge	220	5
Magnetic tape	224	5

Table 10.4
PDP-11 interrupt service routine for Teletype printer/punch

Label	Op code	Operand	Comment
TYPPB	=	177566	; TTY PUNCH BUFFER
	.=	64	; INTERRUPT VECTOR FOR TTY ; PUNCH
	.WORD	TYPPV	; START OF ROUTINE TYPPV
	.WORD	200	; PRIORITY IS 4
TYPPV:	MOV	(%0)+, TYPPB	; MOVE CHARACTER TO PUNCH
	RTI		; RETURN FROM INTERRUPT

8080 interrupt service routine for Teletype printer/punch

Label	Op code	Operand	Comment
TYPPB	EQU	2	; TTY PUNCH BUFFER
TYPPV:	PUSH	PSW	; SAVE A
	MOV	A,M	; MOVE CHARACTER TO A
	OUT	TYPPB	; MOVE CHARACTER TO PUNCH
	INX	H	; INCREMENT POINTER
	POP	PSW	; RESTORE A
	RET		; RETURN FROM INTERRUPT

Simple interrupt service routines for the Teletype printer/punch are shown in Table 10.4. The routine moves the character to which a pointer register (0 for the PDP-11; HL for the 8080) points to the Teletype printer/punch and then increments the register. Even though we use the pointer register in this routine, we do not save and restore its contents. We assume that the main program uses it as a pointer to a stack of characters that it wishes to have punched. The service routine then uses this register as intended by the main program. We need to save and restore registers only when the service routine uses those registers for a different purpose than does the main program. For example, in the 8080 routine we save A (part of the PSW). In other words, we must not disrupt the registers used by the main program. Coordination between the main program and the interrupt service routines requires careful attention.

An interrupt service routine may be written either as a subroutine or as a coroutine. If the service routine should always be entered at the beginning when an interrupt occurs, it should be a subroutine. If at the next interrupt it should resume operations where it stopped after the last, it should be a coroutine. The coroutine is the more general form.

We can illustrate the problem of saving and restoring registers in an interrupt service routine that can be entered at the point of its previous exit. Assume that we have an interrupt service coroutine that we have used once, exiting at point INTROU. Because both the main program and the interrupt service routine are complex, we wish to save the contents of registers 1 through 5 of each routine before going to the other. We call this **saving the state** of the program. We have subroutine SAVEM to save the state of the main program before entering the interrupt service routine. We have RSTORM to restore the state of the main program after returning from the interrupt. Similarly, we have subroutines SAVEI and RSTORI to save and restore respectively the state of the interrupt service routine. These subroutines are simple because they just involve saving register contents on a stack or in special memory locations. Hence we will not show them here. Instead, we will concern ourselves with their use in the interrupt service routine.

Table 10.5 shows a program segment in which an interrupt service routine resumes from the point at which it had been left. The state of the main program is saved, and the state of the interrupted program is restored. After some other instructions, the next return address for the interrupt routine is placed in the interrupt vector. Then the state of the interrupt routine is saved and the state of the main program is restored. Finally a character is sent to the Teletype printer/punch. This order may appear puzzling. Why don't we first move the character to the punch and then restore the state of the main program? That is, why not write

```
MOVB CHAR,TYPPB
JSR  %0, RSTORM
RTI
```

The answer is that if we wrote the instructions in this order, the program might not execute correctly. The intent of the instructions is to have the punch punching a character while the RSTORM subroutine is executing. If the punch is fast enough to finish punching before the end of the RSTORM subroutine and hence before the RTI instruction, the punch can then issue another interrupt— an interrupt of the RSTORM subroutine. As a result the interrupt routine will

Table 10.5
PDP-11 program segment showing interrupt service routine for Teletype printer/punch

Label	Op code	Operand	Comment
INTROU:	JSR	%0, SAVEM	; SAVE STATE OF MAIN PROGRAM
	JSR	%0, RSTORI	; RESTORE STATE OF INTERRUPT ROUTINE
		-------------------------------	; OTHER INTERRUPT ROUTINE INSTRUCTIONS
	MOV	NEXTCO, TYPPV	; SAVE NEXT INTERRUPT ROUTINE
			; RETURN ADDRESS IN INTERRUPT VECTOR
	JSR	%0, SAVEI	; SAVE STATE OF INTERRUPT ROUTINE
	JSR	%0, RSTORM	; RESTORE STATE OF MAIN PROGRAM
	MOVB	CHAR, TYPPB	; MOVE CHARACTER TO TTY PUNCH
	RTI		; RETURN TO MAIN PROGRAM

be reentered. The state of the RSTORM subroutine will be saved by the SAVEM subroutine. If the SAVEM subroutine uses the same locations as the RSTORM subroutine, it will overwrite these locations. The original contents of these locations, the state of the main program, will be lost. Although a Teletype printer/punch operates so slowly that this situation is unlikely, the possibility presents a real timing problem for faster devices.

We can learn two things from this example. First, we cannot let an input/ output device interrupt its own interrupt service routine. We can easily prevent this occurrence in a multiple priority interrupt system by giving the interrupt service routine a priority at least as high as that of the device. Second, interrupt service routines require sensitive attention to timing. It is difficult to write interrupt routines correctly and to analyze them because their timing can be tricky. A poorly written interrupt service routine can operate correctly several times and then fail because of a slight change in device timing.

Further complications can occur when two or more devices can interrupt a program. If two devices of different priorities attempt to interrupt at the same time, the device with the higher priority is serviced first. Then the lower-priority device is serviced. In rare cases, two devices of the same priority may try to interrupt simultaneously (that is, during execution of one instruction). The conflict will usually be resolved in favor of the devices physically closest to the CPU. Devices are commonly wired to the bus in a chain so that the closest device in the chain to the CPU has interrupt privileges over devices further away. This scheme, called a **daisy chain**, is a way of resolving conflicts by means of hardware.

A higher-priority device can interrupt the servicing of a lower-priority device. Suppose that the interrupt service routine for the Teletype (priority 4) is being executed when an interrupt from a clock (priority 6) occurs. The clock interrupt causes the following actions.

1. The state of the Teletype service routine is saved on the stack.
2. A return address in the Teletype service routine is saved on the stack.
3. The clock is serviced.
4. The Teletype service routine is reentered at its return address.
5. The state of the Teletype service routine is restored.

The clock interrupt causes a delay between execution of two instructions in the lower-priority Teletype service routine. The only possible timing problem arises if the delay occurs between the MOVB and RTI instructions. Assume that the clock interrupts the Teletype service routine of Table 10.6 between the MOVB and RTI instructions. Assume also that the Teletype service routine has priority 4, the same as the Teletype priority. If the Teletype completes the MOVB character transfer before the clock service routine has finished executing, the Teletype will try to interrupt. Because the Teletype has lower priority than the clock, the interrupt will not be processed. When the clock service

Table 10.6
PDP-11 subroutine for reading line of characters ending with carriage return

Label	Op code	Operand	Comment
TYKRS	=	177560	; TTY KEYBOARD/READER STATUS REGISTER
TYKRB	=	177562	; TTY KEYBOARD/READER BUFFER REGISTER
	.=	1200	; ORIGIN IS 1200 OCTAL
LINE:	MOV	#1277, POINT	; INITIALIZE POINTER AT 1277
	MOV	#1, TYKRS	; ENABLE READER FOR FIRST CHARACTER
CHAR:	INC	POINT	; INCREMENT POINTER
WAIT:	TSTB	TYKRS	
	BPL	WAIT	
	MOVB	TYKRB, @ POINT	; ENABLE READER FOR NEXT CHARACTER
	CMPB	@ POINT, #215	; COMPARE CHARACTER WITH CARRIAGE
			; RETURN CODE
	BNE	CHAR	; IF NOT, READ NEXT CHARACTER
	RTS		
POINT	.WORD	0	; POINTER

routine has finished executing, control will return to the RTI instruction of the Teletype service routine. The pending Teletype interrupt will still not be recognized because it has just the same priority as its service routine. Hence control will return to the main program, which is of lower priority. Then, finally, the pending Teletype interrupt will be allowed to interrupt the main program and be serviced.

Because the PDP-11 allocates four priority levels to input/output devices, up to four interrupts can be nested. Nesting interrupts is much like nesting subroutines. The hardware interrupt action saves the program status word and return address in the stack; the RTI instruction restores them. Figure 10.7 shows the stack contents for three levels of interrupt. The main program has been interrupted by the Teletype of priority 4. The Teletype interrupt service routine has been interrupted by a disk of priority 5. The disk interrupt service routine in turn has been interrupted by a clock of priority 6. The figure assumes that the interrupt service routines save only the PSW and return address—not register contents.

A lower-priority device cannot interrupt the service routine of a higher-priority device. Thus if a Teletype requests an interrupt while the interrupt service routine for a clock is being processed, the Teletype must wait until the clock routine has finished. After control returns to the main program via an RTI, the Teletype may interrupt the main program. The result is the same as if the Teletype interrupt request occurred just after execution of the clock service routine. The higher-priority interrupt service routine is not interrupted, and no timing errors can occur.

We have seen that an interrupt service routine usually has the same priority as its device. What would happen if it had a different priority? If the routine had

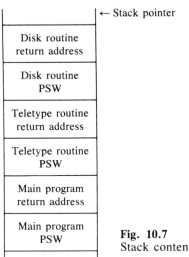

← Stack pointer

Disk routine return address
Disk routine PSW
Teletype routine return address
Teletype routine PSW
Main program return address
Main program PSW

Fig. 10.7
Stack contents for three levels of interrupt.

a higher priority than the device—for example, if a Teletype routine had priority 5—the main result would be that the service routine could not be interrupted by devices with the same priority as the routine. If the routine had a lower priority, such as a Teletype service routine with a priority of 3, timing problems could occur. You might think that a fast device could repeatedly interrupt its own lower-priority service routine; hence the device would never be completely serviced. However, the PDP-11 avoids this problem. It does not allow an interrupting device to request a second interrupt until the device buffer register is changed.

Nonetheless, the interrupt service routine can fail if the device is extremely fast. Suppose the device acts so rapidly that it requests another interrupt between executions of the MOVB instruction and the RTI instruction. If it does this many times, so many copies of the program status word and the return address will be pushed on the stack that the stack will overflow. To avoid this problem we insist that the interrupt service routine have a priority that is the same as or higher than the interrupting device.

Sometimes we prefer to disable the interrupt system while we are servicing an interrupt. We can effectively do this for the PDP-11 by setting the priority of the interrupt service routine to 7. No other device can then interrupt execution of the service routine. After the RTI instruction the interrupt system will be automatically enabled, at least for devices of higher priority than the main program. This method has the disadvantage of ignoring interrupt requests from high-priority devices while servicing a lower-priority device.

Some computers—including most microcomputers—have special instructions for disabling and enabling interrupt systems. Thus the interrupt system can be disabled while the registers of the interrupted program are saved and enabled during the rest of the interrupt routine. We distinguish between a computer's interrupt enabling system and a device's interrupt enable bit mentioned earlier. Both must be enabled for an interrupt to occur. The PDP-11 combines these two concepts by allowing the programmer to set and clear the interrupt enable bit in the device control and status register. We can clear the interrupt enable bit (INT ENB = bit 6) of the Teletype keyboard/reader with the bit clear instruction

```
BIC #100, TYKRS
```

Similarly, we can set the same INT ENB bit with the bit set instruction

```
BIS #100, TYKRS
```

Other computers have **interrupt mask registers.** The bits of this register are ANDed with the interrupt request bits to mask out or disable undesired interrupts. Only interrupt requests with bits that match the mask bits are serviced. A computer may also have a programmable priority register that prevents any interrupts of priority less than n, where the user can set n.

10.5 *Direct Memory Access*

Interrupt systems provide faster input/output because the CPU does not waste time in wait loops waiting for input/output devices to be ready. Even faster input/output can be achieved by removing the CPU from the data path between the input/output device and memory. By passing data directly between the device and memory, the load on the CPU is decreased. To do this we need a special input/output system called a **direct memory access (DMA)** interface. Transfers of large blocks of data often use DMA.

A DMA interface for a computer is normally an addition to the regular interface of the input/output device it serves. It has four registers:

- An address register
- A data register
- A control/status register
- A word-count register

In a DMA output transfer, the CPU first loads the address register with the starting address in memory of the block of data to be moved. It then loads the word-count register with the number of words to be moved and sends a control signal to start the transfer. The DMA device then requests access to memory. During the next memory cycle, one word from memory is transferred directly to the device data register while the CPU suspends activity for that memory cycle. When the device is ready for another word, it again requests a memory cycle and obtains it at the expense of the CPU's operations. This operation is called **cycle stealing.** The DMA device "steals" cycles from the CPU for input/output transfers. Cycle stealing slows down other operations of the CPU but allows both input/output operations and CPU processing to proceed. Transfer continues until the word-count register shows that all words have been transferred. Input DMA transfers occur in a comparable manner.

10.6 *Buffers and Queues*

10.6.1 *Buffers*

Except for DMA our examples of input/output so far have dealt with transfers of a single character. This is unrealistic. Usually we wish to transfer strings of characters such as 8-digit numbers, names, or lines of assembly code. That is, we wish to transfer blocks of data that are logically connected. In this section, following the presentation of Stone and Sieworek, we will see how to process strings of characters. Suppose we wish to input an assembly language instruction coded in ASCII. A typical input line might be

```
LOOP: CLR X
```

We want to read this into memory, have the computer process it, and then read another instruction. We will structure our input program so that the input assembly instruction will be read into a special area of memory that we will call a **buffer.** Until the end of the instruction has been signalled by a carriage return (CR) symbol, the line will be stored in consecutive locations in memory. We will allocate a large enough area in memory that we will be able to store any line written on the Teletype keyboard. Once the CR symbol signals the end of the line, the CPU will begin processing the instruction. A subroutine using a wait loop to read a line of characters and store them in a buffer is shown in Table 10.6; its flowchart is shown in Fig. 10.8.

In the preceding example we assumed that the buffer was long enough to store a line of characters. Sometimes we prefer to assign a buffer of a fixed length. Suppose we wish to read characters into a buffer that can hold at most 8 characters. A buffer like this is shown in Fig. 10.9. It occupies 8 consecutive locations in memory beginning at location labeled BUFFER. At any time there may be from 0 to 8 characters in the buffer. MBLONG is the maximum buffer length, in this case 8 characters. A pointer (BUFPTR) points to the last character in the buffer; the number of characters currently in the buffer is called OBLONG for current buffer length. OBLONG is always less than or equal to MBLONG.

Figure 10.10 shows a flowchart of an interrupt routine to read characters into this buffer. When an interrupt by the reader occurs, a character is read into the buffer, the pointer is incremented, and the status of the buffer is determined. If the buffer is not full, the reader is enabled so that another character can be read into it. If it is full, the reader is not enabled; some other part of the program will have to move at least one character out of the buffer before the reader is enabled so that another character can be read. The program segment for this interrupt is shown in Table 10.7.

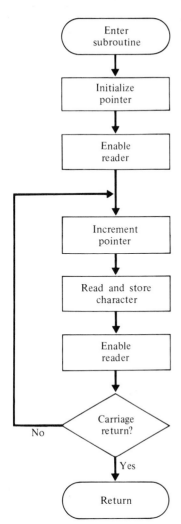

Fig. 10.8
Flowchart for subroutine to read and store line of characters ending with carriage return.

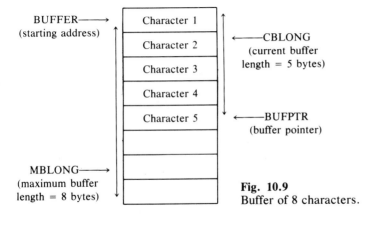

Fig. 10.9
Buffer of 8 characters.

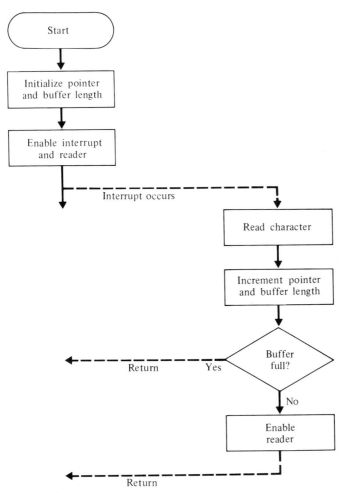

Fig. 10.10
Flowchart of interrupt routine to read characters into a
fixed-length buffer.

Buffers allow more efficient input/output processing. By allowing the computer to read several characters into a buffer before processing them, the
overlap between input operations and CPU processing is improved. The CPU
can perform other operations during most of the time that the characters are
being read into the buffer. Then, while it is processing characters from the
buffer, other characters can be read. Buffers can also be hardware devices, as
we will see in Chapter 13.

10.6.2 *Queues*

The buffers of the last section are best suited to applications in which one line
of code is to be read and processed as a unit. In that case we wish to read the

Table 10.7
PDP-11 program segment using 8-byte buffer to store characters read from Teletype
keyboard/reader on interrupt

Label	Op code	Operand	Comment
TYKRS	=	177560	; TTY KEYBOARD/READER STATOS REG.
TYKRB	=	177562	; TTY KEYBOARD/READER BUFFER REG.
MBLONG	=	10	; MAXIMUM BUFFER LENGTH IS 8
			; CHARACTERS
	.=	1000	
	.WORD	TYKRV	; START OF TTY KR SERVICE ROUTINE
	.WORD	200	; PRIORITY IS 4
	MOV	#BUFFER, BUFPTR	; INITIALIZE BUFFER POINTER TO
			; BUFFER STARTING ADDRESS
	MOV	#101, TYKRS	; ENABLE INTERRUPT AND READER
			; CODE OF MAIN PROGRAM
TYKRV	MOVB	TYKRB, @ BUFPTR	; READ CHARACTER INTO BUFFER
	INCB	BUFPTR	; INCREMENT BUFFER POINTER
	INC	CBLONG	; INCREMENT CURRENT BUFFER LENGTH
	CMP	MBLONG, CBLONG	; COMPARE MAX, AND CURRENT LENGTH
	BEQ	GOBACK	; IF EQUAL, BUFFER IS FULL
	INC	TYKRS	; BUFFER NOT FULL, ENABLE READER
GOBACK:	RTI		
BUFFER:	.BLKB	MBLONG	; BUFFER IS BLOCK OF MBLONG BYTES
BUFPTR:	.WORD	0	; BUFFER POINTER
CBLONG:	.WORD	0	; CURRENT BUFFER LENGTH
	.END		

line into a buffer starting at the beginning of the buffer. When we process the code, we again will start at the beginning of the buffer. We will process the line of code and empty the buffer completely before reading more characters.

Sometimes, however, we wish to process characters one at a time. We want a buffer only to gain the speed advantages that parallel operations with a buffer offer. We will read characters into a buffer one at a time starting at the beginning. As we read characters into the buffer, we may also begin processing them. That is, we may read four characters, process two, read three more, process five, and so on. We may not empty the buffer before reading more characters. Hence we must keep track of the locations of both the last character read into the buffer and the last character processed by the CPU. It is helpful to imagine that we are using a circular buffer or queue, as shown in Fig. 10.11. Of course, the memory locations are not actually arranged in a circle, but we can treat them as if they were.

We usually think of a queue as a line of people writing for service, perhaps at a ticket window. The person at the **head** of the queue is the next one to be served by the ticket seller. A person who wishes to enter the queue must enter at its **tail.** The queue length varies as new people enter the queue at the tail

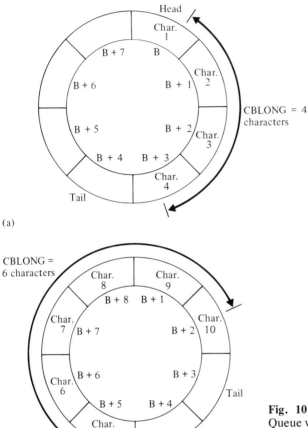

(a)

(b)

Fig. 10.11 Queue of length 8. (a) Queue with four characters read into first four locations. (b) Queue after ten characters have been read in and removed.

while others leave the queue at the head. A queue is also known as a first-in, first-out (FIFO) structure.

A queue in memory is much the same except that the locations of the head and tail move. We keep track of them with separate pointers. The queue shown in Fig. 10.10 can hold at most 8 characters. We will assume this is an input queue. In an **enqueue operation,** characters are read into the tail of the queue by an input program. In a **dequeue operation,** they are removed from the head of the queue for processing by the main program.

The queue begins at memory location B and occupies 8 consecutive locations, numbered B, B + 1, and so forth. Initially, the head of the queue is at B. Figure 10.10(a) shows the queue after four characters have been read into it. The head of the queue is at location B; it points to the first character to be serviced by the main program. The tail of the queue is at location $B + 4$, next to the last character read by the input program. It points to the next empty location. The queue length, called CBLONG as before, is four characters.

Figure 10.10(b) shows the queue some time later. The head of the queue has moved to location $B + 5$; it points to the next character to be serviced by the main program. The tail has wrapped around past the original starting location of the queue to $B + 3$. The queue length, CBLONG, is now six characters. CBLONG must never exceed the maximum queue length, MBLONG, which is again 8 characters in this example. If CBLONG exceeded MBLONG, the tail would pass by the head, and some characters at the head would be overwritten.

We wish to program the operations of reading a character into the queue and getting it from the queue. We will use an interrupt service routine READ to read a character into the queue when the reader is ready. We will use a subroutine GET to take a character from the queue when the main program needs it. Naturally, we must avoid reading a character into the queue when it is already full. To do this we will use a counter, CBLONG. When CBLONG equals MBLONG, we will set a flag FULL to 1. When a character is taken from the queue by GET, we can reset the flag. We will use pointers HEAD and TAIL to keep track of queue locations. HEAD and TAIL can be incremented and decremented in the usual way except at the lowest and highest memory locations. A pointer at the highest memory location, $B + MBLONG - 1$, is incremented by being set to B.

Flowcharts of the interrupt routine READ and the subroutine GET are shown in Figs. 10.12 and 10.13. Their corresponding coded routines are shown in Tables 10.8 and 10.9. The two routines share variables in common that must be initialized in common. HEAD and TAIL must be initialized as B, CBLONG and FULL must be initialized as 0. The other common parameters—B and MBLONG—are set to the lowest address and the length of the queue, respectively.

In this example the interrupt routine READ and the subroutine GET deal with the same data. GET may decrement a value and then be interrupted by READ, which increments the same value. A better programming practice is to combine into one program all routines that update the same variables. This prevents mistakes that can occur when two routines update the same variables in an unanticipated way.

As an example, consider a timing problem that can occur if these two routines were written for another computer. Most small computers can increment or decrement the contents of a memory location. Some computers cannot. They must instead transfer the contents of the memory location to a register, increment or decrement the contents of the register, and then transfer the updated value back to memory. Thus the segment of READ which for the PDP-11 reads simply

```
INC CBLONG
```

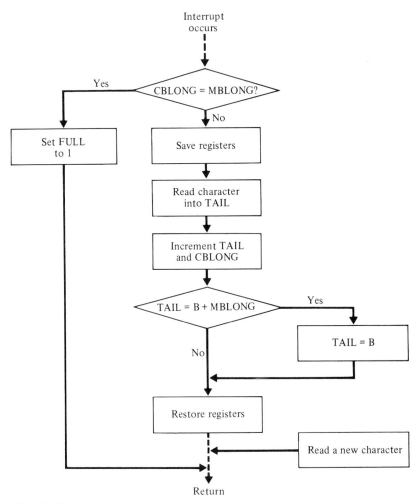

Fig. 10.12
Flowchart of interrupt service routine READ for reading character into queue.

requires three operations for some other computers. For the Fairchild F8 it might read

```
LM    CBLONG  ; LOAD CBLONG INTO ACCUMULATOR
INC           ; INCREMENT ACCUMULATOR
ST    CBLONG  ; STORE NEW VALUE IN MEMORY
```

Suppose that CBLONG has a value of 4 as the GET routine begins. Suppose that READ interrupts between the instruction loading CBLONG into the accumulator and the instruction decrementing it. At that time the copy of CBLONG stored in memory has the value 4. The READ routine increments

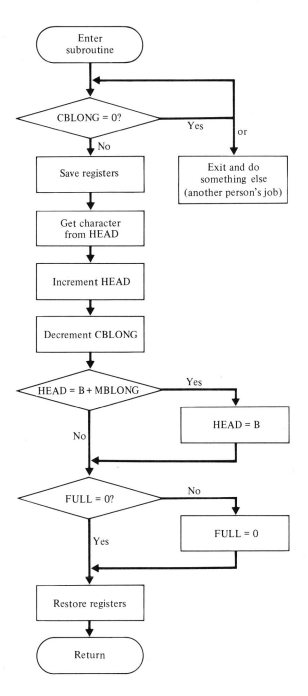

Fig. 10.13
Flowchart of subroutine GET to get character from queue.

Table 10.8
Interrupt routine READ to read character into queue

Label	Op code	Operand	Comment
	.=	60	; INTERRUPT VECTOR FOR TTY READER
	.WORD	READ	; TTY READER SERVICE ROUTINE
	.WORD	200	; PRIORITY IS 4
	.=	1000	
READ:	CMP	MBLONG, CBLONG	; SEE IF QUEUE HAS SPACE
	BNE	OKAY	; IF QUEUE HAS SPACE, PROCEED
	INCB	FULL	; IF NOT SET FULL FLAG
	BR	GO BACK	
OKAY:	MOV	%0, -(%6)	; SAVE R0 ON STACK
	MOV	TAIL, %0	; MOVE TAIL TO R0
	MOV	TYKRB, (%0)+	; READ CHARACTER INTO QUEUE
			; AND INCREMENT POINTER
	INCB	TYKRS	; ENABLE READER
	INC	CBLONG	; INCREMENT QUEUE LENGTH
	CMP	%0, #B+MBLONG	; CHECK FOR HIGHEST LOCATION
	BNE	NEXT	; IF NOT REACHED, PROCEED
	MOV	B, %0	; IF REACHED, RESTART AT LOWEST
			; LOCATION
NEXT:	MOV	%0, TAIL	; RESTORE TAIL
	MOV	(%6)+, %0	; RESTORE R0
GO BACK:	RTI		; RETURN FROM INTERRUPT

Table 10.9
Subroutine GET to get character from queue

Label	Op code	Operand	Comment
	.=	3000	
	.WORD	GET	; START OF GET CHARACTER ROUTINE
	.WORD	0	; PRIORITY 0 TO ALLOW
			; INTERRUPTIONS
GET:	TST	CBLONG	; TEST QUEUE LENGTH
	BEQ	GET	; IF 0, TEST AGAIN
	MOV	%0, -(%6)	; SAVE R0 ON STACK
	MOV	HEAD, %0	; MOVE HEAD TO R0
	MOVB	(%0)+, %1	; MOVE CHARACTER TO R1 AND
			; INCREMENT POINTER
	DEC	CBLONG	; DECREMENT QUEUE LENGTH
	CMP	%0, #B+MBLONG	; CHECK FOR HIGHEST LOCATION
	BNE	DOWN	; IF NOT REACHED, PROCEED
	MOV	#B, %0	; IF REACHED, RESTART AT LOWEST
			; LOCATION
DOWN:	MOV	%0, HEAD	; RESTORE HEAD
	TSTB	FULL	; TEST FULL FLAG
	BEQ	LAST	; IF FULL IS 0, CONTINUE
	CLRB	FULL	; OTHERWISE CLEAR FLAG
LAST:	MOV	(%6)+, %0	; RESTORE R0
	RTS		; RETURN FROM SUBROUTINE

CBLONG to 5 and then returns control to GET. The DEC REG instruction decrements its contents, the old copy of CBLONG, from 4 to 3; it does not decrement the current value of CBLONG of 5 to 4. Thus this sequence of operations results in a value of CBLONG that is smaller by 1 than the correct value.

One solution to this problem is to disable the interrupt system before any critical operations. We could prevent interrupts from occurring during execution of the three instructions needed to decrement CBLONG. We must, however, be careful not to disable the interrupt system for too long. Some devices must be serviced within a short period of time or their information is lost. If we execute many instructions with interrupts disabled, we may have a backlog of several devices waiting for service. Yet the purpose of the interrupt system is to allow peripheral devices to be serviced without waiting and without requiring the CPU to poll them. Therefore, we lose the main advantage of interrupts if we disable them too often.

Another solution to the problem is to let one of the routines be in charge of updating the variables. Suppose we choose to let the READ routine keep the correct copies of the variables. Then when the GET subroutine is called, it must ask READ to supply the correct values. This procedure involves a **supervisor call,** a transfer of control from the user's program to the supervisor program by an interrupt. The user, before executing his program, must tell the supervisor where his queue or queues are to be located. The supervisor then takes charge of filling the queues by an interrupt-driven program, such as READ. It provides any queue addresses, such as TAIL, to the user's program when the user executes a supervisor call.

10.6.3 *Input and Output Queues*

The running example of the last section dealt with an input queue to store characters read from a reader until they were needed by the main program. We may need a similar queue at the output to store characters supplied by the main program in an output queue until a slow output device, such as a punch, can output them. Figure 10.14 shows a main program with both an input and an output queue. An input routine transfers characters from the reader or other input device to the tail of the input queue; the main program operates on characters beginning at the head of the input queue. The main program sends characters to the tail of the output queue. An output routine transfers characters from the head of the output queue to the output device.

Input and output queues have two purposes. They allow us to perform main program calculations and input/output operations at the same time. They also smooth out variations in speed between input and output devices. The slowest device or procedure dominates the overall speed. If the input device is quite slow, as shown in Fig. 10.15(a), the main program will often have to stop calculations until it receives another character. In this case the input queue is empty most of the time. As soon as the input routine puts a character into the input queue, the main program removes it.

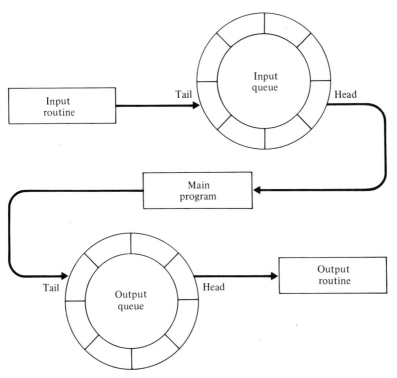

Fig. 10.14
Main program with input and output routines and queues.

Figure 10.15(b) shows the activity when an output device is very slow. Much of the time both the CPU and input device are idle while the output device is processing a character. The output queue is nearly always full. As soon as a character is removed, the CPU performs more calculations until it can send another character to the output queue. The input queue is also full most of the time with characters to be processed by the main program.

Sometimes both input and output devices can be very slow relative to the speed of the main program. Figure 10.15(c) shows activity when speed is limited by both the input and output devices. The input queue is usually empty and the output queue is usually full in this case; see Fig. 10.15.

In these three cases the length of the queue does not matter so long as it is at least 2. (Why?) In the more desirable case, shown in Fig. 10.15(d) queue length is important. In that case the speed of processing is not limited by the input or output devices. Most of the time the input devices, output devices, and CPU are all working. The speed of calculations in the CPU limits the overall **throughput** (rate or amount of information processed). If the speeds of the input and output devices can vary, the queue length should be long enough to smooth

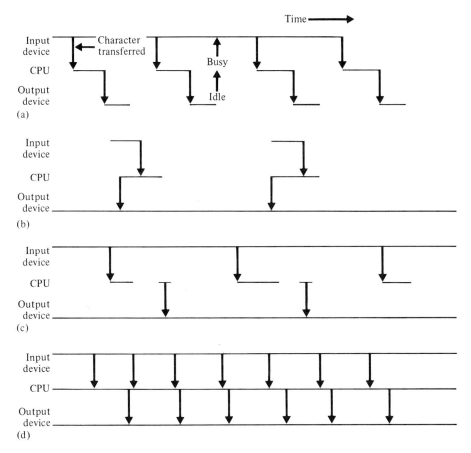

Fig. 10.15
Activity of CPU and peripheral devices.

out these variations. Then the CPU will not need to wait for either device. Increasing queue lengths beyond that point will have no effect.

Flowcharts of input and output routines and the main program are shown in Fig. 10.16. The input routine operates like those we saw earlier. It inputs a character (or other data) from the input device to the tail of the input queue; then it begins the next input operation so that input and other procedures can proceed at the same time. Similarly, the output routine sends a character from the head of the output queue to the output device; then it gets the device ready for the next output operation.

The main program is shown as an endless loop. It takes a character from the head of the input queue, performs calculations, and sends the result to the tail of the output queue. In practice, of course, the processes end when there is no more input data. We will not be concerned here with the end, nor will we be

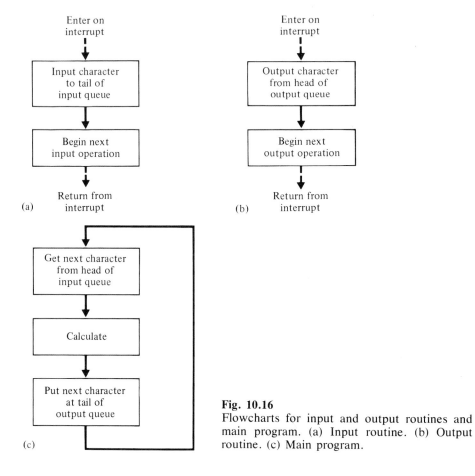

Fig. 10.16
Flowcharts for input and output routines and main program. (a) Input routine. (b) Output routine. (c) Main program.

concerned with the initializations needed at the beginning. Instead, we will concentrate on the interaction of these three processes.

The processes will proceed smoothly so long as the queues do not become either full or empty. Because we cannot guarantee the operations of the devices or of the main program, the queues may empty or fill during program operation. We must anticipate and provide for these cases if our program is to work correctly.

In an earlier input/output example we used a flag FULL that was set to 1 when the input queue was full. For the two queues now four similar flags are used. (Note that for queues longer than one character, full and empty are not opposites.)

FULLIN—Input queue is full.
MPTYIN—Input queue is empty.
FULLOT—Output queue is full.
MPTYOT—Output queue is empty.

Details of their use may be found in the references.

10.S   *Summary*

In this chapter we have briefly viewed a few common input/output devices, such as the Teletype and paper-tape reader, and common methods of input/ output operations. A recurring theme has been timing problems. We have emphasized the need to construct and examine input/output programs carefully to make sure that they will execute correctly no matter when input/output events occur.

Each input/output device has a buffer register to store data and a control or status register containing bits, such as READY or BUSY, to show device status and bits like INTERRUPT ENABLE that are controlled from the CPU. It also has a transducer to convert information from electrical signals to another form of energy or vice versa.

The three main methods of input/output transfer are programmed input/ output, interrupts, and direct memory access. In programmed input/output operations, transfers of information occur under program control. Typically, when the program needs an I/O transfer, the CPU must stay in a wait loop until the device is ready; this can waste hundreds or thousands of CPU cycles. A more efficient method is using interrupts. In an interrupt system a device that is ready for a transfer is allowed to interrupt the CPU at the end of an instruction execution. An even faster method of transfer, used mainly for large blocks of information, is direct memory access. In this method transfer occurs directly between the input/output device and memory, bypassing the CPU. The time needed for the transfer is obtained by stealing cycles from the CPU.

Another recurring theme of input/output operations is the need for over-lapping operations. For efficiency, it is best to have as many devices operating in parallel as possible. Thus when we finish transferring information, we immediately prepare the device to begin a new transfer. Then the device can be operating while the CPU is performing other operations.

For greater efficiency, information from input devices and information to be transferred to output devices is stored temporarily in buffers or queues. A buffer is a set of memory locations for temporary storage. A queue is a buffer organized in a circle; information enters the queue at its head and leaves it at the tail. A main program can get information from an input queue and store results in an output queue.

Key Terms

buffer	echo
buffer register	ENABLE bit
BUSY bit	enqueue
control register	head, tail
cycle stealing	interrupt
data register	interrupt service routine
dequeue	interrupt system
direct memory access	interrupt vector
DONE bit	keyboard/reader

polled interrupts	status register
printer/punch	Teletype
priority	throughput
programmed input/output operations	transducer
queue	vectored interrupts
READY bit	wait loop

10.R *References*

Flores (1973) discusses many input/output devices; although it is primarily concerned with input/output for large computers, it does include material on devices for small computers. Finkel (1975) discusses interfacing for minicomputers; it is somewhat more hardware-oriented than this chapter has been. The texts recommended for Chapters 8 and 9 have information on input/output programming for the PDP-11 and other minicomputers. Stone and Sieworek (1975) has an excellent chapter on input/output that details many of the concepts presented here.

10.P *Problems*

Section 10.2

10.1. Write a program to enter your name on a Teletype and echo it back.

10.2. Write a program to store a string of ASCII characters read in from a Teletype. The string ends with a carriage return symbol. When your program sees a carriage return, it should halt.

10.3. Write a program to ring the Teletype bell every time the letter B is read in.

10.4. Write a program to ring the Teletype bell every time the word BELL is read in. You will want to compare each letter as it comes in, first with B, then with E if B is found, and so on.

10.5. Write a program that will store an incoming message in memory and print it out when requested.

10.6. Write a program that reads in number-letter pairs and echoes the letter that number of times. For example, the program should expand 5Q to QQQQQ and output it. The number can be restricted to the range 1 through 7.

Section 10.3

10.7. Write an interrupt service routine for the Teletype printer/punch.

10.8. Write an interrupt service routine for the paper-tape punch.

10.9. Write instruction sequences for SAVE and RESTORE for the main program and for the interrupt service routine. Assume that registers 0 to 4 must be saved for the main program and that 0 and 1 must be saved for the input/output routine.

11 Data Structures

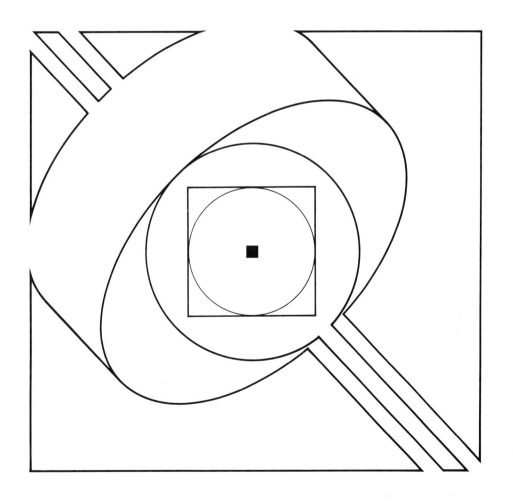

11.1 *Introduction*

Until now we have been primarily concerned with writing and running programs that have manipulated simple data elements, such as bits or words. Now we will consider **data structures**—collections of data that are related in some way. The data in a data structure may be related by position; vectors and matrices are examples. Alternatively, the data may be related in some more complex way as, for example, in a library card catalog. There books may be related by having the same title, or by sharing the same author, or by discussing the same subject, or by being at the same level, and so forth.

Understanding data structures and how they may be stored and used efficiently is important to good programming. We can store a set of data in many different data structures. The storage required for different data structures may vary by as much as ten to one. In addition, the data structure chosen affects processing speed. Judicious choice of a data structure and its associated **algorithm** (or procedure for processing the data) may reduce processing time even more than it reduces memory requirements.

Suppose that n is a parameter of a set of data. We may have five different data structures, D_1 to D_5, that can store the data. The time required to process the data might vary as follows.

Data structure	Time for processing
D_1	n
D_2	$n \log_2 n$
D_3	n^2
D_4	n^3
D_5	2^n

If we assume that with structure D_1 we can process an input of 1000 items in one second, then with structure D_5 we can process an input of no more than 9 items in one second.

Even if we use a much faster computer, the data structure selected still greatly affects speed of processing. Suppose that we use a computer that is ten times faster. This computer can now process 10,000 items in one second for D_1. But for D_5 it can process only 13 items in one second; a tenfold speedup has resulted in the processing of only four more items of data! This example illustrates a general principle for selecting data structures and algorithms. We prefer data structures for which the computation times grow only linearly in n, such as n or $3n$, to those whose times grow algebraically, such as n^2 or n^3. Similarly, we prefer data structures whose associated algorithms have linear or algebraic times to those whose algorithms have times that grow exponentially, such as 2^n.

In this chapter we will look at simple data structures. Some of them are structures that we encountered earlier in a different context. We will now view them in the context of related data structures. In just one chapter we can only provide a glimpse of this subject, which can easily fill two or three courses. In fact, if you are already taking or will soon take a course on data structures, you may wish to skip this chapter. It will, however, be useful to students who need a brief introduction to the structures most commonly used with small computers.

11.2 *Arrays*

11.2.1 *One-Dimensional Arrays*

An **array** is a collection of similar data elements such that each data element can be individually identified by integer indices. A **one-dimensional array** is the simplest and most common data structure. It is a list of similar data elements such that each element can be uniquely identified by its integer index. Suppose we have a one-dimensional array GRADE with 10 elements; its index ranges from 0 to 9. This array stores the test grades of students with student numbers from 0 to 9, as shown in Fig. 11.1. GRADE[0] is the first item and has a value of 71. GRADE[9] is the last item and has a value of 89; GRADE[5], near the middle of the array, has a value of 78.

Student number (index)	Grade
0	71
1	89
2	93
3	65
4	99
5	78
6	93
7	88
8	81
9	89

Fig. 11.1
Array GRADE, consisting of test grades of students with student numbers 0 through 9.

We store the elements of a one-dimensional array in sequence in memory so that we can take advantage of a computer's addressing abilities. We can calculate the address of any item in the array by adding a constant to the address of the first item of the array. Suppose that each item is two bytes long. (This may seem wasteful for the grades as shown, but we may be storing the grades in BCD and we need to allow for grades of 100.) We can create an array GRADE with 10_{10} words by the PDP-11 instruction

```
GRADE:  .  =  .+20
```

Similarly, we would use the 8080/8085 instruction

GRADE: DS 20

or the M6800 instruction

GRADE: RMB 20

These instructions allow 20_{10} bytes for array GRADE and associate the name GRADE with the first word, GRADE[0]. We can calculate the address of the second word, GRADE[1], by adding 2 to the address of GRADE[0].

The simplest way to address arrays on the PDP-11 or the M6800 is to use index addressing. The effective address for the index addressing mode is the sum of the address word and the contents of an index register. We denote index addressing for array GRADE with index register 4 by GRADE [4]. GRADE is the value of the address word; in this example it is the address of the first item of the array.

Suppose we wish to scan array GRADE to locate the highest grade. Our procedure is simple. We start by assuming that the first grade is the highest. Then we compare the rest of the grades, one at a time, with the highest grade we have seen. Whenever we find a higher grade, we call it the highest.

The PDP-11 program in Table 11.1 finds the highest grade and puts HIGH, the value of the highest grade, in register 0. It puts its index, STUNO—the student number of the student with the highest grade—in register 1. GRADE[0] is handled as a special case and is the first value of HIGH. For student numbers 1 through 9, a loop is used. First the index is doubled, because each array element takes two bytes. The array address is then calculated, and the value of the element addressed is compared with the current HIGH grade. If a new HIGH grade is found, HIGH and STUNO are changed to the new values. STUNO is incremented and compared with LENGTH, the length of the array. If STUNO is less than LENGTH, the loop is repeated.

Note in Table 11.1 that the branch back to the loop occurs only when STUNO is less than LENGTH. If, instead, we allowed the branch to occur when STUNO is less than *or equal to* LENGTH, the loop would repeat more than 60,000 times if LENGTH were 0! Although we do not ever expect LENGTH to be 0, we should consider this possibility. Tests of equality, such as LENGTH equals 0, are especially sensitive to bad data. Thus we should avoid tests of equality unless we are sure that excessive iterations will not occur. We can check the data at the beginning of the program to insure that they will not cause undesired looping.

Any one-dimensional array has two important integers associated with it. The **lower bound** is the index of the first element of the array; the lower bound of GRADE is 0. Similarly, the **upper bound** is the index of the last element; the upper bound of GRADE is 9. The **length** of a one-dimensional array is calculated as

length = upper bound − lower bound + 1.

Table 11.1
PDP-11 program to find the highest grade in the array GRADE

Label	Op code	Operand	Comment
HIGH	=	%0	; REGISTER 0 WILL HOLD
			; HIGHEST GRADE
HISTU	=	%1	; REGISTER 1 WILL HOLD INDEX
			; (STUDENT NO.) OF HIGHEST GRADE
TEMP	=	%2	; TEMPORARY STORAGE
STUNO	=	%3	; CURRENT STUDENT NUMBER
LENGTH:		10.	; LENGTH OF ARRAY IS 10
GRADE:.	=	.+20	; ARRAY GRADE TAKES 20 BYTES
	CLR	HISTU	; START WITH STUDENT 0
	MOV	GRADE, HIGH	; MOVE GRADE[0] TO HIGH
	MOV	#1, STUNO	; BEGIN LOOP WITH STUDENT 1
LOOP:	MOV	STUNO, TEMP	; MOVE INDEX TO TEMP
	ASL	TEMP	; DOUBLE INDEX
	CMP	GRADE(TEMP), HIGH	; COMPARE WITH HIGH
	BLE	NEXT	; IF GRADE(TEMP) ≤ HIGH, BRANCH
			; TO NEXT
	MOV	GRADE(TEMP), HIGH	; OTHERWISE SAVE NEW HIGH
	MOV	STUNO, HISTU	; AND SAVE NEW STUDENT NUMBER
NEXT:	INC	STUNO	; INCREMENT STUDENT NUMBER
	CMP	STUNO, LENGTH	; COMPARE STUNO WITH LENGTH
	BLT	LOOP	; IF STUNO < LENGTH, GO TO LOOP
	HLT		; OTHERWISE HALT

Adding 1 is necessary because we count both the upper and lower bounds. For GRADE,

length = $9 - 0 + 1 = 10$.

To avoid errors we often check indices to make sure that they are in range, that is, no less than the lower bound and no more than the upper bound. A sequence of PDP-11 instructions to check indices is shown in Table 11.2 for array GRADE. Because the lower bound is 0, a simpler check could be used. However, a more general check is given.

11.2.2 *Multidimensional Arrays*

Handy as they are, one-dimensional arrays are not adequate for some sets of data. Suppose each student in our example for array GRADE takes three tests, as shown in Fig. 11.2. We may represent the test scores in a two-dimensional array. We will call this array GRADES[I,J]. I is the first index of the array. It is the student number and has a lower bound of 0 and an upper bound of 9, as before. J, the second index of the array, is the test number. It has a lower bound of 1 and an upper bound of 3. Calculation of the address of each test

Table 11.2
PDP-11 program segment to test index of array to insure it is in range

Label	Op code	Operand	Comment
STUNO:		0	; STUDENT NUMBER IS INDEX
LOWER:		0	; LOWER BOUND IS 0
UPPER:		9.	; UPPER BOUND IS 9
TEST	=	%4	; TEST IS REGISTER 4
	MOV	STUNO, TEST	; MOVE INDEX TO TEST
	CMP	TEST, UPPER	; COMPARE WITH UPPER
	BGT	UERROR	; IF TEST EXCEEDS UPPER, GO TO UERROR
	CMP	TEST, LOWER	; COMPARE WITH LOWER
	BLT	LERROR	; IF TEST IS LESS THAN LOWER, GO TO LERROR
UERROR:			; INSTRUCTIONS FOR EXCEEDING UPPER BOUND
LERROR:			; INSTRUCTIONS FOR EXCEEDING LOWER BOUND

score is a little more complicated. We will show two methods for the calculation.

We will obviously want to store the grades in sequence in memory. Suppose that we prefer to store the three test grades of student 1, and so on. Our data in sequence then will be 71, 84, 79, 89, 85, ... This order is **row-major form,** meaning that the array is stored by rows. That is, the major ordering is by rows; within each row, ordering is by columns. Thus the first index is the row index.

If we had stored the scores on test 1 for each student followed by the scores on test 2 for each student and so on, the storage would be in **column-major form.** The first index would be the column index. The data would then be 71, 89, 93, 65, . . . , 89, 84, 85, ... (ANSI FORTRAN requires array storage in column-major form.)

Student number (index)	Test 1	Test 2	Test 3
0	71	84	79
1	89	85	92
2	93	95	93
3	65	60	72
4	99	92	97
5	78	81	74
6	93	97	100
7	88	82	89
8	81	85	87
9	89	80	90

Fig. 11.2
Two-dimensional array GRADES.

We can calculate the address of any item in GRADES[*I,J*] stored in row-major form by the equation

address = base + [*I* · 3 + *J* − 1],

where the base is the address of the first item in the array. The quantity in brackets is called the **address polynomial.** It is the position relative to the base. If the address of GRADES[0,1] is 220_{10}, the address of GRADES[8,2] is

address = 220 + [8 · 3 + 2 − 1]
        = 245.

(Here we are assuming storage in consecutive full-word locations.)

If GRADES[*I,J*] is stored in column-major form, the address is calculated as

address = base + [(*J* − 1) · 10 + *I*].

Thus the address of GRADES[8,2] in column-major form is

address = 238. = 220 + [(2−1) · 10 + 8]

More generally, an *M* × *N* two-dimensional array *X*[*I,J*] with row index *I* ranging from 1 to *M* and column index *J* ranging from 1 to *N* has the address equations

address = base + [(*I* − 1)*N* + *J* − 1]

for row-major form and

address = base + [(*J* − 1)*M* + *I* − 1]

for column-major form. These equations can be extended to give addresses for multidimensional arrays with any number of dimensions. The extension is left as an exercise.

The address equations just given convert two-dimensional (or multidimensional) indices into a single index. In other words, the two-dimensional (or multidimensional) array is mapped into a one-dimensional array. The address polynomial gives the relative position of each data element in the equivalent one-dimensional array. For example, we have seen that when GRADES is stored in row-major form, GRADES[8,2] is in position 25, meaning that it is stored 25 locations beyond the location of the first element. When GRADES is stored in column-major form, the same data element occupies position 18.

The address equations become more complex as the number of dimensions increases. Even worse, the number of multiplications required also increases with the number of dimensions. While a two-dimensional address calculation requires only two-term multiplications, a three-dimensional address calculation requires three-term multiplications. For small computers that lack hardware multipliers, the programming and the execution time required for these calculations are formidable. Fortunately, there is another procedure that requires no multiplications.

By using indirect addressing, we can easily access data from an array. As an example, assume that GRADES is stored in row-major form. We will access GRADES with an index STU that is an array of length 10. Each element of STU contains the address of GRADES corresponding to the first test score for the student STUNO. We then can obtain the address of the remaining test scores by adding the number of the test to the appropriate address of STU.

More precisely, we can calculate the address of GRADES[STUNO, TESTNO] as follows. The element STUNO of array STU contains the address of GRADES[STUNO,1], the first element of row STUNO of GRADES. To obtain the address of GRADES[STUNO, TESTNO], we must add TESTNO − 1 to the address of row STUNO; the subtraction of 1 is needed because TESTNO begins at 1. Instructions to implement this calculation are shown in Table 11.3. Note that most of the instructions deal with the address calculation.

Table 11.3
PDP-11 program segment to obtain data elements of array GRADES[STUNO, TESTNO] with indirect addressing

Label	Op code	Operand	Comment
ADDR	=	%0	; ADDRESS OF DATA WILL BE IN R0
DATA	=	%1	; DATA ELEMENT WILL BE IN R1
TEST	=	%2	; R2 WILL HOLD VALUE OF TESTNO
GRADES:	.=	+60.	; ARRAY GRADES TAKES 60 BYTES
		GRADES+6.	; ADDRESS FOR STUDENT 2
		GRADES+12.	; ADDRESS FOR STUDENT 3
		GRADES+18.	; AND SO ON
		GRADES+24.	
		GRADES+30.	
		GRADES+36.	
		GRADES+42.	
		GRADES+48.	
		GRADES+54.	
STU:	.WORD	GRADES	; STU HAS ADDRESS OF FIRST ELEMENT
			; OF GRADES
STUNO:	.WORD	0	; ROW INDEX
TESTNO:	.WORD	1	; COLUMN INDEX
	MOV	STUNO, ADDR	; MOVE ROW INDEX TO ADDRESS
	ASL	ADDR	; DOUBLE ROW INDEX
	MOV	STU(ADDR), ADDR	; GET ADDRESS OF ROW STUNO
	MOV	TESTNO,TEST	; GET TEST NUMBER (COLUMN INDEX)
	SUB	#1, TEST	; SUBTRACT 1 BECAUSE LOWER BOUND IS 1
	ASL	TEST	; DOUBLE COLUMN INDEX
	ADD	TEST, ADDR	; CALCULATE ADDRESS FOR GRADES
			; (STUNO, TESTNO)
	MOV	@ADDR, DATA	; GET DATA ELEMENT

Then deferred addressing is used to obtain the data element. This program can be expanded to include checks on index bounds and can be changed to allow arbitrary lower bounds.

11.3 *Stacks, Shelves, and Queues*

11.3.1 *Stacks*

We are already familiar with stacks, but with our new knowledge of arrays, we can see that a stack is just a special type of one-dimensional array. Unlike the arrays we have just inspected, a stack usually does not have a fixed length. There may be some maximum length determined by the available storage, but we have generally ignored this.

Information can be pushed onto a stack at just one end, called the top. Similarly, information can be popped from a stack from just one end—the top. Thus one distinction between stacks and other one-dimensional arrays is that at any time we can access just one particular item in a stack—the item at the top of the stack. Another distinction is that when we pop an element from the stack, we effectively erase it. That is, unlike the usual move operation, a pop instruction does not retain a copy of the item at the top of the stack. If we implement the pop operation with a move instruction, we physically retain a copy of the item in memory. However, it is no longer in the stack and cannot be accessed by any stack operations.

To form a stack we must first initialize the stack pointer at the highest memory address of the area intended for the stack. We will illustrate this procedure for the PDP-11; it is much the same for the M6800 and the 8085. Although the PDP-11 uses register 6 as a hardware stack pointer, we can use any register as a stack pointer. To initialize register 4 as a stack pointer at memory location 10000 we write

```
MOV #10000, %4
```

We will also want to establish upper and lower limits for the stack with instructions such as

```
UPPER:   10000
LOWER:   7700
```

These limits are used to check for stack **underflow**—attempts to pop from an empty stack—and stack **overflow**—stack spilling into locations below the lower limit. In this case an attempt to pop data from location 10002 results in underflow; an attempt to push data into location 7676 results in overflow. If either underflow or overflow occurs, an error indication or warning flag should be given.

The instructions of Table 11.4 summarize stack operations, including autoincrementing and autodecrementing for POP and PUSH, respectively.

Table 11.4
PDP-11 instructions for initializing stack pointer, checking for underflow and overflow, pushing, and popping for a word stack

Label	Op code	Operand	Comment
UPPER:		10000	; HIGHEST ADDRESS OF STACK
LOWER:		7700	; LOWEST ADDRESS OF STACK
STACKP:	=	%4	; STACK POINTER IS R4
	MOV	UPPER, STACKP	; INITIALIZE STACK POINTER
PUSH:	MOV	%0, -(STACKP)	; PUSH CONTENTS OF R0 ON STACK
	CMP	STACKP, LOWER	; COMPARE STACK POINTER WITH LOWER
	BLT	FULL	; IF STACK POINTER ≤ LOWER, STACK
			; IS FULL OR HAS OVERFLOWED
POP:	CMP	STACKP, UPPER	; COMPARE STACK POINTER WITH UPPER
	BGT	UNDER	; IF STACKP > UPPER, STACK HAS UNDERFLOWED
	MOV	(STACKP)+, %0	; OTHERWISE POP TOP OF STACK TO R0
FULL:			; INSTRUCTIONS FOR STACK FULL OR OVERFLOW
UNDER:			; INSTRUCTIONS FOR UNDERFLOW

11.3.2 *Shelves*

A double-ended stack is called a **shelf.** Information may be pushed on or popped from a shelf at either end in a last-in, first-out manner for that end. We arbitrarily call one end the top and the other end the bottom. Since we have previously called the lowest address in the stack the top, we will continue that usage for shelves. The highest address is the bottom of the shelf. Figure 11.3

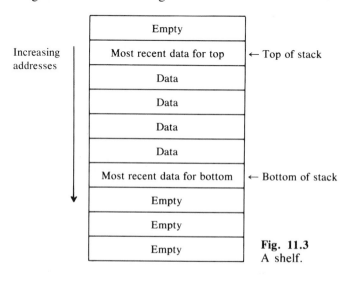

Fig. 11.3
A shelf.

shows a shelf. Like other stacks, shelves have the property that the pop operation effectively erases data. The addressing modes of the PDP-11 make programming a stack quite easy. We need to implement four operations:

- PSHTOP—Push data onto the top of the stack.
- POPTOP—Pop data from the top of the stack.
- PSHBOT—Push data onto the bottom of the stack.
- POPBOT—Pop data from the bottom of the stack.

The instructions for working with data at the top of the stack are the same as before. The instructions for the bottom of the stack are a little different. We will use register deferred addressing instead of autoincrement and autodecrement. To execute PSHBOT, we must first increment the stack pointer and then move data into the stack. Assume STACKB is the register that is the stack pointer for the bottom of the stack and that register 0 holds the data to be pushed. The following PDP-11 instructions are used:

```
PSHBOT: ADD#2, STACKB
        MOV %0, (STACKB)
```

Similarly, to pop data from the bottom of the stack to R0 we must first move the data and then decrement the pointer:

```
POPBOT: MOV (STACKB), %0
        SUB #2, STACKB
```

Similar instructions can be written for these operations on the M6800. Assume that the index register points to the bottom of the stack and that A holds the data (8-bit rather than 16-bit). Then the following M6800 instructions are used:

```
PSHBOT: INX
        STA A 0,X
```

Similarly, to pop data from the bottom of the stack to A, we write

```
POPBOT: LDA A 0,X
        DEX
```

Checking for underflow and overflow on shelves is more complicated than its counterpart for simple stacks. We must not allow a PUSH operation to overwrite any data stored in the shelf. We may want to allow a POP operation to pop data originally stored at either end of the shelf. Shelves, in fact, are most useful for applications in which items must be added or deleted at either end of the stack. An example is an inventory problem in which the storekeeper may wish to remove either the items most recently added to the stack (last-in, first-out) or the items first added to the stack (first-in, first-out). In this case the programmer would push items only on the top of the stack but would pop them from either end as desired.

11.3.3 *Queues*

When a shelf is constrained so that items may be pushed only on one end and popped only from the other end, it becomes a queue. First-in, first-out operation is the rule for queues. We can think of items as percolating their way through the queue from head to tail. However, constructing a queue is easier if the items actually stay in one spot while they are in the queue. Pointers for the head and tail of the queue move instead. The instructions needed to store items in the queue (an enqueue operation) or to remove items from the queue (a dequeue operation) were discussed in Chapter 10.

11.4 *Lists*

In the last section we examined variations of a one-dimensional array in which information was added or removed only at its ends. Sometimes, however, we wish to be able to add or remove information at any location of the array. For example, if we have a roster of students in a class, we would like to be able to add to it students who join the class and delete from it students who drop out. If the roster is in alphabetical order, we would like it to stay in alphabetic order as we add and drop students. To do this, we need a more complex structure than before—a structure we will call a **linked list** or just a **list.**

A list is a one-dimensional array of items that are linked together. The list does not need to occupy a block of adjacent memory locations. Instead, each item may be stored anywhere in memory. Each item stored has two parts—a value and one or more pointers to other items in the list. The pointers link the items of the list together.

11.4.1 *One-Way List*

The simplest list is a one-way list, shown in Fig. 11.4. Each item has a **value,** in this case the name of a student. Each item except the last has a **pointer** or **link** to the next item, its **successor.** We can think of the last item as having a

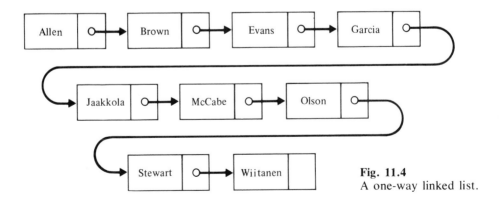

Fig. 11.4
A one-way linked list.

successor that is 0, showing the end of the list. Throughout this chapter we will use 0 to mean that a field is empty.

We need to be able to describe the location of the list in memory. To do this we use a special pointer, called the **head,** to point to the first element of the list. For convenience we may have a second special pointer, called the **tail,** to point to the last item on the list.

There are four basic operations associated with lists: (1) create a list, (2) add an element, (3) delete an element, (4) search for an element. These operations resemble the basic editing operations described in Chapter 6.

Creating a list Suppose we have a list of items. Each item takes four bytes—the first two for data and the second two to point to the item's successor (that is, to hold the address of the successor). We can create the list by assigning two bytes for the head, which we will initially fill with 0's until we know the address of the first item. We will not illustrate list creation since it is so simple.

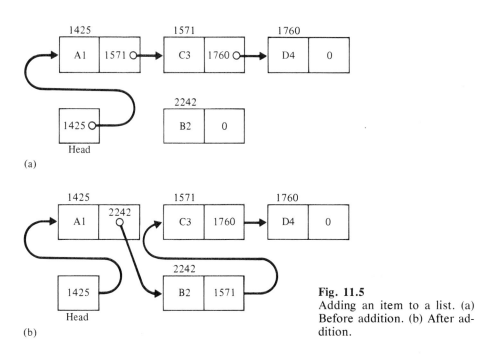

(a)

(b)

Fig. 11.5
Adding an item to a list. (a) Before addition. (b) After addition.

Adding an element To add an element we must insert it into the list as shown in Fig. 11.5. We must enter the element with a pointer to its successor and move the pointer from the previous item that pointed to the successor to the new element. We will add an item with a subroutine ADDLST. It needs two arguments: (1) the position on the list into which the item is to be inserted and (2) the present address of the item. For example, suppose the new element is to become the second one on the list, and its address is 2242. We then can call subroutine ADDLST by writing

```
JSR %4, ADDLST
        2       ;POSITION ON LIST
        2242    ;ADDRESS
```

We can access these two arguments by autoincrement addressing for register 4. The PDP-11 instructions for subroutine ADDLST are given in Table 11.5. For simplicity we have omitted the steps of saving and restoring contents of registers. However, since the subroutine uses four registers, we would probably want to include these steps.

Table 11.5
PDP-11 subroutine ADDLST to add an item to a list

Label	Op code	Operand	Comment
ADDLST:	MOV	(%4)+, %0	; GET POSITION ON LIST FOR COUNTER
	MOV	(%4)+, %1	; GET ADDRESS OF NEW ELEMENT
	MOV	HEAD, %2	; GET POINTER TO HEAD OF LIST
	DEC	%0	; DECREMENT COUNTER
	BEQ	FIRST	; IF POSITION IS 0, JUMP TO FIRST
REPEAT:	MOV	2(%2), %2	; GET LINK ADDRESS OF NEXT ITEM
	DEC	%0	; DECREMENT COUNTER
	BNE	REPEAT	; IF COUNTER IS NOT 0, REPEAT
	MOV	%2, 2(%1)	; LINK NEW ELEMENT TO SUCCESSOR
	MOV	%1, (%2)	; LINK NEW ELEMENT TO PREDECESSOR
RETURN:	RTS		
FIRST:	MOV	%2, 2(%2)	; LINK NEW ELEMENT TO SUCCESSOR
	MOV	%1, HEAD	; PUT ADDRESS OF NEW ELEMENT IN HEAD
	BR	RETURN	

Example 11.1: Adding an element to a list

To help us understand the subroutine ADDLST, we will trace its actions for the example shown in Fig. 11.5. Each element shown consists of a pair of ASCII characters followed by the address of the next element. HEAD contains only 1425, the address of the first element. We wish to insert the ASCII pair B2 as the second item on the list. This element is stored in the four-byte memory locations starting with 2242. The last two bytes originally hold 0's, showing that the element has no successor.

The subroutine ADDLST is called by the instructions given above. The first instruction moves the desired list position of the new element, 2, to R0, which will serve as a counter. The second instruction moves the address of the new element, B2, to R1. Then the value of HEAD, 1425—the address of the first item on the list—is moved to R2, which will serve as a pointer to list items.

Now, R0 is decremented and tested. If it is 0, the new element will become the first one on the list, and a branch is made to special instructions to accomplish this. Otherwise the subroutine continues by moving the link address of the first item to R2. In this case, 1571, the address of item C3, is moved to R2. R0 is decremented again. Because it was originally 2 and has been decremented twice, it is now 0. (If it were not, control would loop back to repeat the last two instructions.)

Since R0 is 0, the new element should be inserted. Two instructions accomplish this. The first links the new element to its successor; it moves 1571, the address of C3, from R2 to the second word of B2. The second links the new element to its predecessor; it moves 2242, the address of B2, from R1 to the second word of A1.

We can now compare the efficiencies of a one-way linked list and a one-dimensional array. Suppose we wish to add an element to the N elements already present in both structures. We would first locate the position for the item; this would require about the same number of instructions for both structures. We would then insert the item. For the one-way list, as we have seen, only a few instructions are needed to insert the item. The time required for adding the item once its position on the list has been located is independent of the position of the item. It is also independent of the length of the list.

For the one-dimensional array, however, the time required to add the item does depend on its position in the array. Each item following it in the array must be relocated. On the average, the item will be in the middle of the array of N items, so that about $N/2$ items must be moved. Hence we can see that for storing many items, a linked list is more efficient in processing time. It does, however, require extra memory locations for pointers.

Deleting an element Deletion is handled in a similar manner and the mechanics are left as an exercise. Let us note, however, that the delete routine should make the locations of the deleted items available for use. Otherwise the list ties up unneeded memory locations. Practically speaking, we rarely have so much memory that we can afford to ignore memory used by deleted items. The memory available for small computers is far too small to hold both active lists and all items that have ever been on lists.

One solution to this problem, popular some years ago but still useful for small computers, is to use a **free-storage list** to keep track of available memory. Initially all available locations are placed in the free-storage list. When we want to add an item to an active list, we take the first available locations from the free-storage list. When an item is deleted from a data list, its memory locations are added to the free-storage list. The programmer usually must write the instructions for memory management unless he or she is using a list processing language such as LISP.

Today a method called **garbage collection** is more commonly found. Its colorful name describes the method. Each memory location is given a one-bit tag that is ordinarily 0. When free memory locations are needed, a garbage-collection program traces all active lists and sets the tags of their items to 1. The remaining locations, those with 0 tags, are then known to be garbage and are put on a free-storage list. This method is useful when items may occur on several lists so that deletion of an item from one list does not mean that it can be deleted from other lists to free the location. Garbage collection is usually handled by the operating system; the programmer does not have to specify it. (We say that garbage collection is **transparent** to the programmer.)

Searching for an element The fourth list operation—searching a list for a particular data item—can be handled by a SEARCH subroutine. The subroutine call specifies the data to be found. If the item is located, the subroutine return gives the address of the data and its position on the list. If the item is not found, the computer will halt after returning from the subroutine.

We could modify the program and calling instructions so that the computer would take some other action if the item is not found. Again, we assume an item consists of one data word followed by a one-word address of the next item. Table 11.6 shows this PDP-11 subroutine, which can be called with

```
JSR %4, SEARCH
        12345   ;DATA TO BE LOCATED
        0       ;ADDRESS TO BE RETURNED
        0       ;LIST POSITION TO BE RETURNED
```

Table 11.6
PDP-11 subroutine to search list for specific data

Label	Op code	Operand	Comment
SEARCH:	MOV	(%4)+, %0	; MOVE DATA TO R0
	MOV	#1, %1	; R1 HOLDS POSITION OF ITEM
	MOV	HEAD, %2	; R2 HOLDS ADDRESS OF ITEM
AGAIN:	CMP	%0, (%2)	; LOOK FOR DESIRED ITEM
	BEQ	FOUND	; IF EQUAL, GO TO FOUND
	MOV	2(%2), %2	; MOVE LINK ADDRESS TO R2 POINTER
	TST	%2	
	BEQ	RETURN	; IF LINK IS 0, LIST IS DONE
	INC	%1	; ADD 1 TO LIST POSITION
	BR	AGAIN	; EXAMINE NEXT ITEM
FOUND:	MOV	%2, (%4)+	; ADDRESS OF LOCATED DATA
	MOV	%1, (%4)+	; POSITION OF LOCATED DATA
RETURN:	RTS	%4	

One important application of linked lists is text editing. Suppose we have a manuscript of a politician's speech stored in computer memory. So that the politician can use the same basic speech in several cities, we wish to change every occurrence of "New York" in the manuscript first to "Denver," then to "San Francisco," and so on. If we have stored the text of the speech in an array with each array element containing the same number of characters, we will have problems. We will find it hard to replace the eight characters of New York by the six of Denver or the thirteen of San Francisco. However, if we have stored the text as a linked list, substitution is relatively easy. Searching for the name "New York" requires about the same amount of time in either representation, but inserting the new name is much quicker and simpler for the linked list. We gain processing time at the cost of some extra memory for pointers.

We can reduce the memory needed for pointers by packing many characters, say 64, into each data field. Each element of a linked list would then have 64 characters followed by a pointer to the next element. We could then replace "New York" by "Denver" anywhere in the text without moving more than 64 characters. Again, there is a trade-off between the memory required for pointers and the processing time. As the number of characters per data field increases, the memory needed for pointers decreases but the processing time for additions and deletions increases.

One-way linked lists can be read only from beginning to end. If we have one element on the list, we can find any elements that follow it, but we usually cannot find any elements that precede it. By adding a link from the last element back to the head or to the first element, we can find any element on the list from any other. This variation of a one-way linked list is called a **circular list.** Examples are shown in Fig. 11.6.

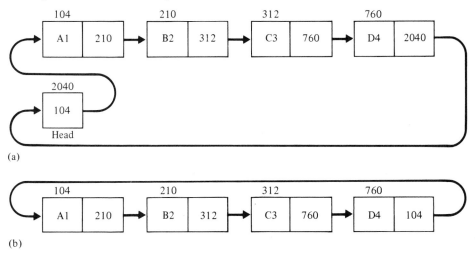

(a)

(b)

Fig. 11.6
Circular lists. (a) With separate head. (b) Without separate head.

11.4.2 *Two-Way Linked Lists*

If we wish to scan a list in both directions, we should have a **two-way linked list.** Each element of a two-way linked list has three fields—a data field, a pointer to its **successor,** and a pointer to its **predecessor.** An example is shown in Fig. 11.7. A 0 in the predecessor field of the first element shows that it is the head. Similarly, as before, a 0 in the successor field of the last element shows that it is the tail. We can extend the basic list operations of addition, deletion, and searching to a two-way list.

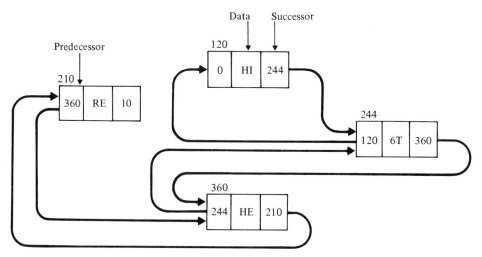

Fig. 11.7
A two-way linked list.

Although a two-way list offers more flexibility, it normally requires twice as much storage for pointers. Adding and deleting elements takes longer because twice as many pointers must be changed. Hence we usually use two-way lists only when we need to scan the list in both directions.

By exercising some ingenuity, however, we can reduce storage for pointers in a two-way list. In fact, we can store the information needed to calculate both pointers in the space usually occupied by just one pointer. The trick hinges on the fact that we reach an element by scanning the list either forwards or backwards. In either case we know the address of one neighbor of the current element—either its predecessor (PRED) or its successor (SUC). Suppose that in the pointer space we store the EXCLUSIVE-OR (XOR) of the two pointers, SUC $\oplus$ PRED. Then if we scan the list from head to tail, we always know the predecessor of any element. We can calculate its successor by the equation

$$\text{SUC} = (\text{SUC} \oplus \text{PRED}) \oplus \text{PRED}.$$

That is, we XOR the pointer with the known predecessor.

Similarly, if we scan the list from tail to head we can find the predecessor of an element by XORing the known successor with the pointer SUC ⊕ PRED:

PRED = (SUC ⊕ PRED) ⊕ SUC.

11.4.3 *Threaded Lists*

By adding more pointers to a two-way linked list, we can create more complex structures. For example, we can think of a two-dimensional array in which each element has four links—one each for its neighbors above and below, to the right and to the left. These four links "thread" the list element. Thus we call such a structure a **threaded list.**

Person
Mother
Father
Next younger sibling
Spouse
Oldest child

Fig. 11.8
A threaded-list element for a family tree.

A classic example of a threaded list is a family tree. Suppose we represent a person and some of his or her family relationships as shown in Fig. 11.8. The first field of the person's element is his or her name. The next five fields are pointers—mother, father, next younger sibling, spouse, and oldest child. Figure 11.9 shows part of a family tree and a threaded-list structure for it. We can trace a person's children by following the link to oldest child. From there we follow the links to the next younger sibling until that field is 0, showing the youngest child. How can we find a person's grandparents with this structure? How can we find aunts, uncles, and cousins?

Consider the problem we would have in tracing family relationships if we did not use a threaded list. Suppose we stored the same relationships for each person in a single block of memory locations without pointers. In the first location would be the person's name, Elizabeth, for example. In the next locations would be her mother, father, next younger sibling, spouse, and oldest child. If we then wished to find her paternal grandmother, we would first look for her father's name and find Bruce. We then would need to search through the entire array to find where Bruce and his relationships are stored, since there are no pointers to lead us. The threaded list is much quicker to use in tracing relationships than is a simple array.

A practical application of threaded lists is a membership roster. Usually we like to keep an alphabetic roster so that we can easily look up members in a

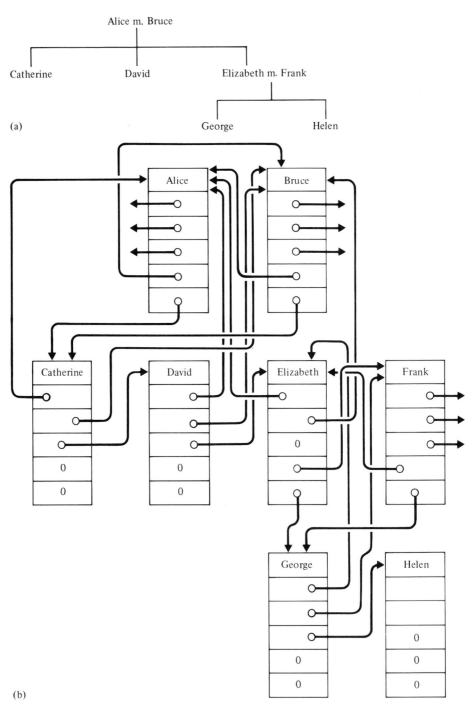

(a)

(b)

Fig. 11.9
A family tree. (a) Part of a tree. (b) A threaded-list structure for it.

printed directory. We may also wish to link members in the same zip code regions so that we can take advantage of postal rates for mailings with common zip codes. We may also want to link members in the same states or other geographic regions so that area meetings can be easily arranged. We may wish to link members in certain specialty groups or those who belong to related organizations that give reduced membership fees. Thus we may wish to develop a threaded-list structure with several threads. Each thread may be a one-way linked list, a two-way linked list, or some other structure.

While the flexibility of threaded lists may tempt us to add many threads, we must consider storage and processing costs. We should add extra threads only when we can justify the increased time for adding and deleting elements and the increased memory required.

Before we leave the subject of lists, we should mention list-processing languages. As you will discover when you attempt some of the problems at the end of the chapter, programming list operations in assembly language is not easy. For this reason, some high-level languages have been designed specifically for working with lists and similar data structures. LISP is one example. These languages are often found on large and medium-size computers; they are becoming available for small computers.

11.5 *Trees*

A **tree** is another variation of a one-dimensional array or linked list. We will examine one type of tree, called a **rooted tree,** which we will refer to as simply a tree. We are intuitively familiar with trees as structures that are found in all aspects of life. Trees in nature are the most obvious examples, but we can also think of family trees, tournament schedules, tables of contents, moves in a game, and the like. Any time that we regard items as being ordered in a hierarchy, a tree is a natural structure by which to represent them.

Our discussion of trees will closely follow Knuth (1973). A tree can be defined as a graph consisting of **nodes** and of **branches,** each of which links two nodes. The tree begins at the top with a **root** node. All branches connect an upper node—a **predecessor**—with a lower node—a **successor.** Except for the root node, which has no predecessor, every node has exactly one predecessor. Every node except the root node is connected to the root by exactly one path that begins at the root and ends at the node. Every node on that path, except the root, is a successor of another node on that path. A tree has no closed loops.

Figure 11.10 illustrates the features of trees. The root node is R; it is a predecessor of all other nodes. We can describe branches by the two nodes they connect; RA is a branch. Similarly, we can label paths by the nodes located on them. Path RBGL connects nodes R and L; it is the only path that connects those nodes.

It may strike you as odd that the tree in Fig. 11.10 grows from the root downward—not at all like the trees we see outdoors! The reason for this is just

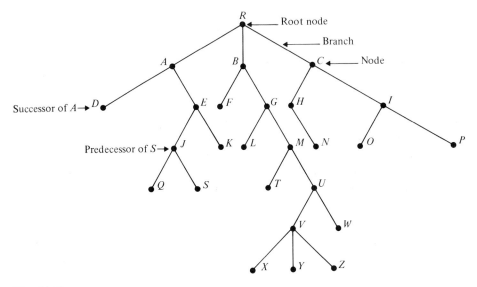

Fig. 11.10
A tree.

convention. Perhaps because of the way we write, it seems easier to draw a chart from the top down instead of from the bottom up. Computer scientists have recognized this and have agreed to regard trees as growing downward from their roots.

Nodes are either roots, leaves, or branch nodes. In Fig. 11.10, node M is a **branch node;** it has both a predecessor and a successor. Node X is a **leaf,** a node with no successor. Each leaf or branch node can be viewed as the root of a tree consisting of the node, its successors, their successors, and so on. We call such a tree a **subtree** of the original tree. A subtree can be as small as a single leaf.

Associated with each node is an integer called a **level,** which describes the distance of that node from the root. The root is at level 1. Nodes that are just one branch away from the root are at level 2, and so on. The level of any node is one more than the number of branches on the path connecting the root to that node. The greatest level in Fig. 11.10 is 7, for nodes X, Y, and Z.

The **degree** of a node is the number of its immediate successors. Leaves have degree 0. Nodes R and V in Fig. 11.10 have degree 3.

We can think of many applications of trees. A family tree, such as the one discussed in the last section, can be diagrammed as a tree if we omit marriages and show only descendents. That is, to correspond to the definition of a tree given here, a family tree must begin with a single ancestor (the root) and branch downward through all his or her descendents.

A tournament diagram for a basketball championship is an example of a binary tree. A **binary tree** has nodes of degree 2 or less. Binary trees are useful for showing calculations, because most arithmetic and logical operators are

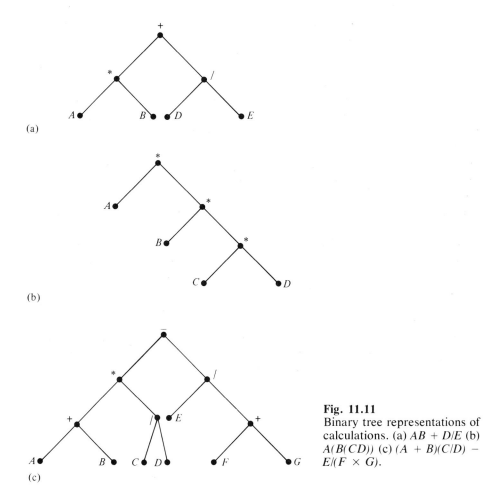

(a)

(b)

(c)

Fig. 11.11
Binary tree representations of
calculations. (a) $AB + D/E$ (b)
$A(B(CD))$ (c) $(A + B)(C/D) - E/(F \times G)$.

binary—they combine two operands. Other operators are unary—involving single operands—and can also be represented in a binary tree. Figure 11.11 shows binary trees that represent calculations.

Each node of a binary tree has at most two successors. By drawing branches that slant to the left or the right, we can distinguish **right successors** and **left successors.** No node can have two left successors or two right successors.

We **traverse** a tree by scanning through it in such a way that each node is scanned just once. We picture a tree as being divided into its root, a left subtree, and a right subtree. We can traverse the tree in three ways—called **preorder, inorder,** and **postorder.** Each subtree has a root and its own right and left subtrees, which are traversed in the same way as the original tree. Each type of traversal requires three steps for each tree or subtree. Of course, if a subtree is empty, it is traversed by doing nothing. The three methods differ only in their order of traversing. In all three a left subtree is always traversed before the corresponding right subtree, this convention being simply another consequence of our way of writing. The three methods, to be clarified in the examples that follow, are listed below.

Preorder traversal

- Go to the root.
- Traverse the left subtree in preorder.
- Traverse the right subtree in preorder.

Inorder traversal

- Traverse the left subtree in inorder.
- Go to the root.
- Traverse the right subtree in inorder.

Postorder traversal

- Traverse the left subtree in postorder.
- Traverse the right subtree in postorder.
- Go to the root.

Example 11.2: Tree traversal

Let us apply these three methods to the binary tree shown in Fig. 11.12.

In preorder traversal we start with root A. Then we traverse the left subtree beginning with its root B and proceeding to its left and right subtrees, consisting of the single branches to nodes D and E, respectively. Then we traverse the right subtree in the same order. The resulting order is

A B D E C F H G I J

In inorder traversal we visit the root between the nodes of each subtree.

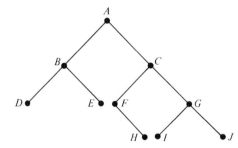

Fig. 11.12
A binary tree for Example 11.2.

We would get the same order if we projected the nodes down onto a horizontal line and scanned from left to right. The resulting order is

D   B   E   A   F   H   C   I   G   J

Inorder traversal is sometimes called **symmetric order.** By scanning the root in the middle, it treats the left and right subtrees symmetrically.

In postorder traversal we scan both the left and right subtrees before going to the root. The resulting order is

D   E   B   H   F   I   J   G   C   A

Example 11.3: Traversal involving a calculation

Consider these three different traversals for a binary tree representing a calculation, such as the one in Fig. 11.13. Its leaves are all operands; the other nodes are operators. The results of the three types of traversal are shown below.

Preorder   * + * *CDA* − *B/EF*
Inorder   *C * D + A * B = E/F*
Postorder   *CD * A + BEF/−**

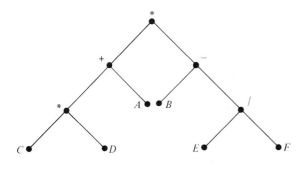

Fig. 11.13
A binary tree representation of a calculation for Example 11.3.

We can store a binary tree as an array in computer memory by giving each item four fields. The first is for its array index; the other three are the node, its left successor, and its right successor. Thus the binary tree of Example 11.3 (Fig. 11.13) can be stored in the array of Table 11.7. Once we have the tree stored in an array, we can traverse it or process it as we like. How could we find the root of the tree?

This kind of storage can be considered a generalized form of a one-way linked list. There are no links pointing to the root or pointing back to any predecessor. Another data structure uses special pointers to point to predecessors. This structure is called a **threaded tree.**

Table 11.7
An array representing the tree of Fig. 11.13.

Index	Node	Left successor	Right successor
1	*	2	3
2	+	4	5
3	−	6	7
4	*	8	9
5	A	0	0
6	B	0	0
7	/	10	11
8	C	0	0
9	D	0	0
10	E	0	0
11	F	0	0

11.6 *Recursion*

A **recursive structure** is one defined in terms of itself. For example, we can define a tree recursively as follows:

A tree is a set of nodes connected by branches. One node is a root. The other nodes are divided into sets, each of which form a tree.

Similarly, a **recursive function** is defined in terms of itself. The classic example of a recursive function is the factorial. We can define $f(N) = N!$ recursively. We define

$$f(0) = 1$$

and

$$f(N) = N * f(N - 1) \qquad \text{for integer } N \geqslant 1.$$

With this definition, we must find 8! before we can find 9!; we must find 7! before we can find 8!; and so on.

Many computer algorithms are written recursively. Any one may be implemented as a **recursive subroutine** that calls itself. Each recursive routine must have some part, called the **basis part,** which is not defined recursively. For the factorial function, the statement $f(0) = 1$ is the basis part. If a recursive subroutine does not have a basis part, it will continue calling itself indefinitely and can never exit.

We meet two problems when we write recursive procedures in assembly language. The first problem is saving the return address. A recursive subroutine can be called several times before returning to the main program. The return addresses for all calls need not be the same. The first return address will normally be in the main program; the subsequent return addresses will usually be in the recursive subroutine. Thus we cannot save the return address in a fixed location, such as in the first location of the subroutine. The best place to save the return addresses is in a stack, so that we may recover them in a last-in, first-out order. This means that if a computer saves the return address in one location, we must write instructions in the subroutine to move the address to a stack. (See Problem 11.25.)

A second and related problem is passing sets of parameters to and from the subroutine. Using a stack for parameter transfer solves this problem also. The instructions needed for this were discussed earlier.

Table 11.8
PDP-11 instructions for a recursive subroutine

Label	Op code	Operand	Comment
	JSR	%7, RECURS	; CALL FROM MAIN PROGRAM
RECURS:			
			; CALCULATIONS OF SUBROUTINE
	MOV	ARGN, −(%6)	; PASS ARGUMENTS TO STACK
			; IN PREPARATION FOR
	MOV	ARG1, −(%6)	; RECURSIVE CALL
	JSR	%7, RECURS	; RECURSIVE CALL
			; PREPARATION FOR RETURN TO MAIN PROGRAM
	MOV	(%6)+, %1	; SAVE RETURN ADDRESS IN R1
	ADD	#2N, (%6)	; MOVE STACK POINTER UP 2N PLACES
	MOV	(%1), −(%6)	; RESTORE RETURN ADDRESS TO STACK
	RTS	%7	; RETURN TO MAIN PROGRAM

PDP-11 instructions for working with a recursive subroutine, RECURS, having parameters PARAM1 to PARAMN, are shown in Table 11.8. Register 7, the program counter, is used as a subroutine linkage register. Just before the subroutine is called for the first time, the top N items in the stack are the N parameters of the subroutine, with PARAM1 at the top. When the subroutine is called, the contents of the linkage register are pushed onto the stack. Because the linkage register is the program counter, the return address is stored on the stack. The parameters can be accessed by indexing relative to the stack pointer. When the subroutine calls itself recursively, N new parameters are pushed on the stack, followed by the new return address. To exit from the subroutine we first transfer the return address to a temporary storage. Then we advance the stack pointer past the N parameters. Finally we move the return address back onto the stack. The stack is the same after a return from RECURS as it was before RECURS was called. The stack contents at various times are shown in Fig. 11.14.

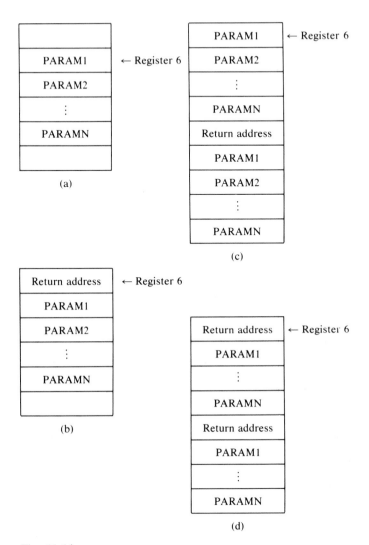

Fig. 11.14
Stack contents for subroutine RECURS. (a) Before first subroutine call. (b) After first subroutine call. (c) Before first recursive call. (d) After first recursive call.

Example 11.4: Application of a recursive subroutine

Consider the programming of the factorial function. We will assume that we have a multiplication procedure MULT that multiplies the contents of register 1 and 2, leaving the product in register 1. The instructions needed are shown in Table 11.9.

Table 11.9
PDP-11 instructions for calculation of *N* factorial

Label	Op code	Operand	Comment
	MOV	N, −(%6)	; TRANSFER POSITIVE INTEGER N TO STACK
	JSR	%7, FACT	; CALL FACTORIAL SUBROUTINE
FACT:	MOV	2(%6), %0	; FETCH N FROM STACK
	BEQ	VALUE1	; RETURN WITH VALUE 1 IF N IS 0
	DEC	%0	; OTHERWISE CALCULATE N − 1
	MOV	%0, −(%6)	; PUSH ONTO STACK
	JSR	%7, FACT	; CALL FACTORIAL RECURSIVELY
	MOV	2(%6), %1	
	MOV	%0, %2	
MULT:	--------------------------------		; MULTIPLY CONTENTS OF R2 AND R1
			; FORMING N*FACT(N − 1) IN R1
	MOV	%1, %0	; MOVE N! TO R0
	BR	RETURN	
VALUE1:	MOV	#1, %0	; FACTORIAL IS 1
RETURN:	MOV	(%6)+, @%6	; MOVE RETURN ADDRESS FROM TOP OF
			; STACK TO PARAMETER SPACE
	RTS	%7	

11.7 *Sorting*

Sorting an array of numbers into numerical order is a common occurrence. A simple method is called the **bubble sort.** Its name refers to the way in which small numbers "float" to the top of an array when this method is used. The method involves comparing the contents of adjacent locations and exchanging them, if necessary, to put the smaller number first. More specifically, the bubble-sort procedure is:

1. Clear a flag to 0.
2. Scan through the array from beginning to end. Examine all pairs of adjacent locations. If the second location (the one with a higher index) holds a smaller number, exchange the numbers and set the flag to 1.
3. Examine the flag after the scan is finished. If it is 1, return to step 1 and repeat. If it is 0, the sort is finished.

The flowchart of this procedure is shown in Fig. 11.15. Table 11.10 shows the results of each scan through the bubble-sort algorithm for a small array. Note that the results of the last two passes are the same. Why?

We would like to know how many passes and how many exchanges we need to make to sort *N* numbers. The worst case occurs when the array is initially arranged in reverse order, from largest number to smallest. In that case, each time the array is sorted, the smallest number will move up one

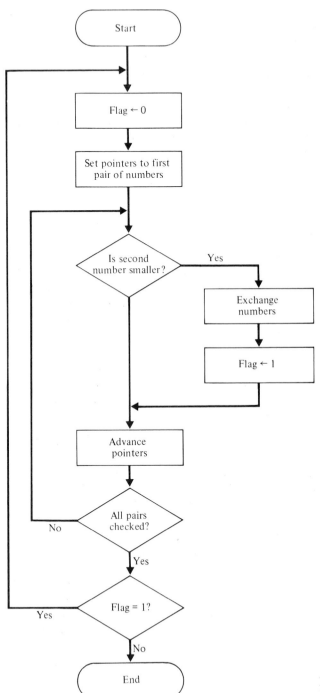

Fig. 11.15
Flowchart of bubble sort.

Table 11.10
Results of a bubble sort of a small array

Array index	Unsorted array	After pass 1	After pass 2	After pass 3	After pass 4	After pass 5
1	12	1	1	1	1	1
2	1	4	4	4	3	3
3	4	9	6	3	4	4
4	9	6	3	6	6	6
5	6	3	9	9	9	9
6	3	12	12	12	12	12

position. After $N - 1$ passes, the array will be in numerical order. Counting the last pass, N passes are needed. The maximum number of exchanges is at most $N(N - 1)$.

Usually the array will not be in reverse order. Hence we are interested also in the average number of passes that will be needed. The calculation is much more complicated and will not be done here, but the result is that the average number of passes is about $0.875N$. Thus if we were sorting an array of 100 numbers, we would expect to make about 87 or 88 passes. At most we would need 100 passes. The average number of exchanges required increases approximately as N^2.

We can simplify the bubble sort by eliminating the steps of setting and testing a flag. We then must sort $N - 1$ times. Most of the time we will sort a few more times than necessary, but we save the steps of the flag and insure that we never will sort N times.

The bubble sort can be improved. One possibility is the "cocktail shaker" sort, in which passes alternate from one end to the other. This reduces the number of passes needed somewhat. Another improvement is a strategy that moves small numbers to the top as rapidly as it moves large numbers to the bottom.

Other sorting algorithms are based on organizing the data from an array into a tree and then rearranging the tree into a sorted list. These algorithms, which are characterized by the maximum number of comparisons as $N \log_2 N$ instead of as N^2, are discussed in the references.

11.8 Searching

As we have seen, we often want to search a list for a particular item. In the past we have used a naive procedure that required us to proceed through the list comparing the desired item with each item in sequence until a match was found. In the worst case we must perform N comparisons if the list has N items. However, if we assume that the list we are searching has been sorted into numerical order, we can search more rapidly.

11.8.1 *Binary Searching*

Suppose we have a table of numerically sorted data. We will arrange to search in such a way that we halve the area to be searched on each pass. We illustrate the procedure by an example. Suppose that we wish to search the following sorted array to see whether it contains 13.

Index	1	2	3	4	5	6	7	8	9	10	11	12	13	14	15
Value	1	3	4	6	7	9	10	11	12	14	16	17	18	19	21

This array contains 15 items. We first examine the middle item, that is, the eighth item. It has a value of 11. This is too low. We now realize that we can confine our search to the upper half of the array. We seek the approximate midpoint of the upper part of the array. We look at the twelfth item, which has a value of 17. This is too high. We now have narrowed our search to the approximate quarter of items with indices between 8 and 12 and with values between 11 and 17. We examine the middle item, with index 10 and value 14. This is too high. We narrow the search further to the only possible remaining item. It has index 9 and value 12. Our search is finished; 13 is not in the array.

A general binary search of N items of an array A to find item X requires the following steps.

1. Set LOW = 0; HIGH = $N + 1$
2. If LOW + 1 ⩾ HIGH, exit with item not found in array.
3. Calculate I = (LOW + HIGH)/2 by integer division, ignoring any fraction.
4. Compare $A(I)$ with X.
   If $A(I) = X$, exit with the item found.
   Otherwise, if $A(I) < X$, set HIGH = I;
                 if $A(I) > X$, set LOW = I.

Repeat steps 2, 3, and 4.

If an item is not in the array, about $\log_2 N$ comparisons are needed to determine its absence. For example, four comparisons were needed to find that 13 was not in an array of 15 items. If the item is in the array, there is one chance that it may be located the first time, two chances that it may be located the second time, four chances that it may be located the third time, and so on. In general, however, almost $\log_2 N$ comparisons are needed to find an item that is in the array.

Comparing the binary search with a straight sequential search, we note that the number of comparisons required for the latter is about $N/2$ if the item is in the array and N if it is not.

11.8.2 *Hash Addressing*

Sometimes we want to find items even more rapidly than we can with a binary search. For example, consider the list of items in Table 11.11. There are eight

Table 11.11
Symbol table entries

Index	Item	Hash index
1	A	1
2	LOOP	4
3	HERE	4
4	SYMBOL	6
5	X1	2
6	X2	2
7	RETURN	6
8	MOVES	5

items, each with one to six characters, that might be labels in a symbol table. Each item has an index that gives its location in the table. It also has a **hash index,** a search parameter that directs us to the item. In this case the hash index is an integer between 1 and 6 that equals the number of characters in the item. Because there are eight items, some of them have the same hash index. No item has hash index 3. Ordinarily the number of characters is not a particularly good hash index, but it will work for this example.

If we wish to find some item that may be in the table, we first compute its hash index. Then we use the hash index as an entry to another table, Table 11.12. We compare the item for which we are searching with the first item of that hash code in the table. If we find it, we are done. If the first entry is 0, no items with that hash code are in the table, and we are done. Otherwise we look at the second item of the table for a match, 0 entry, or no match. Because, in this simple example, no more than two items have the same hash code, at most two comparisons are needed. A binary search could require three comparisons; a straightforward search through Table 11.11 could require as many as eight comparisons.

Hash addressing is a search procedure that limits the amount of calculations needed by using an index to the array. The parameter is the hash index. It basically partitions the original list of N items into M separate sets, where M is

Table 11.12
A hash-addressing array containing the symbol table entries

Hash index	Column 1	Column 2
1	A,1	0
2	X1,5	X2,6
3	0	0
4	LOOP,2	HERE,3
5	MOVES	0
6	SYMBOL,4	RETURN,7

the number of values that the hash code can assume. (In the preceding example, N was 8 and M was 6.) To find an item, we first compute its hash code and then search the sublist of items with that hash code. Hashing is much like picking a starting point in a telephone directory based on the city in which the desired phone is located. On the average, if we have chosen the hash code carefully, the search will involve only $1/M$ of the items on the original list.

To see how this works in a general case, suppose we have a list LIST of N items. We select, in a way to be explained later, a hash code HASH that can assume the values 1, 2, . . . M. We calculate the hash code for each item in LIST. We put all items with the same hash code into a one-way linked list. We store all N items in an array ARRAY of length N and store the linkage information in LINK (also of length N). In this way the item that follows ARRAY[I] on one of the linked lists is ARRAY [LINK[I]]. The first item on each linked list of items with the same hash code can be found from HINDEX, a list of length M. For example, HINDEX[H] contains the index in ARRAY of the first item on LIST that has hash code H. If HINDEX[H] = 0, the array has no item of hash index H.

Before we try to enter the first item into ARRAY, we must initialize LINK and HINDEX to 0. This ensures that all linkages and other information not entered are 0. We also need a variable NEXT that will show the next open place in the array. NEXT is initialized to 1 for the first item. Once these values are properly initialized, the procedure to enter an ITEM into ARRAY proceeds as follows.

1. H = HASH (ITEM). (Calculate the hash code of the item.)
2. Place HINDEX[H] in LINK[NEXT] so that ARRAY [HINDEX[H]] will be searched after ARRAY[NEXT].
3. NEXT = NEXT + 1. (Increment NEXT; this causes a search to begin at ARRAY[NEXT]. The array should be tested to avoid overflow.)
4. ARRAY[NEXT] = ITEM
5. LINK[NEXT] = HINDEX[H]
6. HINDEX[H] = NEXT

To illustrate this procedure, consider entering the items of Table 11.11. Figure 11.16 shows the resulting contents of HINDEX, ARRAY, and LINK. Note that the linkage information goes backward through the array. Thus a value of HINDEX of 6 points to RETURN with index 7; LINK[7], in turn, points to SYMBOL, the fourth item in ARRAY. Contrast this structure with that of Table 11.12.

To search ARRAY for an ITEM, we first compare ITEM with HINDEX [HASH(ITEM)]. We call this index the **index of the first probe** of the table. If we find a match, we have successfully ended the search. If we find a 0, we know that ITEM is not in the table. Otherwise we trace through the linked list of entries that have the same hash code as ITEM. We find the second item by

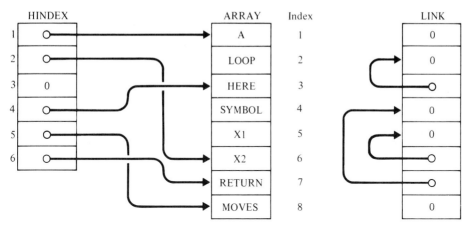

Fig. 11.16
Entering items with a hash index.

using the index of the first probe as an index to LINK. That entry in LINK is
the **index of the second probe**; it is the next to be compared with ITEM. We
continue tracing through LINK until we find a match and conclude the search
successfully or find a 0 and conclude the search unsuccessfully.

A hash addressing search proceeds as follows.

1. Set INDEX = 0. (INDEX is a dummy variable that will give the index of
   ITEM if the search is successful or will be 0 if the search is unsuccessful.)
2. Compute I = HINDEX[HASH(ITEM)].
3. If I = 0, exit. The search has concluded unsuccessfully.
4. If ARRAY[I] = ITEM, exit. The search has concluded successfully;
   INDEX gives the index of ITEM in ARRAY.
5. If ARRAY(I) = ITEM, calculate the next value of I from I = LINK I.
   Return to step 2.

The worst case in a hash addressing search occurs when all N items have
the same hash code. We then search only one list in the same way as for any
one-way linked list. At worst we would have to examine all N items.

The average case is much better. While we will not analyze rigorously, we
can intuitively think about it. If we have M hash codes, each sublist will
average about $1/M$ items. If the item for which we are searching is in the array,
we will need to search through half of these $1/M$ items, on the average. If the
item is not in the array, we must search through all $1/M$. Thus by hash
addressing we do about M times better than we would in a simple sequential
search.

If hash addressing is to partition the N items of a list into M subsets of
about equal size, we must pick a hash function carefully. Our goal is to hash or

randomize the items as uniformly as possible, just as a good dish of hash has evenly spread pieces of meat, potatoes, and so on. A good hash function is the EXCLUSIVE OR function. It results in a hash code that depends on every bit in the item and is evenly distributed between 0 and $2^k - 1$, where k is the number of bits in the hash code.

For example, suppose we wish to use hash addressing for a symbol table containing names composed of one to six 8-bit characters. A typical entry can be represented as

$C_1C_2C_3C_4C_5C_6$.

We can construct an 8-bit hash code by

$$\text{HASH} = C_1 \oplus C_2 \oplus C_3 \oplus C_4 \oplus C_5 \oplus C_6.$$

This hash code can assume any of the 256 values from 0 to $2^8 - 1$. Table 11.13 shows PDP-11 instructions for this.

Table 11.13
PDP-11 instructions to calculate a hash address

Label	Op code	Operand	Comment
	MOV	#HINDEX, %1	; PUT HASH INDEX LOCATION IN R1
	CLR	@%1	; CLEAR R1
	MOV	#CHARAD, %0	; PUT CHARACTER ADDRESS IN R0
LOOP:	MOVB	@%0, -(%6)	; DECREMENT STACK POINTER
	BICB	@%1, A6	; EXCLUSIVE-OR NEXT
	BICB	(%0)+, %1	; CHARACTER WITH CONTENTS
	BISB	(%6)+, %0	: OF R1 (3 INSTRUCTIONS)
	CMP	%0, #CHARAD+5	; CHECK FOR ALL 6 CHARACTERS
	BLE	LOOP	; IF NOT DONE, REPEAT

Another possible hash function is addition. We could add the six characters together, ignoring carries beyond 8 bits. This also would give us well-distributed hash codes. In either case we should avoid selecting k equal to the number of bits in each character, namely 8 in this example. Doing so might lead to a nonuniform distribution of hash codes. Another possibility is dividing by a prime number p and taking the remainder, which is uniformly distributed between 0 and $p - 1$.

The most serious disadvantage of hash addressing is the memory required for storing pointers for the linked list. In our example we stored these pointers in LIST. Other data structures can be used in hash addressing to save memory. An alternative is to use a variation of hash addressing that requires no pointer storage. Pointers are needed only when two or more items have the same hash code. When that occurs, we can examine the item in the table at that hash index. If it does not match, we can look elsewhere in the table to continue the search. One possibility—though not the best—is to examine the next items in sequence until we find either a match or a 0. During entry we will have placed the second item with the same hash code in the first available location after the first item with that hash code. Some of the references discuss this approach in detail.

11.9   *Examples of Tables*

One of the most useful data structures is the **table,** which we may think of as a generalized array. In an array, all entries are usually of the same form and length. In a table, entries may be of different lengths. A symbol table, in which entries may be from one to six characters long, is an example. Tables are often used in programming small computers, especially microcomputers, to regularize the structure of a problem, to give results without calculation, or to isolate one part of a program from another. The following examples illustrate these features.

Example 11.5: BCD multiplication

Suppose we wish to multiply parts of decimal digits. We can write a subroutine to do so, using decimal adjust instructions. However, the subroutine will take considerable time to execute. Alternatively, we can construct a BCD multiplication table, as shown in Fig. 11.17, and store it in ROM. It will take substantial

ROM address	Contents
00	00
01	00
02	00
	⋮
46	24
47	28
48	32
	⋮
96	54
97	63
98	72
99	81

Fig. 11.17
A BCD multiplication table.

memory but will speed the multiplication process. It can also be the basis for multiplication of N-digit numbers. The two digits to be multiplied combine to give an 8-bit address for entry to the table. The contents of the location addressed are the two-digit product. For example, if the multiplicand is 4 and the multiplier is 7, the table is entered at ROM address 47. The product of 28 is the contents of that location.

Example 11.6: Jump table

We can use a jump table to isolate subroutines from our main program. When we call a subroutine in our main program, control will be transferred to the location of the same name in the jump table. There, instead of all the instructions of the subroutine, we find only a jump statement that transfers control to the main part of the subroutine. The subroutine ends with a return statement that transfers control back to the statement following the call in the main program as usual.

Figure 11.18 illustrates this procedure. When the main program reaches the statement CALL SUBA, control transfers to location SUBA in the jump table. In that location is stored the command JUMP ASUB. (We are speaking somewhat generally here; an 8-bit microcomputer would ordinarily need three bytes of memory to store that command.) Hence control transfers to location ASUB to begin the main actions of the subroutine. The subroutine ends in the usual manner with a RETURN statement that transfers control back to the appropriate point in the main program—not the jump table. (Why?)

In this way subroutines are isolated from the main program. Now if the

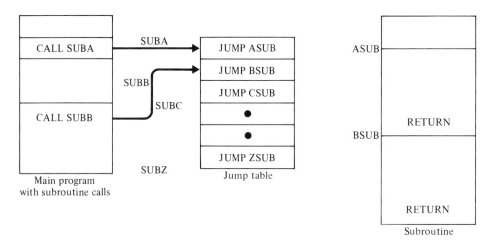

Fig. 11.18
Use of a jump table to isolate main program from subroutines.

subroutine is enlarged and must be relocated in memory, nothing in the main program needs to be changed. Instead, an address in the jump table is changed. This can help to prevent errors when a subroutine is called several times in a main program.

Example 11.7: Handling multivalued decisions

Decisions that lead to many alternatives can be regularized through use of a jump table such as the one shown in Fig. 11.19. Here it is assumed that there are 16 alternatives, numbered from 0 to F (in hexadecimal). The table is entered with the value of the variable that governs the decision. The contents of that location are a jump address to the routine for handling the chosen alternative. Indirect addressing is used.

Entry
number

Entry number	Address
0	4 A 00
1	4 A 39
2	5 B 01
3	5 C FE
F	6 E 08

Fig. 11.19
Handling multi-valued decisions.

11.S *Summary*

In this chapter we have seen several types of data structures. We began by considering arrays. An array is a collection of similar data elements such that each element can be identified by an integer index or indices. Arrays may be one-dimensional or multidimensional. We then reexamined stacks and queues in context as data structures. A double-ended stack is a shelf.

A special form of one-dimensional array is a list. Lists may be one-way linked, two-way linked, or threaded. A free-storage list can keep track of available memory freed from lists. A garbage collection routine may also be used to identify free memory locations.

A tree is another variation of the one-dimensional array or linked list. A tree begins at a root node. Successive nodes are successors. The level of a node describes its distance from the root. The degree of a node is the number of its successors. A binary tree has nodes of degree 2 or less. A tree is traversed by scanning through it in such a way that each node is scanned just once. Trees may be traversed in preorder, inorder, or postorder.

A recursive structure is one defined in terms of itself. It must have some part, called a basis part, that is not defined recursively.

Sorting and searching are common processing operations. A simple sort is the bubble sort, in which small numbers float to the top of an array. Binary searching is a method of finding an item by halving the area to be searched on each pass. Hash addressing is a searching procedure in which the programmer picks a hash code that controls the number of searching operations needed.

Tables are generalized arrays that may be used to provide results without calculation, to regularize the structure of a problem, or to isolate parts of a program.

Key Terms

address polynomial	list
algorithm	lower bound
array	multidimensional array
binary search	node
binary tree	one-dimensional array
branch	one-way linked list
branch nodes	overflow
bubble sort	postorder
circular list	predecessor
column-major form	preorder
data structure	queue
degree	recursive
dequeue	right successor
enqueue	root
free-storage list	rooted tree
garbage collection	row-major form
hash addressing	shelf
hash code	stack
hash function	subtree
hash index	successor
hash table	symmetric order
head	table
index of the first probe	tail
index of the second probe	threaded list
inorder	threaded tree
jump table	traverse
leaf	tree
left successor	two-way linked list
level	underflow
linked list	upper bound

11.R   *References*

The classic reference for data structures is the series of books by Knuth. Other sources include Elson (1975), Aho, Hopcroft, and Ullman (1974), and Stone and Siewiorek (1975). Eckhouse (1975) relates data structures to PDP-11 programming. Peatman (1977) and Leventhal (1978a,b) apply data structures to microcomputer programming.

11.Q   *Questions*

1. What is the difference between an array and a list?
2. How can elements in a multidimensional array be located?
3. Distinguish between a shelf, a stack, and a queue.
4. How many lists may be linked?
5. What is the purpose of garbage collection?
6. Give some examples of trees.
7. Explain the three ways in which a tree may be traversed.
8. Give an example of a recursive routine.
9. Explain the principle of a bubble sort.
10. Explain hash addressing.
11. Explain the use of a jump table in isolating subroutines from a main program.

11.P   *Problems*

Section 11.2

11.1. Write a program to find the maximum and minimum numbers in an array of 200_{10} positive bytes.

11.2. Rewrite the program of Table 11.1 using autoincrement addressing.

11.3. Rewrite the program of Table 11.1 including tests on upper bound and lower bound.

11.4. Calculate the addresses for both row-major and column-major forms of the data elements below for a $20_{10} \times 80_{10}$ array X with a base address of 1782_{10}.

   a) $X(1, 70)$ b) $X(19, 79)$ c) $X(10, 40)$

11.5. Calculate the addresses for both row-major and column-major forms of the data elements below for a $100_{10} \times 100_{10}$ array Y with a base address of 2000_{10}.

   a) $Y(100, 100)$ b) $Y(50, 50)$ c) $Y(29, 84)$

11.6. Write the address equations for both row-major and column-major forms using an address polynomial for a three-dimensional array $Z(I,J,K)$

with indices I ranging from 1 to M, J ranging from 1 to N, and K ranging from 1 to P.

11.7. Redo Problem 11.6 assuming that indices I, J, and K have arbitrary lower bounds A, B, and C, respectively.

11.8. Revise the program of Table 11.3 to include checks on index bounds.

11.9. Revise the program of Table 11.3 for a general array $X(I,J)$ where I and J may have arbitrary lower bounds.

Section 11.3

11.10. Write instructions to check for underflow and overflow of a shelf.

11.11. Write instructions to pop data from a stack without saving a copy of the data in memory by the stack.

Section 11.4

11.12. Write instructions to delete an item from a one-way list.

11.13. Modify the program of Problem 11.12 to add deleted items to a free-storage list.

11.14. Write a garbage-collection program. You may assume that everything in memory except list LIST is garbage.

11.15. Write a subroutine to add an element to a two-way linked list.

11.16. Write a program to delete an element from a two-way linked list.

11.17. Modify the program of Problem 11.15 to use the single pointer field SUC $\oplus$ PRED.

11.18. Modify the program of Problem 11.16 to use the single field SUC $\oplus$ PRED.

11.19. Construct a figure to show the threaded-list elements and structure for the membership roster described in the text.

11.20. Develop a threaded-list structure for a list of students at your school. Consider the threads needed. Show figures for the elements and an example of several related elements.

Section 11.15

11.21. Perform preorder, inorder, and postorder traversals on the binary trees of Fig. 11.11.

11.22. Show how to store the binary tree of Fig. 11.12 in an array.

11.23. Show how to store the binary trees of Fig. 11.11 in arrays.

Section 11.6

11.24. Assume that you have a computer that stores subroutine return addresses in a fixed location. Flowchart the steps necessary to save the return addresses in a stack and restore them to the fixed location for eventual return.

High-Level Languages

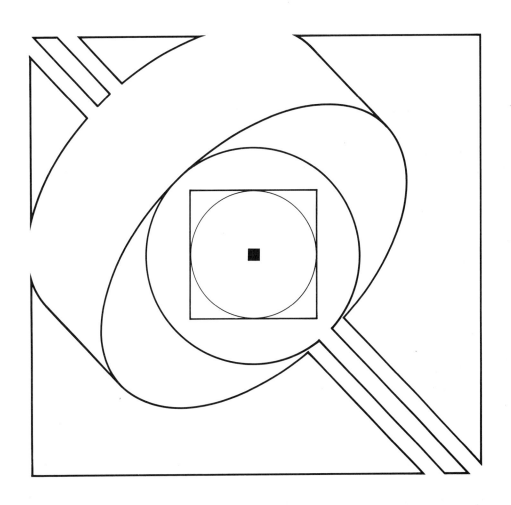

12.1 *Introduction*

12.1.1 *High-Level Versus Assembly Language*

In earlier chapters we examined machine and assembly language programming. We have seen that these languages are closely related to the hardware of a computer. For example, the number of registers and the type of logic circuits on a computer determine many of its instructions. With assembly language programming we can directly control the sequence of instructions a computer executes. If we are good assembly language programmers, we can write highly efficient programs—ones that execute quickly and take little memory.

Yet we are well aware of the disadvantages of assembly language programming. The instructions we can use are very simple. We may have to write a dozen or more statements to multiply two numbers together. If we have little time, we might gladly sacrifice the efficiency of assembly language programming for the convenience of writing a single statement to perform several arithmetic operations, such as

$$X = A + B * (C/(D - E)).$$

Furthermore, we may prefer to write programs that are **machine independent** —programs that will run on several different computers. Assembly language is **machine dependent;** a program written for one type of computer will not run on another. We must learn a new assembly language for each new computer. The situation is much like that of learning foreign languages. Learning one foreign language helps us develop skills that may make learning the second easier. A second foreign language usually has some words that are similar to those of the first, or to English words. Similarly, in assembly language programming we will see identical or similar mnemonics such as HALT or HLT. Sentence construction in two foreign languages may be similar; instruction types in two assembly languages may be the same. Yet no matter how much two foreign languages or two assembly languages may be alike, we still long for a universal language.

High-level languages attempt to satisfy our needs for powerful, machine-independent languages. They are oriented toward general procedures rather than toward specific computers. In this chapter we will look at high-level languages commonly used on minicomputers and microcomputers. BASIC is a relatively simple language that can be used for both scientific and business problems. FORTRAN is the most common scientific language for both large and small computers. Versions of PL/I, another scientific language, are used on some microcomputers. Pascal is a relatively new language that is well suited to handling data structures. Our discussions of each language are brief and are intended to compare features of the languages. If you want to program in any of these languages, you will want to consult a manual of that language for your computer. We will also look at the programs that translate high-level language programs into machine instructions.

High-level languages give us a choice. When we write in assembly language we are limited to the instructions that the computer designer has selected. When we write in high-level languages we can do the choosing, because many small computers offer compilers for several high-level languages. Thus, it is important to consider their relative advantages and disadvantages so that we can select the one that is best for our application. Of course, if our computer offers only one high-level language, we have less freedom. Even so, we may be able to persuade someone to write a compiler for another high-level language for us, or we can learn to write one ourselves. Hence, we should always be aware of the relative strengths and weaknesses of the most common high-level languages.

12.1.2 *Structured Programming*

In looking at each high-level language, we will keep in mind good programming practices. As we noted in the discussion of assembly language programming, we should write programs as collections of modules, such as subroutines. A well-written program consists of clearly defined modules, each of which has a definite purpose. The rigid formats of assembly language make it difficult for us to identify modules, except through comments. Most high-level languages have more flexible formats. With them we can distinguish between major and minor modules. We can use top-down programming; that is, we can solve our problem by dividing it into modules and then subdividing each module into submodules until we arrive at statements that can be coded. Then, when we have written the lines of code for each module, we can arrange the modules in such a way that the structure of the program is apparent—each time we go from a major module into a submodule, we indent the lines of code. This technique is especially helpful when we have loops nested within loops. We can also comment frequently to identify the purpose of each module.

An important feature of high-level languages is their control structure. Language experts consider some control structures more desirable than others. For example, they think that unrestricted jumps, usually called GO TO statements, are undesirable because they can detract from the modular structure of good programs. Certainly, GO TO statements can make programs harder to follow and to debug. We will elaborate on this point when we examine each of these languages.

Another feature we will consider is permissible **identifiers,** or names for variables. As in assembly language programming, we like names to be descriptive. Colorful names can clarify and help to document programs. Thus we prefer names such as SUM, ARRAY, SQROOT, and the like. Assembly languages usually restrict variable names to six alphanumeric characters with no embedded spaces. This restriction cramps our style. We can't name variables MULTIPLICAND or SQUARE ROOT. High-level languages vary considerably in the variable names they allow.

High-level languages handle labels in a different way from assembly languages. Statement labels are not given descriptive names. Instead, two of the languages we will study use statement numbers. The third language, because of its structure, needs no statement labels.

12.2 BASIC

Because of its small number of commands, BASIC is one of the simplest high-level languages to learn. Its name is an acronym for Beginner's All-Purpose Symbolic Instruction Code. BASIC was developed at Dartmouth College by John G. Kemeny and Thomas E. Kurtz. It lets the user communicate interactively with the computer. The user types a series of numbered statements, using common English words and mathematical notation.

12.2.1 BASIC Example 1: Temperature Conversion

The clarity of BASIC programs is demonstrated by the example in Table 12.1. We can understand most of it without prior knowledge of BASIC. Let us examine the program as a whole and then consider each line in turn.

Table 12.1
BASIC program to convert fahrenheit to celsius

```
10   REMARK TEMPERATURE CONVERSION
20   PRINT "FAHRENHEIT", "CELSIUS"
30   FOR F = 0 TO 100 STEP 1
40        LET C = (9/5) * (F −32)
50        PRINT F, C
60   NEXT F
70   END
```

First we note that each line begins with a **line number.** Line numbers identify the statements of the program—10, 20, 30, and so on. They also show the order in which the statements should be executed. The instructions may be typed in any order. Before the program is run, the computer will sort and edit the statements, rearranging them into the order of their line numbers. We have chosen line numbers that are multiples of 10. This choice allows room for later insertion of statements to change the program. For example, if we wish to insert an instruction between lines 40 and 50, we can write it at the end of the program and give it a line number of, say, 45. The computer will handle the insertion; the corrected program can be printed in its desired order.

After each line number comes a simple, clear English word that shows the type of statement. BASIC has several types of statements, six of which are illustrated in this first example.

Although it may not be clear from the example, spaces have no significance in BASIC except in statements to be printed, which are enclosed in quotation marks. Spaces can even be placed in the middle of a word; for example, PR I N T is as acceptable as PRINT. Spaces may be inserted as desired to make a program neater and more readable. We will use spaces to indent submodules of our programs.

Now that we appreciate these general comments on BASIC programs, we can proceed through the program in Table 12.1 line by line. The first statement,

```
10    REMARK TEMPERATURE CONVERSION
```

is a comment statement. All such statements in BASIC must begin with the syllable REM or the word REMARK. The computer disregards anything on the same line following REM. Thus it disregards the ARK part of REMARK as well as the words TEMPERATURE CONVERSION, which give the purpose of the program.

The second statement,

```
20    PRINT "FAHRENHEIT", "CELSIUS"
```

is a print statement. It directs the computer to print the two expressions within the two sets of quotation marks. We need not worry about the spacing of these two titles. The BASIC system takes care of spacing and formatting problems for us. BASIC may contrast in this respect with FORTRAN. As we will see in the next section, some versions of FORTRAN require users to state formatting requirements explicitly.

The third statement,

```
30    FOR F = 0 TO 100 STEP 1
```

begins a loop. The loop operations are to be done for all values of F from 0 to 100 in steps (increments) of 1. That is, the operations will be done for F = 0, 1, 2, . . ., 100. If a step is not assigned, the computer assumes a step of +1.

The fourth statement,

```
40    LET C = (9/5) * (F - 32)
```

is a LET statement, which gives a formula to be evaluated. It directs the computer to set variable C equal to the expression on the right side of the equals sign. (The asterisk * shows multiplication.) We have indented this statement to show that it is within a module, in this case, a loop.

The fifth statement,

```
50    PRINT F, C
```

is another PRINT statement, which prints the values of F and C for each step of F. This statement is also indented because it is in a loop.

The sixth statement,

```
60    NEXT F
```

marks the end of the loop. Each time the NEXT statement is reached, the computer increases the value of the loop index (F) by one step (that is, by 1) and checks to see that the index has not exceeded its terminal value (100). As long as the index is less than or equal to its terminal value, the loop operations are repeated. Once the index exceeds it upper bound, control passes to the first statement outside the loop.

The seventh statement,

```
70    END
```

signals the end of the program

12.2.2 *BASIC Example 2: Area of Triangles*

A slightly longer BASIC program is shown in Table 12.2. Its flowchart is given in Fig. 12.1. Many of the BASIC statements are familiar, but there are a few new ones that deal with data. The fourth statement,

```
40    READ A, B, C
```

directs the computer to read data from the four data statements near the end of the program. This contrasts with the preceding example, in which "data" were generated by the FOR statement. The data are read in the order given in the READ statement. The first value read is considered to be A, the second is considered to be B, and so fourth. Data are read from the data statements, for example,

```
90    DATA 4, 5, 6
```

The result is A = 4, B = 5, and C = 6.

Table 12.2
BASIC program to compute area of triangles

```
10    REMARK TRIANGLE AREA PROGRAM
20    PRINT "A", "B", "C", "AREA"
30    FOR I = 1 TO 4
40        READ A, B, C
50        LET S = (A + B + C)/2
60        LET X = (S * (S − A) * (S − B) * (S − C))  ↑ 0.5
70        PRINT A, B, C, X
80    NEXT I
90    DATA 4, 5, 6
100   DATA 10, 15, 20
110   DATA 8, 8, 8
120   DATA 12, 15, 18
130   END
```

The only other new item in this program is the arrow ↑ in statement 60. It shows an exponent. In this case, the expression within the outer parentheses will be raised in the 0.5 power; that is, its square root will be taken.

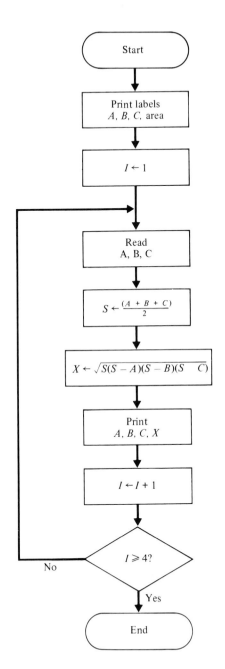

Fig. 12.1
Flowchart for computing areas of triangles.

Table 12.3
BASIC program to calculate the number of selections of 5 of 12 objects

```
10    REMARK CALCULATE 12!/(5! * 7!)
20    REMARK CALCULATE 12 FACTORIAL
30    LET N = 12
40    GO SUB 600
50    LET X = F
60    REMARK CALCULATE 5 FACTORIAL
70    LET N = 5
80    GO SUB 600
90    LET Y = F
100   REMARK CALCULATE 7 FACTORIAL
110   LET N = 7
120   GO SUB 600
130   LET Z = F
140   REMARK CALCULATE NUMBER OF COMBINATIONS
150   C = X/(Y * Z)
160   PRINT "THE NUMBER OF WAYS OF SELECTING"
170   PRINT "5 OBJECTS FROM 12 OBJECTS", C

600   REMARK—N FACTORIAL SUBROUTINE
610   REMARK ENTER SUBROUTINE WITH N
620   LET F = N
630   LET A = 1
640   LET F = F * (N − A)
650   LET A = A + 1
660   IF A < N THEN 640
670   REMARK F = N FACTORIAL (N!)
680   END
```

12.2.3 BASIC Example 3: Selection of Objects

BASIC programs can call subroutines. The call subroutine command is GOSUB N, where N is the line number (not the name) of the subroutine. Because BASIC ignores spaces, we can write the call as GO SUB if we wish. Table 12.3 shows a BASIC program that calculates the number of ways that five items can be selected from 12 objects. A subroutine is used for the factorial function, N factorial, written $N! = (N)(N-1)(N-2) \cdots 2 \cdot 1$. For example, $5! = 5 \times 4 \times 3 \times 2 \times 1$. The main program calculates

$$\frac{12!}{(5!)(7!)}$$

which is the mathematical expression for the desired selection. See any book on probability for an explanation.

12.2.4 BASIC Example 4: Sales Computation

Our final BASIC example, shown in Table 12.4, illustrates array calculations. Its flowchart is shown in Fig. 12.2. The name of an array in BASIC consists of

Table 12.4
BASIC program to compute sales

```
10    DIM P(4)
11    REMARK P(4) GIVES PRICE OF 4 PRODUCTS
20    FOR I = 1 TO 4
30         READ P(I)
40    NEXT I
50    DIM S(4,6)
51    REMARK S(4,6) GIVES NO. OF EACH PRODUCT SOLD BY
52    REMARK EACH OF 6 SELLERS, STORED IN ROW-MAJOR ORDER
60    FOR I = 1 TO 4
70         FOR J = 1 TO 6
80              READ S(I,J)
90         NEXT J
100   NEXT I
101   REMARK COMPUTE TOTAL SALES PER SELLER
110   FOR J = 1 TO 6
120        LET T = 0
130        FOR I = 1 TO 4
140             LET T = T + P(I) * S(I,J)
150        NEXT I
160        PRINT "TOTAL SALES FOR SELLER" J, "$", T
170   NEXT J
180   DATA 1.99, 4.76, 21.76, 3.95
181   REMARK PRICES PER PRODUCT FOR P(I)
190   DATA 42, 75, 100, 82, 61, 90
191   REMARK NUMBER OF PRODUCT 1 SOLD BY SELLERS 1 TO 6
192   REMARK FIRST ROW OF S(I,J)
200   DATA 51, 40, 29, 33, 17, 40
210   DATA 6, 9, 3, 7, 11, 2
220   DATA 29, 31, 14, 42, 18, 16
230   END
```

a single letter, such as A. Its elements can be designated by numbers in brackets or parentheses such as A(1), A(2), B(2,3), and so on. A dimension statement gives the maximum number of elements. Thus

```
10    DIM P(4)
```

means that array P has four elements. Similarly,

```
50    DIM 5(4,6)
```

means that array S has 24 elements arranged in four rows and six columns. DIM statements are not executed when programs are run. They simply provide information about array sizes to the BASIC system. If a dimension statement is omitted, the BASIC system may assume a maximum value for each dimension, such as 10. We call this value a **default option,** because the system assumes it. It is good practice to state dimensions explicitly rather than relying on the default option. When we state the dimensions of the array, the computer will save exactly the space the array needs; otherwise it will save the default value and

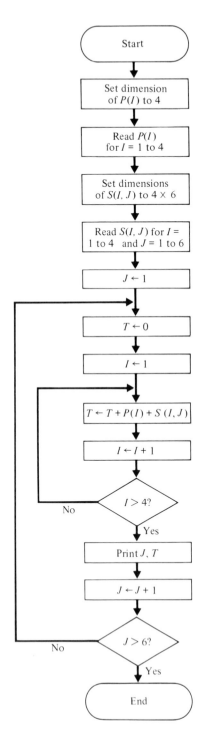

Fig. 12.2
Flowchart of program to compute sales of six sellers.

may waste space. For example, if we omitted the dimension statement of line 50, and if the default value is 10, the computer would save space for a 10×10 array instead of the actual 4×6 array.

The program calculates total sales for six sellers, each of whom sells four products. Array P holds the prices of the four products. Array S holds the quantity of each product sold by each seller; any row I of S holds the quantity of product I sold by each seller. That is, the rows represent the types of products; the columns represent the sellers. Nested FOR statements are given again in lines 110 through 170 to calculate and print total sales per seller. This program can be used again by modifying line 180 if prices change. It can be reused by changing lines 190 through 220 for new sales in another sales period. What lines must be changed if a new product is added? If a new seller is added?

12.2.5 BASIC Features

We could continue giving BASIC examples, but we have seen enough to appreciate the simplicity of this language. We can now turn our attention to its features. BASIC deals only with decimal numbers. It accepts any number with a decimal point and assumes a decimal point after the rightmost digit of any number without one. It also accepts numbers in an exponential notation of the form $xxEn$, which it interprets as xx times 10^n. Thus 24.3E-8 means 24.3×10^{-8}.

Variables are algebraic symbols representing numbers. A variable in BASIC may be identified by either a single letter or a single letter followed by a single digit. Thus A, C, X2, and D3 are acceptable variables. Because variable names are so restricted, we cannot give variables descriptive names, such as TEMPERATURE, AREA, or SUM.

The standard arithmetic operations of addition, subtraction, multiplication, division, and exponentiation can be applied to any variables or constants. Parentheses can be used to improve clarity or to establish priority. Common relational operators—equal to, less than, less than or equal to, greater than, greater than or equal to, and not equal to—can be used.

All high-level languages have **precedence** rules that state the order in which operations are to be performed. BASIC precedence rules can be summarized as follows.

1. Operations within parentheses are performed first.
2. In the absence of parentheses, the order of operations is
   a) exponentiation,
   b) multiplication or division (equal priority),
   c) addition or subtraction (equal priority).
3. In the absence of parentheses, operations of equal priority are performed from left to right.

Thus the computer would execute the BASIC statement

```
X = 2 * B ↑ 3 + C/D + E
```

in the following order.

1. Raise B to the third power.
2. Multiply by 2.
3. Divide C by D.
4. Add B^3 + C/D (the results of the last two operations).
5. Add E.

We can always insert parentheses if we wish to change this order. For example, in what order would the computer execute the operations in the following equation?

X = (2 * B) ↑ 3 + C/(D + E)

Precedence rules of other high-level languages are similar. We will not discuss those of FORTRAN and PL/I. Consult your programmer's manual if in doubt. Or just insert parentheses.

BASIC statements are summarized in Table 12.5. We have already discussed several of them; the meaning of the rest can be ascertained from the examples. As mentioned earlier, it is essential to consult a programming manual for the BASIC system on which the program is to be run before writing a program. BASIC systems differ in the limitations placed on BASIC features. For example, limits on the size of arrays differ from one computer to another. The input and output commands that refer to a particular device, such as a Teletype, may also differ.

Table 12.5
BASIC statements

Statement		Example	
REM	text	20	REMARK
READ	variable(s)	40	READ X, Y, Z
INPUT	variable(s)	37	INPUT A, B, D4
DATA	constant(s)	70	DATA 47, 61, 20
PRINT	expression(s)	64	PRINT "X=", X
LET	variable = expression	42	LET X = A * B ↑ 2
GO TO	line number	50	GO TO 70
IF	expression operator expression THEN line number	60	IF X = 4 THEN 100
FOR	variable = expression TO expression STEP expression	70	FOR A = 0 TO 50 STEP 2
NEXT	variable	61	NEXT B
END		120	END
GOSUB	line number	40	GOSUB 140
RETURN		80	RETURN

Suppose we have written a simple BASIC program and wish to run it on a small computer. A typical procedure for doing this follows.

1. Load the BASIC system tape into the computer and begin execution. The computer will then type READY.

2. Type your program on a Teletype or other terminal, ending each line by pressing the CARRIAGE RETURN key.

3. If you mistype, delete your errors with the reverse arrow (the shift key above the letter O). To delete an entire line, press ALT MODE.

4. If you make grammatical errors, such as omitting a line number or mistyping a command, the computer will type an error code as soon as it detects your error. You can correct the error immediately by typing a new line with the correct statement.

5. When you have typed your entire program, type RUN and push CARRIAGE RETURN. Your program should now run and print any results requested by your PRINT statements.

6. If the program appears to give wrong answers, you can stop it by typing STOP. Then you can identify the statements causing the errors, correct them, and run the program again.

As with any language, writing a BASIC program is only part of the battle. Debugging it correctly is important. While the error statements provided by the BASIC system can identify errors in construction, only careful attention by the programmer can find all logical and computational errors. Two ways to find such errors are the following.

1. Use test data that should yield known results. For example, knowledge of the correct Celsius equivalent of 2 degrees Fahrenheit can help to identify any error in the first BASIC program of this chapter. (Why is the conversion of 0 degrees Fahrenheit a poor test case?)

2. Insert PRINT statements to print intermediate results. For example, in the third program we could insert PRINT statements after each return from the subroutine so that we could check the correctness of each factorial calculation. We could also insert a PRINT statement after line 650 to print values of the factorial and A for loop calculations.

Many different versions of BASIC are available, especially for microcomputers. They differ primarily in the number of instructions offered and in their speed of execution. As a rule of thumb, the more powerful versions require more memory; hence one can expect an 8K version to be more powerful than a 4K version. You should be sure that any version of BASIC you want to use is adequate for your problems. Comparing BASIC implementations for some of your standard or benchmark problems will be helpful.

12.3 *FORTRAN*

FORTRAN is a more powerful and complex language than BASIC. It is the most common scientific programming language. As we did with BASIC, we will study FORTRAN by examining a series of examples. This procedure lets us immediately note superficial features of one language and compare them with those of another. It also lets us learn features and procedures of a language in context, rather than immediately facing a list of rules.

12.3.1 *FORTRAN Example 1: Calculation of Pay*

Our first FORTRAN example, shown in Table 12.6, is a program to calculate an employee's pay, given the hours worked and the pay rate. We can immediately spot several differences between this program and BASIC programs.

Table 12.6
FORTRAN program for calculating an
employee's pay from hours worked and
rate of pay

```
C      A PROGRAM TO CALCULATE PAY
       READ (1,10) HOURS, RATE
10     FORMAT (2F5.2)
       PAY = HOURS*RATE
       WRITE (1,20) PAY, HOURS, RATE
20     FORMAT (3F10.2)
       STOP
       END
```

Only a few of the lines have line numbers, not every line as in BASIC. In FORTRAN ordinarily only those lines to which another statement of the program refers are given line numbers. In this example, two FORMAT statements—which will be explained shortly—are given line numbers. They are numbered because the READ and WRITE statements must address them. Line numbers do not need to appear in numerical order, nor does the FORTRAN system execute them in numerical order. Not surprisingly, all statements should have different numbers. Line numbers are placed in the first few columns of a line, typically columns 1 through 4. A C in column 1 denotes a comment statement. Just as with a REMARK statement in BASIC, the computer disregards a comment.

These two points show the rigid formatting of a FORTRAN program. Unlike the free spacing of BASIC, the arrangement of FORTRAN programs, in many versions of FORTRAN, is tightly prescribed. Each statement should occupy a single line. If it is necessary to continue a command from one line to the next, a continuation symbol is needed. In many FORTRAN systems, continuation is signaled by a digit placed in column 6.

We also note that variables in FORTRAN are not limited to one or two characters as they were in BASIC. The variable names HOURS, RATE, and PAY show their purposes. We can decipher much of the program from them without guessing at the meanings of initials. FORTRAN variable names may have up to six letters or digits; the first character must be a letter. (Some small computer implementations of FORTRAN require fewer characters, but we will assume six here.)

FORTRAN distinguishes between two types of variables.

- **Integers** never have decimal points; they are whole numbers, such as 6, 538, and 41.
- **Real variables** are decimal numbers; they may have decimal points and fractional parts, such as 12.37.

FORTRAN variable names show the variable type. **Integer variables** must begin with I, J, K, L, M, or N. Thus integer variables must have names like

ITEM
INDEX
KVARI
LENGTH

Real variables must begin with any letter except I, J, K, L, M, or N. Hence real variables must have names like

X
PAY
PAGE4
WEIGHT
ATOM6

This distinction frequently results in programming errors. We must carefully identify all program variables to decide if they may ever take on a fractional part. If so, they should be real variables. We should avoid carelessly naming a real variable LENGTH or MASS; instead we can name it ALENG or AMASS. Similarly, we cannot name an integer variable COUNT; instead, we can choose JCOUNT or KOUNT. Some versions of FORTRAN have a REAL statement that allows declaring a variable as real regardless of its initial letter. Similarly, there is an INTEGER statement that allows declaring any variables as integers. We will assume that we do not have or perfer to use these two statements.

Now that we have noticed these superficial characteristics, we can examine the program of Table 12.6 line by line. We already understand the first line, a comment. The second line,

```
READ (1,10) HOURS, RATE
```

is a READ statement. It directs the computer to read data from device 1, possibly a Teletype, according to the format given by statement 10. (Device numbers are determined by the hardware configuration of a particular computer system.) The first value read will be assigned to variable HOURS, the second to variable RATE. The FORMAT statement

```
10    FORMAT (2F5.2)
```

states that the data are to be read as real variables. Each item within parentheses has a specific meaning. From left to right the items can be decoded as follows:

2   There are two values per line.
F   Values are decimal floating point.
5   Each datum has a field of five columns.
.2   Each datum has two decimal places to the right of the decimal point.

Data begin in column 1 with numbers right-justified. Typical data for this program might be

40.00 3.25

More generally, numeric data can be assigned in one of three forms:

rEw.d   For decimal floating point with E exponents, such as 0.67E-04 for 0.67×10^{-4}.
rFw.d   For decimal floating point.
rIw   For integers.

The codes here have the following meanings.

r   Repetition count, the number of times each datum is repeated on a line, can be omitted if 1.
w   **Field width,** number of columns for each datum.
d   Number of decimal places to the right of the decimal point.

The field width should always be big enough for the decimal point, sign, and exponents. If it is not, most FORTRAN systems print an error message. A number is always treated as right-justified in the field (placed far right). Blanks are ignored. Thus, in an F5.2 format with b representing a blank,

bbb40,   40bbb,   00.40

are all read as the number 0.40.

The next line in the program,

```
PAY = HOURS*RATE
```

is an arithmetic assignment statement. Except for the longer variable names, it looks much like a BASIC statement. In general, the same operators are used in both languages except that in FORTRAN a double asterisk, **, shows exponentiation.

All variables in this assignment statement are real variables. It is best to write any assignment statement with only one type of variable, either only real variables or only integer variables. Statements with both real and integer variables are called **mixed-mode** statements. FORTRAN compilers for different computers differ in their tolerance for mixed-mode statements; check yours for the ground rules. If the system allows mixed mode, problems can occur. Suppose an arithmetic assignment statement sets an integer variable equal to an expression of real variables. Then any fractional part of the result is dropped. For example, consider the equation

```
MONEY = HOURS*PAY
```

Suppose HOURS = 10.25 and PAY = 3.75. The result, 38.4375, will be truncated to 38 because MONEY is an integer variable. This is an example of real-mode calculations converted to integer.

   To avoid mixed-mode expressions, we must consider forms of constants. Constants may also be real or integer. Real constants are specified with a decimal point, for example,

1.0,   2.25,   48.0.

Integer constants do not have a decimal point, for example,

1,   0,   27.

Consider the differences in results using the two forms:

5/2 = 2   (integer mode),
5/2. = 2.5   (mixed mode).

What do you get when you write

x + 5/2,
I + 5/2,
I + 5./2?

No two compilers seem to be totally consistent on what to do.
   The next two statements,

```
      WRITE (1,20) PAY, HOURS, RATE
20    FORMAT (3F10.2)
```

are WRITE and FORMAT statements, respectively. We can decode most of them from what we know already. Evidently the computer is to write the values of PAY, HOURS, and RATE on device 1 according to format 20. Each will be shown with two places to the right of the decimal point. Although we will not need a field width of 10 for our data—we do not expect values to be greater than 999.99—the extra width allows for spaces. The output will be neater and more readable. Another way to provide spaces is to write

nX

for *n* spaces. We often use this notation for spaces between different types of fields. For example, we might write

```
20    FORMAT (F10.2, 4X, I6, 5X, I8, E5.2)
```

The last two statements of the program are

```
STOP
END
```

A STOP statement says stop processing. An END statement says there are no more statements in the program. STOP and END, in FORTRAN, are analogous to HALT (or HLT) and END statements in assembly language programs.

You may have noticed that this program calculates only one employee's pay each time it is run. It lacks instructions to tell it to read several sets of data so that it can calculate pay for several employees at one time. Later examples will illustrate repeated calculations.

12.3.2 *FORTRAN Example 2: Computation of N Factorial*

Our next FORTRAN example, shown in Fig. 12.3 and Table 12.7, illustrates more complex FORTRAN procedures. A quick glance at this program shows its modular structure. Blocks of the program can be easily identified; statements within a procedure are indented. Let us examine the statements of this program that are new to us.

The first one is a DO statement,

```
DO 10 N = 2, 30
```

A DO statement is a major and powerful FORTRAN procedure. It causes repeated executions of the statements between the DO and the statement number that follows DO. In this case the terminal statement is line number 10, a WRITE statement. Ordinarily, though, the terminal statement is a CONTINUE statement, as shown later in the program at line 3. This is a dummy statement that causes no processing action; it serves only to end the DO. All statements between DO and CONTINUE (or other terminal statement) are said to be in the **range** of the DO statement.

Each DO statement has an index, which is the variable following the statement number, in this case *N*. The next two values are the initial and final values of the index, here 2 and 30. More generally, the DO statement can take either of the following two forms:

DO *ni* = *A*, *B*, *C*
DO *ni* = *A*, *B*

Statements up to *n* are to be executed first with *i* = *A*. After that, *i* is incremented each time by *C*, if it is given, until *i* takes the largest value that does not exceed *B*. If the increment *C* is not given, as in our example, it is assumed to be 1. (*A*, *B*, and *C* must be integer type.)

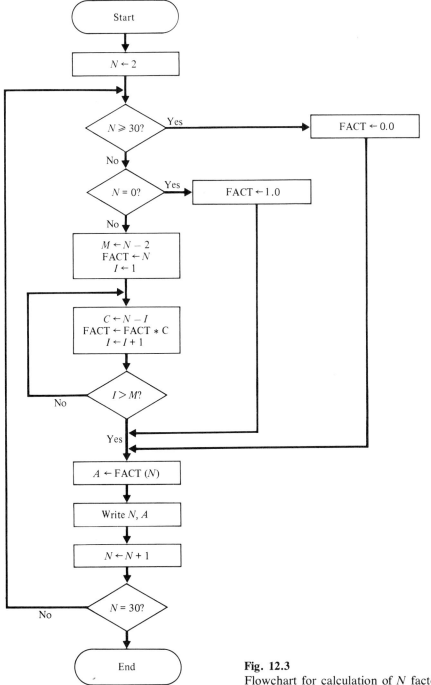

Fig. 12.3
Flowchart for calculation of N factorial.

Table 12.7
FORTRAN program to compute N factorial

```
C       FORTRAN PROGRAM FOR N FACTORIAL
        DO 10 N = 2, 30
              A = FACT(N)
C             OUTPUT STATEMENT AND FORMAT
10            WRITE (1,20) N, A
20            FORMAT (I4, 'FACTORIAL=', E14.7)
        STOP
        END
        FUNCTION FACT(N)
C       COMPUTATION OF N FACTORIAL
C       CHECK TO SEE IF N IS TOO LARGE FOR PROGRAM
        IF (N - 30) 1, 5, 5
1             IF (N) 2, 4, 2
C                   FOR N UNEQUAL TO 0
2                   M = N - 2
                    FACT = N
                    DO 3 I = 1, M
                          C = N - I
                          FACT = FACT *C
3                         CONTINUE
                    RETURN
C             ZERO FACTORIAL
4             FACT = 1.0
              RETURN
5             WRITE (1, 30) N
              FACT = 0.0
              RETURN
30      FORMAT (I4, 'FACTORIAL IS TOO LARGE FOR PROGRAM')
        END
```

The first statement in the range of the DO is

```
A = FACT(N)
```

It sets A equal to the value of the user-defined function FACT(N). [Because FACT(N) is a function, not an array, it does not appear in a DIMENSION statement. FORTRAN has a DIMENSION statement, similar to the BASIC one, that must appear before any other reference to an array.] The next two statements provide output in much the same way as in the previous example.

We note something new in the FORMAT statement

```
20    FORMAT (I4, 'FACTORIAL=', E14.7)
```

It will cause the printing of the alphanumeric material between the single quote marks, namely FACTORIAL=. It follows the integer value of N and the E form for A, resulting in an output such as

```
4 FACTORIAL = 0.24 E+02
```

With this specification, the material between single quotes is reproduced exactly. If we wanted spaces between the value of N and FACTORIAL we could write

```
20    FORMAT (I4, 'FACTORIAL=', E14.7)
```

Another way to print characters is with an H field. We could print the same message with a FORMAT statement.

```
20    FORMAT (I4, 13H FACTORIAL=, E14.7)
```

The 13H means that the characters, including spaces, after the H are to be printed. More generally, the notation

$$n \, H c_1 c_2 c_3 \cdots c_n$$

means that the characters c_1 through c_n should be printed (or read). The disadvantage of this notation, as contrasted with surrounding the characters with quote marks, is that we must count the characters. If we miscount, we will receive an error message.

The FORMAT statement ends the DO procedure, and the main program ends.

The rest of the program defines the function FACT(N). After two comments it begins with another major FORTRAN procedure, an arithmetic IF statement:

```
IF (N - 30) 1,5,5
```

This statement checks the value of the quantity within parentheses, namely $N - 30$. It directs the system to branch to one of the following three statements as follows:

Branch to statement numbered...	if (N − 30) is
1	less than 0
5	equal to 0
5	greater than 0

More generally, an arithmetic IF statement takes the form

IF (expression) A, B, C

Control transfers to statements numbered A, B, or C depending on whether the value of the expression is less than 0, equal to 0, or greater than 0, respectively.

Arithmetic IF statements have the disadvantages of being hard to read and of possibly transferring control from one module of a program into another module. If the programmer is not careful when using IF statements, he or she can lose track of the main flow of control. Procedures like DO, which keep control within a module, are preferred. Control can and should transfer from one module to another in sequence. It is best to avoid statements that allow control to branch to any of three places that may be anywhere in a program. In the next example we will see another type of IF statement that is less disadvantageous.

Returning to our program, we can see that if N is less than 30 (so that $N - 30$ is less than 0), the next statement executed is 1, which we will discuss momentarily. Otherwise control goes to statement 5. In this case N is too large for the factorial function programmed here. Statement 5 begins a module that prints the message that

```
N FACTORIAL IS TOO LARGE FOR PROGRAM
```

with the value of N stated.

When N is less than 30, the next statement executed is another IF statement

```
IF (N) 2, 4, 2
```

We realize this means to proceed to statement 4 if N equals 0; otherwise proceed to statement 2. (The program interprets the factorial function of $-N$ to be the same as for N.) If N is 0, control transfers to a statement that sets the factorial function FACT to 1.0. (Why doesn't it set it to 1?) Then control returns to the main program with the statement

```
RETURN
```

Definitions of FORTRAN functions always end by transferring control to the main program with a RETURN statement. This function definition in fact has three RETURN statements—one for normal return, one for return when N is too large, and one for return when N is 0.

When N is between 0 and 30, control transfers to the module beginning with statement 2 for calculation of the factorial. Within this module is a submodule consisting of a DO statement and its range. You should trace through the calculations for a small value of N, say $N = 5$, to convince yourself that the process works.

12.3.3 FORTRAN Example 3: Calculating Grades with a Subroutine

Our next FORTRAN example, shown in Table 12.8, is substantially more complex than the preceding two. It uses a subroutine to sort an array of grades and calculate several statistics for it. The main program calls the subroutine three times to sort the grades and calculate statistics for three groups of students—all students, freshmen, and sophomores. This program might be used at a community college. After reading it, you should be able to extend it to calculate grades for juniors and seniors also, so that it might be used at a four-year college. We will examine the main program first.

The main program begins with a series of comments that describe the purpose of the program and explain the full meaning of all variable names. This type of documentation is important in a large program where there are many variables. Not only does it make a program clearer to other people, but it also helps the programmer review a program written some days or weeks before. Without these comments, we would have to search through the program to learn that TEST is an array and GRADE is a single test score. DIMENSION statements for arrays TEST, SOPH, and FR immediately follow the comments and precede other references to these arrays. The test scores are to be read with each student's score followed by a code that shows his or her class. A series of up to 100 pairs of test scores and class codes are to be read. After the last pair comes an input called a **sentinel,** which signals the end of the scores. In this program the sentinel is a negative score. Each score is checked to see whether it is the sentinel by a logical IF statement:

```
IF (GRADE .LT. 0.0) GO TO 30
```

In a logical IF statement, the expression within parentheses is checked to see if it is logically true. If so, some action is taken; in this case, control passes to statement 30 if GRADE is less than 0, as shown by

```
GO TO 30
```

Otherwise control proceeds in sequence. The second part of the statement is called a GO TO procedure for evident reasons. Programming experts frown on GO TO statements because they allow control to transfer out of a module without automatically providing for return to the module. One other part of this IF statement needs explanation, the notation .LT. This mean "less than." FORTRAN has similar relational operators for the other **equality** relations:

.EQ.   Equal to
.NE.   Not equal to
.LE.   Less than or equal to
.GT.   Greater than
.GE.   Greater than or equal to

Until the sentinel is read, each value of GRADE is read into two arrays—the main test array and either the freshman or sophomore array, as determined by the student code. Then the pointers are incremented. Another IF statememt,

```
IF (KTEST .LE. 101) GO TO 10
```

assures that no more than 100 scores will be read even if the sentinel is not found. (Why is the limit actually 100 instead of 101?) After the scores have been read, *N* is calculated.

Then the subroutine SCORES is called:

```
CALL SCORES (TEST, N, TOP, BOT, AMEAN, AMEDN, RANGE)
```

We can see that the general form of the subroutine call command is CALL, followed by the name of the subroutine, SCORES in this case. All parameters of the subroutine are listed in parentheses in the order determined by the

Table 12.8
FORTRAN program to calculate class grades using a subroutine

```
C       A PROGRAM TO CALCULATE SCORES ON AN EXAMINATION BY CLASS
C       VARIABLE NAMES
C       TEST        UNSORTED ARRAY OF ALL TEST SCORES
C       GRADE       TEMPORARY STORAGE FOR EACH TEST SCORE
C       SOPH        SOPHOMORE GRADES
C       FR          FRESHMAN GRADES
C       KSOPH       INDEX OF SOPHOMORE ARRAY
C       KFR         INDEX OF FRESHMAN ARRAY
C       KTEST       INDEX OF TEST ARRAY
C       KODE        CODE SOPH = 2, FR = 1
        DIMENSION   TEST (101), SOPH(101), FR(101)
C       INITIALIZE POINTERS
        KTEST = 1
        KSOPH = 1
        KFR = 1
10      READ (1,20) GRADE, KODE
20      FORMAT (F10,0, I1)
C       CHECK FOR END OF SCORES - A NEGATIVE SCORE
        IF (GRADE .LT. 0.0) GO TO 30
C       ENTER GRADE INTO APPROPRIATE ARRAYS
        TEST (KTEST) = GRADE
        IF (KODE .EQ. 2) SOPH (KSOPH) = GRADE
        IF (KODE .EQ. 1) FR(KFR) = GRADE
C       INCREMENT POINTERS
        IF (KODE .EQ. 2) KSOPH = KSOPH + 1
        IF (KODE .EQ. 1) KFR = KFR + 1
        KTEST = KTEST + 1
C       A MAXIMUM OF 100 SCORES MAY BE READ
        IF (KTEST .LE. 101) GO TO 10
C       PROCESS COMPLETE TEST GRADES FIRST
30      N = KTEST - 1
        CALL SCORES (TEST, N, TOP, BOT, AMEAN, AMEDN, RANGE)
        WRITE (1,40)
40      FORMAT (1X, 'TOTAL GRADES')
        WRITE (1,50)
50      FORMAT (5X, 'N', 6X, 'TOP SCORE', 1X, 'BOTTOM SCORE',
        14X. 'MEAN', 7X, 'MEDIAN', 7X, 'RANGE')
        WRITE (1,60) N, TOP, BOT, AMEAN, AMEDN, RANGE
60      FORMAT (5X, I3, 4X, 5F 12.2)

C       PROCESS SOPHOMORE GRADES
        N = KSOPH -1
        CALL SCORES (SOPH, N, TOP, BOT, AMEAN, AMEDN, RANGE)
        WRITE (1,90)
90      FORMAT (1X, 'SOPHOMORE GRADES')
        WRITE (1,50)
        WRITE (1,60) N, TOP, BOT, AMEAN, AMEDN, RANGE

C       PROCESS FRESHMAN GRADES
        N = KFR - 1
        CALL SCORES (FR, N, TOP, BOT, AMEAN, AMEDN, RANGE)
        WRITE (1,100)
```

Table 12.8 (cont.)

```
100     FORMAT (1X, 'FRESHMAN GRADES')
        WRITE (1,50)
        WRITE (1,60) N, TOP, BOT, AMEAN, AMEDN, RANGE
        STOP
        END


C       SUBROUTINE SCORES SORTS AN ARRAY OF SCORES AND CALCULATES
C       MEAN, MEDIAN, TOP SCORE, BOTTOM SCORE, AND RANGE
C       VARIABLES
C       A          ARRAY OF SCORES
C       N          NUMBER OF
C       TOP        TOP SCORE IN ARRAY
C       BOT        BOTTOM SCORE OF ARRAY
C       NMI1       N-1, OUTER LOOP PARAMETER
C       I          OUTER LOOP INDEX
C       IPL1       I + 1, INNER LOOP PARAMETER
C       J          INNER LOOP INDEX
C       TEMP       TEMPORARY STORAGE
C       AMEAN      ARRAY MEAN
C       AMEDN      ARRAY MEDIAN
        SUBROUTINE SCORES (A, N, TOP, BOT, AMEAN, AMEDN, RANGE)
        DIMENSION A(100)
C       SORT ARRAY
        NMI1 = N - 1
        DO     25  I = 1, NMI1
            IPL1 = I + 1
            DO     15  J = IPL1, N
                IF (A(I) .LE. A(J)) GO TO 15
                    TEMP = A(I)
                    A(I) = A(J)
                    A(J) = TEMP
15          CONTINUE
25      CONTINUE
C       CALCULATE SUM OF GRADES
        SUM = 0.0
        DO     35  K = 1, N
            SUM = SUM + A(K)
35      CONTINUE
C       CALCULATE MEAN AND MEDIAN
        AMEAN = SUM/N
        NHALF = N/2
C       MEDIAN FOR EVEN N
        AMEDN = (A(NHALF) + A(NHALF + 1))/2.0
C       MEDIAN FOR ODD N
        IF (2 * NHALF .NE. N) AMEDN = A(NHALF + 1)
C       CALCULATE TOP, BOTTOM, AND RANGE
        TOP = A(N)
        BOT = A(1)
        RANGE = TOP - BOT
        RETURN
        END
```

subroutine. In this program we call subroutine SCORES three times. Only the first two parameters differ as they are passed to the subroutine. The first name given is the array of grades to be processed, the second is the number of grades. The remaining parameters will be calculated by the subroutine and passed back to the main program. After each return from the subroutine all parameters are printed.

We next examine the subroutine. Like the main program, it begins with explanations of all variables. The array is sorted in ascending order with a bubble sort routine, as in Chapter 11, that uses nested DO statements. Then all desired statistics are calculated. The FORTRAN statements for these calculations are familiar. The subroutine ends with the command

```
RETURN
```

12.3.4 *FORTRAN Features*

Although we could continue with FORTRAN examples, we have already seen most of the procedures and can now compare FORTRAN with BASIC. Here we will summarize some of the main features of FORTRAN as they are typically implemented on small computers.

We have already discussed FORTRAN constants, variables, and expressions. We noted that FORTRAN allows more descriptive names than BASIC and more types of constants and variables. However, it constrains our selections of names by rules for the first letter. Barring special statements to the contrary, integer constants and variables must begin with I, J, K, L, or M; real constants and variables must begin with any other letter. In other respects, FORTRAN expressions resemble BASIC expressions except for minor differences in notation. However, in FORTRAN we must be careful in the way we specify numbers. We should avoid mixed-mode expressions. FORTRAN systems differ in their tolerance of incorrectly specified numbers (a real for an integer, for example) and of mixed-mode expressions.

FORTRAN has five types of statements: arithmetic, input/output, control, specification, and subprogram.

Arithmetic statements define calculations to be performed. They have the general form

```
VARIABLE = EXPRESSION
```

The expression on the right side is calculated; the resulting value is assigned to the variable on the left. Examples are:

```
N = N + 1
ALPHA = 3.0*BETA + GAMMA/2.0
```

Input/output statements control data transfers between input/output devices and computer memory. They may be executable statements, such as

READ and WRITE, or nonexecutable FORMAT statements. Examples are:

```
    READ (1, 20) A, B, C
    WRITE (1,30) X, Y, Z
40  FORMAT (I6, 4X, 3F7.2, 2X, E9.2, 'FOR X')
```

Control statements govern the sequence of execution of statements. Examples are:

```
GO TO 20
GO TO (10, 20, 30) K
IF (X-2.0) 4, 5, 6
IF (X .GE. 10.0) GO TO 50
DO 20 ITEM = 1, 50, 2
CONTINUE
PAUSE
STOP
END
```

Some of these statements are new to us. An unconditional GO TO statement, such as

```
GO TO 20
```

transfers control unconditionally to the statement whose number is given. A computed GO TO statement, such as

```
GO TO (10, 20, 30) K
```

transfers control to the first statement named if the variable is 1, the second statement named if it is 2, and so on. In this case, control transfers to statement 10 if $K = 1$, to statement 20 if $K = 2$, or to statement 30 if $K = 3$. Computed GO TO statements can be troublesome. Consider what happens if K is not 1, 2, or 3. All GO TO statements are best avoided.

The PAUSE statement stops execution until the operator presses the CONTinue key on the console. It may be used when the operator needs to change tapes or perform some other action. Similarly, the STOP statement ends execution.

Specification statements provide the FORTRAN system with information about variables, constants, and arrays. When used, they must appear before any executable statements of a program. Examples are:

```
DIMENSION A(100)
COMMON X, Y, Z
EQUIVALENCE (A, B)
```

We have not yet discussed these last two statements. A COMMON statement causes the variables or arrays named to be stored where other programs can access them. It lets a main program and subprogram share a common storage area much as global variables do in assembly language programs. The EQUIVALENCE statement saves storage space by assigning the same location to each variable within a pair of parentheses. The statement

```
EQUIVALENCE (A, B)
```

means that *A* and *B* have the same value and hence may be assigned the same storage location. The same variables may not appear in both COMMON and EQUIVALENCE statements.

Subprogram statements define the form and provide for the control of subprograms. Examples are:

```
FUNCTION FACT(N)
SUBROUTINE AMULT (X, Y, Z)
CALL AMULT (A1, A2, PROD)
RETURN
```

Besides the user-defined functions and subroutines previously discussed, most FORTRAN systems have **library functions,** such as SIN and SQRT. Library subprograms are available to all users, much like books in a library.

For quick reference and for comparison with BASIC, these statements are summarized in Table 12.9.

Table 12.9
Summary of FORTRAN statements

Abbreviations Used:

var = variable   *d* = device number
exp = expression   *f* = field descriptors
  n = statement number   *i* = integer

Statement	Example
var = exp	A = 4.0B + C
READ (*d,n*) var, var	READ (1,20) X, Y, Z
WRITE (*d,n*) var, var	WRITE (1,30) ITEM, J
FORMAT (*f,f,f*)	FORMAT (4I, 2X, 3F5.2)
GO TO *n*	GO TO 20
GO TO (*n,n,n,n*)*i*	GO TO (12, 15, 17, 14) I
IF (exp) action	IF (Y−2.0) GO TO 30
	IF (X) Y = Z
IF (exp) *n,n,n*	IF (Y = X ↑ 2) 14, 18, 19
DO *n* var = *i,i,i*	DO 45 N = 5, 100, 5
DO *n* var = *i,i*	DO 31 N = 1, 20
CONTINUE	CONTINUE
PAUSE	PAUSE
STOP	STOP
END	END
DIM array (*i,i*)	DIM A(4, 6), C(50)
COMMON var, var, var	COMMON - ITEM, INDEX, X1
EQUIVALENCE (var, var)	EQUIVALENCE (WHITE, BLACK)
FUNCTION name (var, var)	FUNCTION CALC (DIF, J)
SUBROUTINE name (var, var)	SUBROUTINE GIVE (ME, INFO)
CALL name (var, var)	CALL GIVE (YOU, KFACTS)
RETURN	RETURN

The next high-level language we will study is PL/I. Various subsets of PL/I have been implemented for small computers, especially microcomputers. These subsets or versions of PL/I differ more from PL/I as implemented on large computers and from each other than is the case with BASIC or FORTRAN. Intel has its PL/M; Motorola has its MPL; and each feels free to substitute characters and devise restrictions as suits its need. Consequently, rather than closely following a particular microcomputer version of PL/I, we will instead examine PL/I as it exists on larger computers. Occasionally we will point out differences in microcomputer versions.

12.4.1   *PL/I Example 1: Sum of Two Variables*

As we did with the other two languages, we will begin our discussion with a simple example. Table 12.10 presents a PL/I program to compute the sum of two variables.

Table 12.10
PL/I program to compute the sum of two variables

```
SUM_OF_2:   PROCEDURE OPTIONS (MAIN);
            /* PROGRAM CALCULATES SUM OF TWO INTEGERS */
            DECLARE
                  NUMBER_1 FIXED DECIMAL (6,0),
                  NUMBER_2 FIXED DECIMAL (6,0),
                  TOTAL FIXED DECIMAL (6,0);
            GET LIST (NUMBER_1, NUMBER_2);
            TOTAL = NUMBER_1 + NUMBER_2;
            PUT DATA (NUMBER_1, NUMBER_2, TOTAL):
            END SUM_OF_2;
```

As before, we first note several gross features of the language. Having grown accustomed to the line numbers of BASIC and FORTRAN, we immediately note their absence in this PL/I program. The absence of line numbers means less bookkeeping for the programmer. No more remembering which of three statements an IF statement should branch to or what FORMAT goes with what WRITE statement! (PL/I does have numbers called level numbers, but we will not be concerned with them.) Besides lacking line numbers, PL/I uses few labels of any kind, which again means less bookkeeping.

Next we notice that all PL/I statements end with semicolons. Because a semicolon rather than a new line shows the end of a PL/I statement, we are free to continue PL/I statements from one line to the next, as shown by the DECLARE statement in this program. If we liked, we could also write two or more PL/I statements on one line. However, in this text we will always begin each new PL/I statement on a new line. We recommend this practice for clarity.

The sole exception to the rule that every PL/I statement end with a semicolon is comments. As we can guess by reading the program, PL/I comments begin with /* and end with */. Everything between these two identifiers is ignored by the PL/I system. If desired, comments can be inserted in the middle of other PL/I statements. For example, the DECLARE statement could be rewritten:

```
DECLARE NUMBER_1 FIXED (6,0) /* ADDEND IS
     READ FROM DATA */, NUMBER_2 FIXED (6,0) /*
     AUGEND IS READ FROM DATA */, TOTAL
     FIXED (6,0) /* SUM WILL BE OUTPUTTED */;
```

Each comment then describes a variable. This usage of comments is sometimes called a **variable dictionary.** Writing a variable dictionary forces the programmer to think about the purpose of each variable and may facilitate using each variable consistently throughout the program.

We note that variable names in PL/I can be longer than in FORTRAN. For example, our short program featured names such as NUMBER_1 and NUMBER_2. Most versions of PL/I allow variable names to be as long as 31 characters, a length that allows complete spellings of most descriptions. Because PL/I allows such long descriptions, we have no excuse for choosing shorter names, such as X or Y. Naturally there are some other restrictions:

1. Each name must begin with a letter or with one of the special characters @, #, or $.
2. Each character of the name may be any of the above, a digit, or the underscore character, _. The underscore primarily substitutes for spaces (not allowed) and provides readability, for example, THIS_ IS_ A_ LONG_ VARIABLE_ NAME. (In PL/M the dollar sign is used instead of the underscore, for example, THISISA$LONG$VARIABLE$NAME. The developers of PL/M claim that the dollar sign improves readibility; you can decide for yourself whether they are right.)
3. Words with special meanings in PL/I (and PL/M) cannot serve as variable names.

Let us now note that PL/I programs consist of modules called procedures. Each procedure is a sequence of statements that begins with

PROCEDURE

and ends with

END

So that different procedures can be distinguished, each one has a name, called an **entry name.** It is followed by a colon. In Table 12.10, SUM_OF_2 is an entry name. The end of each procedure is clearly identified by also placing the entry name after its END statement.

One procedure in a program must be the **main procedure.** A statement designating the main procedure has the general form:

```
ENTRY_NAME: PROCEDURE OPTIONS (MAIN);
```

Having made these preliminary observations, let us examine the program in Table 12.10 line by line. The first line,

```
SUM_OF_2:  PROCEDURE OPTIONS (MAIN);
```

designates SUM_OF_2 as the main procedure of this program. (Because this is a simple program, SUM_OF_2 is also the only procedure of the program.)

The next line of the program is a comment that describes the purpose of the program. The third line is a DECLARE statement:

```
DECLARE
      NUMBER_1 FIXED DECIMAL (6,0),
      NUMBER_2 FIXED DECIMAL (6,0),
      TOTAL FIXED DECIMAL (6,0);
```

Each PL/I procedure ordinarily has a DECLARE statement just after the procedure name. This statement gives attributes to the variables of the procedure. DECLARE statements can be omitted, because PL/I has **default conventions** that give attributes to any variables the programmer omits from a DECLARE statement; however, it is best not to rely on the default attributes. Instead, declare the attributes you wish your variables to have.

In this case, each variable is given the attribute FIXED DECIMAL (6, 0). FIXED means that the variables are fixed-point numbers. DECIMAL means that they are decimal. (The default value is binary.) (6,0) means that they have at most 6 significant figures and that 0 of them are to the right of the decimal point. Thus the variables are integers that may range between $-999,999$ and $+999,999$. More generally, the attribute:

FIXED DECIMAL (m,d)

means that the variables described have up to m significance figures, of which d are to the right of the decimal point. In standard PL/I, m may be any integer up to 15.

Numeric variables may also be given the attribute FLOAT, meaning floating-point. The notation

FLOAT DECIMAL (n)

where n is any integer between 6 and 16, shows that the variable named is a decimal floating-point number with up to n significant digits. Standard PL/I can represent numbers from 10^{-75} to 10^{+75}.

Other forms of the DECLARE statement are used for characters. For example, the statement

DECLARE MESSAGE CHARACTER (80) VARYING;

allows the variable MESSAGE to store a string of up to 80 characters. The word VARYING can be deleted if the programmer is certain that the character string will be exactly 80 characters. As many as 256 characters can be declared in a single character string.

Microcomputer versions of PL/I have different DECLARE statements. For example, PL/M allows declarations of BYTE or ADDRESS data. BYTE variables have 8-bit values; ADDRESS variables have 16-bit values. Character strings can also be handled.

When there are several variables with the same attributes they can be listed within parentheses, followed by the intended attribute. For example, in this program the DECLARE statement could be written

```
DECLARE (NUMBER_1, NUMBER_2, TOTAL) FIXED DECIMAL (6,0);
```

The next statement,

```
GET LIST (NUMBER_1, NUMBER_2);
```

is an input statement, called a GET LIST statement in PL/I. It directs the computer to read the next two values from the input data stream and assign them to NUMBER_1 and NUMBER_2. No format statement or device number is needed.

The next statement,

```
TOTAL = NUMBER_1 + NUMBER_2;
```

is an assignment statement much like those in BASIC and FORTRAN.

The output statement

```
PUT DATA (NUMBER_1, NUMBER_2, TOTAL);
```

prints all three values. In this case, the values of all three variables are to be printed. As in the GET LIST statement, we do not need to specify a format. The PL/I system automatically prints the names of variables along with their values in a predetermined format.

As described earlier, the final statement,

```
END SUM_OF_2;
```

ends the procedure.

12.4.2 *PL/I Example 2: Sorting an Array*

Our second PL/I example is sorting an array, following the bubble sort described earlier. The program will repeatedly scan the array, exchanging adjacent elements that are not in ascending order (see Table 12.11). First we must declare the array A to be sorted:

```
DECLARE A(100) FIXED DECIMAL (6,0);
```

This statement declares A to be an array of 100 decimal integers. In the

Table 12.11
PL/I program to sort an array

```
SORT:           PROCEDURE OPTIONS (MAIN);
                /* PROGRAM SORTS ARRAY IN ASCENDING ORDER */
                DECLARE A(100) FIXED DECIMAL (6,0);
                    /* ARRAY TO BE SORTED */
                DECLARE
                     INDEX FIXED DECIMAL (3,0) /* ARRAY INDEX */,
                     NUMBER FIXED DECIMAL (3,0) /* NUMBER OF
                         INTEGERS READ */,
                     FLAG FIXED DECIMAL (1,0) /*FLAG SHOWING
                         ANOTHER SCAN REQUIRED */,
                     TEMP FIXED DECIMAL (6,0) /* TEMPORARY STORAGE
                         FOR EXCHANGING ELEMENTS */,
                     I FIXED DECIMAL (3,0) /* SCAN INDEX */,
                     LAST FIXED DECIMAL (3,0) /* LAST SCAN */,
                /* READ UP TO 100 ELEMENTS INTO ARRAY AND CHECK
                     FOR NUMBER READ */
                ON ENDFILE (SYSIN) FLAG = 1;
                FLAG = 0;
                INDEX = 1;
                GET LIST (A(INDEX));
READ:           DO WHILE ((INDEX < 100) & (FLAG = 0));
                     INDEX = INDEX + 1;
                     GET LIST (A(INDEX));
                END READ;
                NUMBER = INDEX - 1;
                /* BEGIN THE BUBBLE SORT. EXAMINE ADJACENT ELEMENTS
                OF A. EXCHANGE THEM IF THEY ARE NOT IN ASCENDING
                SEQUENCE. CONTINUE THIS PROCESS UNTIL NO ELEMENTS
                ARE EXCHANGED ON ONE COMPLETE SCAN THROUGH A */
                LAST = NUMBER - 1;
                FLAG = 1;
REPEAT:         DO WHILE (FLAG = 0);
                     FLAG = 0;
SCAN_ARRAY:          DO I = 1 TO LAST;
EXCHANGE:                IF A(I) < A(I + 1) THEN DO;
                         /* EXCHANGE AND SET FLAG */
                         FLAG = 1;
                         TEMP = A(I);
                         A(I) = A(I + 1);
                         A(I + 1) = TEMP;
                         END EXCHANGE;
                     END SCAN_ARRAY;
                END REPEAT;
                END SORT;
```

general form of array declaration, the size of the array follows in parentheses after the array name; then comes the array **attributes**—the type of array elements, such as FIXED DECIMAL (6,0) or CHARACTER (VARYING). Each array element must be of the same type.

After the array has been declared, any elements of it can be referenced. For example, we can reference the tenth element as A(10). In the program we declare an array index called INDEX. To read in elements we write

```
GET LIST (A(INDEX));
```

Then each element of A is read.

The array may have up to 100 elements. We do not know in advance exactly how many elements to read. In one of our FORTRAN examples we read data until we met a sentinel. Here we will try a similar but simpler method. We will simply read data into A until there are no more data. At that point, we say we have come to the end of the file (computer scientists like to refer to sets of data as **files**). We can tell the PL/I system to take some action when the data run out and it sees the end of the file. The statement

```
ON ENDFILE (SYSIN) FLAG = 1;
```

directs the computer to set the value of FLAG to 1 when it reaches the end of file. SYSIN stands for SYStem INput and is the name of our data file.

We wish to read data until the end of file is reached or until 100 elements have been read into successive elements of the array. We first initialize the array INDEX to 1 and FLAG to 0 and read the first element. Then we enter a loop to read the remaining elements. The control statement for the loop is:

```
READ: DO WHILE ((INDEX 100) & (FLAG = 0));
```

A DO WHILE statement tells the computer to repeatedly execute a group of statements while a condition remains true. It may have a label to identify it, much as the name of a procedure does. Here the label is READ. The group of statements to be repeatedly executed are those following the DO WHILE statement and ending with

```
END READ;
```

Statements between the DO WHILE statement and the END statement with the same label are said to be in the **range** of the DO WHILE statement.

When the DO WHILE statement is first encountered, its condition must be evaluated. Here the condition has two parts, both of which must be true. The PL/I symbol & means a logical AND. For the condition to be true, INDEX must be less than 100 and FLAG must be 0, meaning that the end of file must not have been reached. If it is true, the statements within the range of the DO WHILE statement will be executed. Then control transfers back to the DO WHILE statement, and the condition is tested again. As long as the condition is true, the process continues. The statements in the range of the DO WHILE statement are executed, and control returns to the DO WHILE statement. If the condition is false, control will skip to the statement following the END READ statement.

The DO WHILE statement is an excellent way to control repeated execu-tion of statements. It has a single entry and a single exit. In fact, the DO

WHILE statement itself is both entry and exit. Control can pass out of the loop only as a result of something done within the loop. In this example, the condition will become false if INDEX equals or exceeds 100 or if FLAG = 1. The first possibility can occur as a result of incrementing INDEX; the second can occur if the end-of-file condition is encountered as a result of the GET LIST statement. Both these conditions are possible results of statements within the range of the DO WHILE statement.

After exiting from the loop, the number of elements read is one less than INDEX. This number is critical to the bubble sorting procedure because it is the number of elements to be sorted and controls the number of pairs of elements we must examine.

The sort itself is controlled by another DO WHILE loop. We set FLAG to 1 before we enter the loop. We then immediately reset FLAG to 0 and begin the sorting process. If we find two adjacent elements that are not in increasing order, we must exchange them and set the FLAG. When the FLAG is 1, we must scan through the array at least once more. These actions are controlled by two new statements which resemble FORTRAN statements. The first of these,

```
SCAN_ARRAY: DO I = 1 TO LAST;
```

is an **iterated** DO statement. Like a DO statement in FORTRAN, it directs the computer to execute the statements within its range. The range ends with the statement

```
END SCAN_ARRAY;
```

Each time the statements are executed, the index of the DO statement is incremented. In this case the index I is incremented from 1 to LAST by 1 each time. If we wished to increment by any other value, we must state it by adding "BY N" with the appropriate N to the DO statement. For example, to increment by N, we would write

```
SCAN_ARRAY: DO I = 1 TO LAST BY N;
```

This choice illustrates the point that the PL/I DO is more powerful than the FORTRAN one. The initial value, final value, and index of a PL/I iterated DO statement may be constants, variables, or arithmetic expressions. To avoid problems we should not write statements to alter any of these values within the range of the DO statement.

The second statement,

```
EXCHANGE:  IF A(I) > A(I + 1) THEN DO;
```

is a PL/I IF-THEN statement. It directs the computer to evaluate the expression following IF, namely $A(I) > A(I + 1)$. If the expression is true, that is if A(I) exceeds A(I + 1), then the statements within the range of the IF-THEN statement are executed. Naturally, the range ends with the statement

```
END EXCHANGE;
```

If the expression is false, control passes to the statement following that END statement.

Like the DO WHILE module, the IF-THEN module has one distinct entry and one distinct exit. Unlike the DO WHILE module, it may have an entry that is different from the exit. (Why?) More important, the DO WHILE and IF-THEN modules have different purposes. DO WHILE is intended for **repetitive** execution; IF-THEN is intended for **alternative** execution. IF some condition is true, THEN some action should be taken. Otherwise no action should be taken in that module, and control should advance to the next module.

PL/I has another alternative statement called IF-THEN-ELSE. It allows either of two alternative actions to be taken. IF the condition is true, THEN the first action is taken; otherwise another action, consisting of statements preceded by ELSE, is taken. Consider the problem of keeping track of gains and losses in a series of football plays. We get a yardage resulting from each play; if it is positive it is a gain, otherwise it is a loss. We wish to consider gains and losses separately. A segment of a program to compute team statistics might look like this.

```
GET LIST (YARDAGE);
IF YARDAGE > 0 THEN
    GAIN = GAIN + YARDAGE;
ELSE
    LOSS = LOSS + YARDAGE;
```

When more than two alternatives should be considered, IF-THEN-ELSE statements may be nested. For example, if we wished to sort a group of people into two sets according to age, we could first divide them into those under and over 40. This would take one IF-THEN-ELSE statement. Then we could divide each subset into two, and so on.

The end of the bubble sort shows nesting of modules. First the IF-THEN module labeled EXCHANGE ends; then the DO module labeled SCAN_ARRAY ends; then the DO-WHILE module labeled REPEAT ends. Finally, the SORT program ends.

For comparison we have included a bubble sort program written in PL/M as Table 12.12. In it the data in the array of length 10 are given. Because the data are given, no read routine is needed. Fewer parameters and labels are used. The algorithm and instructions are basically the same. The program ends with EOF, meaning end of file.

12.4.3 *PL/I Example 3: Finding Peak Snowfall*

Our last PL/I example is given in Table 12.13. It illustrates finding the peak snowfall for four four-county areas. First the peak snowfall in each area is found and then the overall peak for all four areas is determined. The program illustrates calling procedures and passing parameters. Calling procedures resembles calling subroutines in BASIC and PL/I. The main procedure, SNOW-

Table 12.12
PL/M program to sort 10 numbers

```
/* INITIALIZE VECTOR A(10) TO HOLD THE UNSORTED NUMBERS, WHICH */
/* RANGE BETWEEN 0 AND 65535 DECIMAL */
DECLARE A(10) ADDRESS INITIAL
(4000, 21, 693, 3746, 129, 782, 3, 419, 8881, 1000)
/* BEGIN A BUBBLE SORT. SCAN THROUGH A, EXAMINING PAIRS OF */
/* ADJACENT NUMBERS. IF THE FIRST NUMBER OF A PAIR IS GREATER */
/* THAN THE SECOND, EXCHANGE THEM. CONTINUE SCANNING THROUGH A */
/* UNTIL NO MORE NUMBERS ARE EXCHANGED. */
DECLARE (I, SWAP) BYTE,
        TEMP ADDRESS;
SWAP=1;
        DO WHILE SWAP;
        SWAP=0;
        /* SCAN THROUGH A FOR A PAIR TO BE EXCHANGED */
                DO I=0 to 8;
                IF A(I) > A(I+1) THEN DO;
                        SWAP=1;
                        TEMP=A(I);
                        A(I)=A(I+1);
                        A(I+1)=TEMP;
                        END;
                END;
        END;
/* A IS SORTED INTO NONDECREASING ORDER */
EOF
```

FALL, will yield the overall peak snowfall. The second procedure, SNOW, is called by SNOWFALL to read snow data and determine the maximum. It is an **internal** procedure because it is inside a main procedure. SNOW, in turn, calls MAX_OF_FOUR to determine the maximum of any four snow data. Note that SNOWFALL also calls MAX_OF_FOUR. We will say that SNOWFALL is a **parent** of SNOW and of MAX_OF_FOUR.

Before tracing through this program we should consider nesting procedures. A main procedure may have internal procedures. Any procedure defined within another is considered to be a **child.** A main procedure that has children may call any one that is a child as an entire internal procedure. Thus SNOWFALL may call SNOW. A main procedure cannot access only part of an internal procedure. Hence it may not directly call procedures that are internal to one of its internal procedures. That is, it may not call deeply embedded procedures—procedures that are not children of the main procedure. Any internal procedure may have its own internal procedures that it may call as needed.

Nesting procedures naturally affect variables. Any variable declared in a procedure is known to its internal procedures unless the local procedure rede-

Table 12.13
PL/I program to find peak snowfall for four four-county areas

```
SNOWFALL:      PROCEDURE OPTIONS (MAIN);
               /* PROGRAM FINDS THE PEAK SNOWFALL FOR FOUR
               FOUR-COUNTY AREAS */
               DECLARE
                       AREA1 FIXED (5,2),
                       AREA2 FIXED (5,2),
                       AREA3 FIXED (5,2),
                       AREA4 FIXED (5,2);
                       /* PEAK SNOWFALL IN EACH AREA */
               DECLARE MOST_SNOW FIXED (5,2);
                       /* OVERALL PEAK SNOW */
               CALL SNOW (AREA1);
               CALL SNOW (AREA2);
               CALL SNOW (AREA3);
               CALL SNOW (AREA4);
               CALL MAX_OF_FOUR (AREA1, AREA2, AREA3, AREA4);
               PUT SKIP DATA (PEAK);
SNOW:          PROCEDURE (MAXSNOW);
               /* PROCEDURE READS 4 VALUES AND RETURNS MAXIMUM
               IN MAXSNOW */
               DECLARE MAXSNOW FIXED (5,2);
               DECLARE (A,B,C,D) FIXED (5,2);
               /* SNOW DATA FROM EACH OF 4 COUNTIES */
               GET LIST (A,B,C,D);
               CALL MAX_OF_FOUR (A,B,C,D, MAXSNOW);
               PUT SKIP LIST (MAXSNOW);
               END SNOW:
MAX_OF_FOUR:   PROCEDURE (W,X,Y,Z, MAXIMUM);
               /* PROCEDURE FINDS LARGEST OF FOUR VALUES—W,X,Y,Z—
               AND RETURNS IT AS MAXIMUM */
               DECLARE (W,X,Y,Z, MAXIMUM) FIXED 5.2;
               MAXIMUM = W;
               IF X > W, THEN MAXIMUM = X;
               IF Y > MAXIMUM, THEN MAXIMUM = Y;
               IF Z > MAXIMUM, THEN MAXIMUM = Z;
               END MAX_OF_FOUR;
               END SNOWFALL;
```

clares it. Whenever a variable name is used, it refers to the declaration of that name in the same procedure or in the nearest ancestor of that procedure on which the name was declared (first parent, then grandparent, and so on).

The name of a procedure is not known within the procedure itself. Thus no procedure can call itself. (Pl/I does have recursive procedures, but we will not consider them.) A child of a procedure also cannot call that procedure. Hence SNOW cannot call itself, nor can it call SNOWFALL. More generally (and less

usefully), a procedure can call

- its children,
- its siblings (other children of its parent),
- its parent's siblings,
- its grandparent's siblings,
- its greatgrandparent's siblings, and so on.

Thus, in our example, SNOWFALL can call both SNOW and MAX_OF_FOUR. We say that SNOW and MAX_OF_FOUR are siblings. Both SNOW and SNOWFALL can call MAX_OF_FOUR. If MAX_OF_FOUR had been internal to SNOW, SNOWFALL would not have been able to call it.

With this knowledge of procedures, we can easily follow the example. The maximum of any four numbers is calculated by the nested IF-THEN statements of procedure MAX_OF_FOUR. The algorithm first assumes the first of any four numbers is the maximum, and then compares each of the other three numbers to the maximum, replacing the maximum as needed. This procedure is used to determine the maximum snowfall in each four-county area and then in the overall region.

12.4.4 *PL/I Features*

The essence of PL/I is its control mechanisms. It has four.

- **Sequential flow**—statements are executed in sequence unless one of the other three types of control is stated.
- **Repetitive execution**—statements within a loop are repeatedly executed in a DO-WHILE module.
- **Alternative execution**—one of two alternatives is selected by IF-THEN-ELSE or IF-THEN.
- **Execution of internal procedures**—called by CALL.

With these four control mechanisms, programs can be constructed from modules. Flow of control can be so clear and apparent that programs can be easily followed and documented. Programs can be written so that control flows from top to bottom with minor exceptions. Within modules or when another procedure is called, control may temporarily deviate from its usual downward flow.

PL/I does have a GO TO statement that can alter this direction of flow, but most PL/I promoters recommend against using it. The statment

GO TO label;

can transfer control to any statement label. However, using this statement tends to confuse programs, sometimes hopelessly. It is best to stick to the four control mechanisms listed above.

The statements of PL/I, discussed here, are summarized in Table 12.14.

Table 12.14
Summary of PL/I statements

Statement	Example
name: PROCEDURE	BIG_ONE: PROCEDURE OPTIONS (MAIN);
END name;	END BIG_ONE;
DECLARE (variable list) attributes;	DECLARE (A,B,C) FIXED DECIMAL (5,0);
variable = expression;	SUM = A + B + C;
GET LIST (variable list);	GET LIST (A,B,C);
PUT DATA (variable list);	PUT DATA (A,B,C);
label: DO WHILE (condition);	PROFIT: DO WHILE (SUM > 0);
IF expression THEN statement;	IF A > 0 THEN PROFIT = PROFIT + A;
IF expression THEN statement 1; ELSE statement 2;	IF A > 0 THEN PROFIT = PROFIT + A; ELSE LOSS = LOSS − A;
ON ENDFILE (SYSIN) statement;	ON ENDFILE(SYSIN) FLAG = 1
label: DO-statements; . .	POSITIVE: DO; POS_NUMBER = POS_NUMBER + 1; PUT DATA (X);
END;	END;
CALL procedure-name;	CALL TOP;
GO TO label;	GO TO POSITIVE;

12.5 *Pascal*

Pascal is a relatively new programming language. It was developed in 1968 by Niklaus Wirth in Zurich and named after the seventeenth-century French mathematician and philosopher Blaise Pascal. It has been adapted for the PDP-11 and for microcomputers by Kenneth Bowles of the University of California at San Diego. Currently, many different versions of Pascal exist, not all of them compatible, but attempts to standardize the language are proceeding.

Pascal is a block-structured programming language that deals with procedures in a manner much like PL/I. It was designed to be a structured programming language and to improve on the features of the older high-level languages. It is especially powerful for defining data structures and allows a large number of data types including arrays, records, and files. It contains internal typechecking procedures to guard against programmers inadvertently changing data types within a program.

12.5.1 *Pascal Example*

Pascal looks outwardly much like FORTRAN and PL/I so we will content ourselves with the examination of a program, shown in Table 12.15. The

Table 12.15
A Pascal program to solve a substitution cipher

```
PROGRAM DOCUMENT (INPUT, OUTPUT) ;
   TYPE
      RA=ARRAY(.'A'..'Z','A'..'Z'.)OF INTEGER ;
      ARA = RECORD DIF:INTEGER;
              LOWEST:INTEGER;
              LOWIND:CHAR;
              SECLOW:INTEGER;
              SECINY:CHAR;
                 KEY:CHAR
              END;
   VAR
      ARAY:ARRAY(.'A'..'Z'.)OF ARA;
      DUMMY:ARA.
      TAKEN:ARRAY(.'A'..'Z'.) OF BOOLEAN;
      CHARCOUNT,WORDCOUNT,LETTERCOUNT,L,N,M: INTEGER ;
      DOCUMENT: ARRAY(.-1..9000.)OF CHAR ;
      J,I:CHAR ;
      NFREQ,NLL,NFL,FL,LL,FREQ : ARRAY (.'A'..'Z'.)OF INTEGER ;
      DATAFREQ,DATAFL,DATALL: ARRAY(.'A'..'Z'.)OF INTEGER;
      LOWEST,SECONDLOWEST,DIFFERENCE:ARRAY(.'A'..'Z'.)OF INTEGER;
      TABLE,NORFREQ,NORLL,NORFL: RA ;
      SOLUTION,LOWESTINDEX,SECLOWINDEX,ORDERED: ARRAY(.'A'..'Z'.)
        OF CHAR;

   PROCEDURE FREQCOUNT;
      BEGIN
         READLN;
         WRITELN;
         DOCUMENT(.-1.) :=' ';   DOCUMENT(.O.) :=' ';
         FOR I := 'A' TO 'Z' DO READLN(DATAFREQ(.I.));
         FOR I := 'A' TO 'Z' DO READLN(DATALL(.I.));
         FOR I := 'A' TO 'Z' DO READLN(DATAFL(.I.));
         CHARCOUNT:=1;
         WHILE NOT(EOF(INPUT)) DO
           BEGIN
              READ (DOCUMENT(.CHARCOUNT.));
              WRITE (DOCUMENT(.CHARCOUNT.));
              CHARCOUNT:=CHARCOUNT+1
           END;
         DOCUMENT(.CHARCOUNT.) := ' ';
         WRITELN;
         LETTERCOUNT:=CHARCOUNT-1;
         M:=0;
         WORKCOUNT:=0;
         N:=0 ;
         WHILE N<=LETTERCOUNT+1 DO
         BEGIN
            IF ((DOCUMENT(.N.)<'A') OR (DOCUMENT(.N.)>'Z'))
              THEN BEGIN
                M:=M+1;
                IF ( (DOCUMENT(.N-1.)<>' ')
                   AND (DOCUMENT(.N-1.)< = 'Z')
```

Table 12.15 (cont.)

```
                    AND (DOCUMENT(.N-1.)> = 'A'))
                    THEN LL(.DOCUMENT(.N-1.).):=LL(.DOCUMENT(.N-1.).)+1;
            IF ( (DOCUMENT(.N+1.)<> ' ')
              AND (DOCUMENT(.N+1.)< = 'Z')
              AND (DOCUMENT(.N+1.)> = 'A'))
                THEN BEGIN
                  FL(.DOCUMENT(.N+1.).):=FL(.DOCUMENT(.N-1.).)+1;
                  WORDCOUNT := WORDCOUNT + 1
                END
          END
        ELSE FREQ(.DOCUMENT(.N.).):=FREQ(.DOCUMENT(.N.).)+1;
        N:= +1;
    END;
  LETTERCOUNT := LETTERCOUNT - M + 2;
  FOR I := 'A' TO 'Z' DO
    BEGIN
    NFREQ(.I.) := 10000*FREQ(.I.) DIV LETTERCOUNT;
    NFL(.I.) := 10000*FL(.I.) DIV WORDCOUNT;
    NLL(.I.) := 10000*LL(.I.) DIV WORDCOUNT
    END
END;

PROCEDURE TABLES;
  BEGIN FOR I := 'A' TO 'Z' DO
    BEGIN FOR J:= 'A' TO 'Z' DO
      BEGIN
        NORFREQ(.I.) :=ABS(NFREQ(.I.)-DATAFREQ(.J.));
        NORLL(.I,J.):=ABS(NLL(.I.)-DATALL(.J.));
        NORFL(.I,J.):=ABS(NFL(.I.)-DATAFL(.J.));
        TABLE(.I,J.):=NORFREQ(.I,J.)+NORFL(.I,J.)+NORLL(.I,J.)
      END
    END
  END;

PROCEDURE ASSIGN;
  BEGIN
    FOR I:='A' TO 'Z' DO
      BEGIN
        ARAY(.I.).SECLOW:=TABLE(.I,'B'.);
        ARAY(.I.).LOWEST:=TABLE(.I,'B'.);
        ARAY(.I.).LOWIND:= 'B';
        ARAY(.I.).SECIND:= 'B';
        FOR J:='A' TO 'Z' DO
          BEGIN
            IF TABLE (.I,J.)<ARAY(.I.).LOWEST THEN
              BEGIN
                ARAY(.I.).SECLOW:=ARAY(.I.).LOWEST;
                ARAY(.I.).SECIND:=ARAY(.I.).LOWIND;
                ARAY(.I.).LOWEST:=TABLE(.I,J.);
                ARAY(.I.).LOWIND:=J
              END
```

Table 12.15 (cont.)

```
                    ELSE IF TABLE (.I,J.)<ARAY(.I.).SECLOW
                       THEN
                          BEGIN
                            ARAY(.I.).SECLOW:=TABLE(.I,J.);
                            ARAY(.I.).SECIND:=J
                          END;
                 END;
            ARAY(.I.).DIF:=ABS(ARAY(.I.).SECLOW-ARAY(.I.).LOWEST);
            ARAY(.I.).KEY:=I
         END;
      FOR I:='A' TO 'Y' DO
         BEGIN
            FOR J:='Y' DOWNTO I DO
               BEGIN
                  IF ARAY(.SUCC(J).).DIF<ARAY(.J.).DIF THEN
                     BEGIN
                       DUMMY:=ARAY(.J.);
                       ARAY(.J.):=ARAY(.SUCC(J).);
                       ARAY(.SUCC(J).):=DUMMY
                     END
         END
      END;
      FOR I:='A' TO 'Z' DO
         BEGIN
            SOLUTION(.I.):=' ';
            TAKEN(.I.):=FALSE
         END;
      FOR I:="Z" DOWNTO 'A' DO
         IF NOT TAKEN(.ARAY(.I.).LOWIND.)
            THEN
               BEGIN
                 SOLUTION(.ARAY(.I.).KEY.):=ARAY(.I.).LOWIND;
                 TAKEN(.ARAY(.I.).LOWIND.):=TRUE
               END
            ELSE
               BEGIN
                 SOLUTION(.ARAY(.I.).KEY.):=ARAY(.I.).SECIND:
                 TAKEN(.ARAY(.I.).KEY.):=TRUE
               END
END;

PROCEDURE FINAL;
  BEGIN
     FOR M:=0 TO CHARCOUNT DO
        BEGIN
          IF DOCUMENT (.M.)>='A') and (DOCUMENT(.M.)='Z'))
             THEN WRITE (SOLUTION(.DOCUMENT(.M.).));
          IF DOCUMENT(.M.)=' ' THEN WRITE(' ')
        END
  END;
```

Table 12.15 (cont.)

```
BEGIN (* MAIN PROGRAM *)
  WRITELN;
  WRITELN;
  WRITELN;
  WRITELN;
  WRITELN;
  WRITELN;
  WRITELN;('***********  ORIGINAL  TEXT  *************');
  WRITELN;
  WRITELN;
   FREQCOUNT;
  WRITELN('*******************************************');
    FOR I:='A' TO 'Z' DO WRITELN('I=',I,' NLL(I)=',NLL(.I.), NFREQ(I)='
                                 ,NFREQ(.I.),'NFL(I)=',NFL(.I.));

  TABLES;
  ASSIGN;
  WRITELN;
  WRITELN;
  WRITELN;
  WRITELN;
  WRITELN;
  WRITELN;
  WRITELN;
  WRITELN('*************  S O L U T I O N S  **************');
  WRITELN;
  WRITELN;
    FOR I:='A' TO 'Z' DO
      BEGIN
        WRITELN('ENGLISH' ',I,' "CORRESPONDS TO DOCUMENT" ',
             SOLUTION(.I.),' " ')
      END
  WRITELN;
  WRITELN;
  WRITELN;
  WRITELN('**************************************************************');
  WRITELN;
  WRITELN;
  WRITELN;
  WRITELN;
  WRITELN;
  WRITELN;
  WRITELN('********  D E C I P H E R E D  T E X T  ********'):
  WRITELN;
  WRITELN;
   FINAL;
  WRITELN;
  WRITELN;
  WRITELN;
  WRITELN('*************************************************************');
  WRITELN;
END.
```

program is designed to decipher a document enciphered in a simple substitution cipher (in which each letter is replaced by another letter.)

The program begins with a heading naming it (DOCUMENT) and labeling the standard input and output files. The program, as well as its component procedures, labels, and variables, must have a valid identifier—a name beginning with a letter and with continuing letters or decimal digits. The length of an identifier may be limited by the compiler, usually to 8 characters. Next comes a list of type definitions that we choose to use in our program, including types we define. There is a 26 × 26 array that will hold frequency counts of letters in integer form; the indices of the array are the letters A through Z for convenient reference. Next is defined a **record,** a composite variable of mixed data types, here including integers and characters (abbreviated as CHAR). The ability to define a record that includes several types of data is a major advantage of Pascal over FORTRAN or BASIC; some versions of PL/I have similar features.

Next comes a list of variable declarations specifying types including arrays, integers, characters, and Boolean variables. Generally, strings and real variables might also be included. Each variable must be declared before it is used. The listing concludes with a comment line; in implementations of Pascal for small computers, comments begin with * and end with *.

Our example does not show all possible parts of a Pascal program. A general Pascal program consists of a program heading, followed by a block, followed by a period. A general block has six parts:

- Label declarations to mark statements, such as LABEL 234;
- Constant definitions, such as CONST PI = 3.14159;
- Type definitions, such as COLOR = (BLACK, WHITE);
- Variable declarations, such as VAR CHARCOUNT:INTEGER;
- Procedure and function declarations consisting of headings followed by blocks;
- Statements specifying actions.

Pascal procedures are much like PL/I procedures. We can think of a Pascal procedure as a miniprogram within a program. In fact, procedures are defined recursively in the same way as programs; each procedure has a heading and a block; the block may define additional procedures. This structure makes it easy to write top-down programs.

Returning to our example, we note that the next part is a procedure named FREQCOUNT. This procedure does not have the first four parts of a block because it uses only variables and types that were defined earlier and lacks constants and labels. (If we wish, we can define variables and types that will be used only locally within a procedure rather than globally by the whole program.) The procedure consists of a series of statements starting with BEGIN and ending with END. Matching BEGIN and END statements in Pascal set off procedures and **compound statements** (sequences of statements).

The READLN and WRITELN commands mean to read and write a line, respectively. Pascal has two read statements, READ and READLN, and two write statements, WRITE and WRITELN. The commands ending with LN handle an entire line at a time; the others deal with individual variables. The intent here is to read a line and echo it before starting letter and word counts.

Pascal provides several structured statements for controlling program flow, three of which—IF, WHILE, and FOR—are seen in this procedure. The FOR statement controls repetition of an action or actions while a control variable is in a desired range. The compound statement

```
FOR I:='A' TO 'Z' DO
   BEGIN
     NFREQ(.I.):=10000*FREQ(.I.)DIV LETTERCOUNT;
     NFL(.I.):=10000*FL(.I.)DIV WORDCOUNT;
     NLL(.I.):=10000*LL(.I.)DIV WORDCOUNT;
   END
```

provides for normalization of frequency counts of all letters, first letters, and last letters by multiplying by 10,000 and dividing by the number of letters or words as appropriate for all letters A through Z. Note the matching BEGIN and END. Pascal also provides a way to count down rather than up in a FOR statement by writing DOWNTO instead of TO.

A WHILE statement controls repetition of an action or actions a number of times determined by a condition. A simple example in our program provides for updating the character count until an end-of-file marker is read from the input.

```
WHILE NOT (EOF(INPUT))DO
   BEGIN
     READ(DOCUMENT(.CHARCOUNT.));
     WRITE(DOCUMENT(.CHARCOUNT.));
     CHARCOUNT = CHARCOUNT + 1;
   END;
```

The IF statement is like those we have seen in FORTRAN and PL/I. Its basic form is

IF condition THEN statement ELSE statement 2

Our program shows nesting of IF statements. Note the absence of a semicolon between the THEN and ELSE statements.

```
IF((DOCUMENT(.N.)<'A') OR (DOCUMENT(.N.)>'Z'))
   THEN BEGIN
     M:=M+1;
     IF((DOCUMENT(.N-1.)<>' ')
       AND(DOCUMENT(.N-1.)<='Z')
       AND((DOCUMENT(.N-1.)>='A'))
         THEN LL(.DOCUMENT(.N-1.).):=DOCUMENT(.N-1.).)+1;
     IF((DOCUMENT(.N+1.).):<>' ')
       AND(DOCUMENT(.N+1.)<='Z')
       AND(DOCUMENT(.N+1.)>='A'))
```

```
        THEN BEGIN
          FL(.DOCUMENT(.N+1).):=FL(.DOCUMENT(.N+1.).)+1;
          WORDCOUNT:=WORDCOUNT+1
        END
 END
 ELSE FREQ(.DOCUMENT(.N.).):=FREQ(.DOCUMENT(.N.).)+1;
```

The ELSE statement in this example belonged to the outermost IF statement. The statements provide for testing whether characters are letters and testing for the beginning or end of words. Note the use of the logical connectives AND and OR as well as the use of such symbols as $<=$ for less than or equal to and $<>$ for not equal to.

Pascal also offers a REPEAT statement that is similar to but simpler than WHILE. It has the form:

REPEAT statement UNTIL condition

It also offers a CASE statement, which is a generalized form of IF in that it allows as many alternatives as desired instead of being limited to two. The program contains three more procedures, TABLES, ASSIGN, and FINAL, in addition to the main program, which calls the procedures and executes a few other actions. Note that the main program ends with END, thus justifying the statement that a program consists of a heading, followed by a block, followed by a period.

While this look at Pascal has been much too brief for us to learn how to program in it, it does give a bit of the flavor of the language. Note especially the convenience of defining data types and the ease of referring to an array of letters A–Z rather than of the numbers 1–26.

12.6 *High-Level Languages on Small Computers*

The versions of BASIC, FORTRAN, and PL/I available on small computers are generally less powerful and flexible than the implementations found on large computers. To find out just what you can do on a small computer, you must read your user's manual very carefully. Computer manufacturers or software sellers may claim that they implement the standard language with **extensions.** Sometimes extensions allow you to do more than the standard language includes. Sometimes, however, they require you to insert extra instructions or limit the use of some instructions. The problem is more severe on small computers with limited memory. High-level language systems that occupy only 4K or 8K of memory are severely limited. Systems that are kept on a floppy disk or in other secondary memory are likely to be more powerful.

For example, one manufacturer offers a 4K FORTRAN system that is restricted to single-precision arithmetic and to arrays of no more than two dimensions. It has no logical IF statements. It does not allow alphabetic input and it cannot compare variables. Maximum program size is about 100 lines.

The same company offers an 8K FORTRAN system. It also is restricted to single-precision arithmetic and to arrays of two dimensions. It does not permit logical IF statements. Program size is restricted to roughly 200 to 300 lines.

Other restrictions often found on small computers are lack of subroutine calls, standardized formats, prohibitions against mixed mode arithmetic, omission of certain statements, and limited library routines.

12.7 Structured Programming

Now that we have seen examples of three high-level languages, we can return to the topic of good programming practices. In this section we will look at several aspects of programming, following the ideas of Kernighan and Plauger. At the beginning of the chapter we mentioned the importance of modularity. If we write programs as sections of modules with clear transfers of control between modules, our programs will be easy to understand. Since we can write each module separately, our programs will be easy to write. Because any error will occur either within a module or during transfer to another module, our programs will also be easy to debug.

PL/I and Pascal are best suited to structured programming. Because they allow four distinct types of control transfers, they make writing programs easy. However, we can use good programming practices in any language. The ideas that follow are a checklist of good programming practices.

12.7.1 Clarity of Expression

Write your programs so that both you and the computer know what you intend. Say what you mean as simply and as directly as you can. Clarity is always more important than cleverness. It is also more important than efficiency of execution. Computers are intended to take tedious work off our hands; hence we should let them convert decimal numbers to binary and do arithmetic calculations. We shouldn't do by hand what the computer can do more quickly and easily, just to save a few milliseconds of computer time. Some specific hints for writing clear programs follow.

1. *Parenthesize to show what you intend.* The expression

```
A*B**C+D-E/F**G
```

is not clear. The expression

```
((A*B)**C)+D*(E/F**G)
```

is clear. We discussed hierarchies of precedence for BASIC and said that the other languages had similar precedence rules. However, we don't want to worry about precedence rules and about minor differences in them between languages. If we parenthesize, we can always be sure that the computer will interpret an expression as we intend because, in every language, quantities within parentheses are evaluated first.

2. *Use library functions.* We have not discussed library functions in much detail. Every small computer implementation of a high-level language will have some library functions. Typically it will have trigonometric functions such as SIN, TAN, and COS; logarithmic functions such as LOG and LN; and other functions such as random numbers, absolute values, and square roots. Consult your user's manual to learn about them. Always use the library functions your small computer provides instead of writing your own functions. You will save time and increase the clarity of your program. Look at the difference between writing

```
40      y = A + ABS(B)
```

and

```
38      IF B > 0 THEN 40
39      B = −B
40      Y = A + B
```

3. *Choose descriptive variable names.* The languages we have seen differ considerably in the choices they allow for names. In BASIC we have little room for imagination. In FORTRAN, Pascal, and PL/I, however, there is little excuse for unimaginative names like A, B, and C unless we are referring to the angles of a labelled triangle. Besides looking for descriptive names, we should avoid confusion. For example, what is

```
NO1?
```

Is it N, letter O, and number 1? Or is it N, number 0, and number 1? Or maybe it is N, letter O, and letter I? The possibilities for typing or keypunching errors are rampant.

For better visual identification it is best to avoid identifiers that differ only at the end. For example,

```
ASUM and BSUM
```

are preferred to

```
SUMA and SUMB
```

Identifiers that are collections of the same set of letters lead to confusion. Consider the expression

```
MMMM = MMMM + MMM + MM + M
```

It is hard to write this without making errors. It is hard, also, to be sure that MMM is not mistakenly used for MM or MMMM somewhere in the program. Even M4, M3, M2, and M1—unimaginative as they may be—are better choices.

4. *Use few temporary variables.* We have sometimes found temporary variables useful, as in the exchange part of a bubble sort. However, we can easily get into trouble with temporary variables. We must be sure that a temporary variable is initialized before it is used. In the bubble sort we handled this easily by placing one of the array values into TEMP to begin the exchange. However, in a longer program with several variables we may forget to initialize a temporary variable. The result is worthless.

12.7.2 *Structure*

We have already emphasized the main idea here. Write a program as a set of modules with clear transfers of control between the modules. Some specific hints—some new, some old—are listed below.

1. *Avoid unnecessary branches.* Sometimes we must think for a while before we see the simplest way to handle branching. For example, we wish to find the maximum value of an array of 100 elements. We might at first write statements like these.

```
        TOP = A(1)
        DO 20 I = 2, 100
        IF (A(I) .GT. TOP) GO TO 15
        GO TO 20
15      TOP = A(I)
20      CONTINUE
```

The IF statement controls an unnecessary branch. We can simplify the procedure by having the IF statement control a calculation directly.

```
        TOP = A(1)
        DO 20 I = 2, 100
        IF (A(I) .GT. TOP) TOP = A(I)
20      CONTINUE
```

We have eliminated two statements and clarified our program. We should always watch branches carefully. Branching backwards is often confusing. With a little thought we can select a minimum number of branches.

2. *Implement multiway branches with successive* IF-ELSE *statements.* Branching in more than two directions is best handled by IF-THEN-ELSE, IF-THEN-ELSE, IF-THEN-ELSE. We have already discussed the disadvantages of using the FORTRAN arithmetic IF statement for three-way branches; we may lose track of the flow of control. Also, we need labels to show transfers with arithmetic IFs, but we can avoid them with IF-THEN-ELSE. Suppose we wish to write a series of equations describing the weight of an object as a function of its height. We might write the following.

```
IF HEIGHT > 200
    THEN WEIGHT = 100 + 0.5 * HEIGHT;
ELSE IF HEIGHT > 180
    THEN WEIGHT = 90 + 0.6 * HEIGHT;
```

```
ELSE IF HEIGHT > 160
    THEN WEIGHT = 80 + 0.7 * HEIGHT;
ELSE IF HEIGHT > 140
    THEN WEIGHT = 70 + 0.8 * HEIGHT;
ELSE
    WEIGHT = 60 + 0.9 * HEIGHT;
```

Here, nested IF-THEN-ELSE statements control a five-way branch. Note that each new IF-THEN-ELSE statement occurs during the ELSE part of the branch. Thus if a condition is satisfied, WEIGHT is calculated, and we are done. If a condition is not satisfied, we look at the next condition. We can easily understand the flow of control.

3. *Use subroutines to modularize your programs.* Any procedure that is done more than twice is best handled by a subroutine. Avoid repeating the same lines of code with different variables. Instead write a subroutine and call it as necessary.

4. *Avoid* GO TO *statements whenever possible.* As we have discussed, GO TO statements can lead to undisciplined branches. We cannot always avoid them, even in PL/I or Pascal programs, but we can minimize their use. In FORTRAN and BASIC we use GO TO statements to construct loops that could be written with a DO-WHILE statement in PL/I or Pascal.

12.7.3 *Input/Output*

In most of our examples we have been more concerned with the main operations of a program than with input/output. In practical programs we should check input data carefully. You have probably heard the rule, "garbage-in, garbage out." We can minimize the processing of garbage by a series of checks.

1. *Check input data for obvious errors.* Suppose we are writing a program to calculate areas of triangles. Input data to the program may be the lengths of the three sides of each triangle. We should check these lengths to make sure that they can be sides of a triangle. The sum of any two sides of a triangle must be greater than the length of the third side. Otherwise the lengths cannot form a triangle, but only a line. We speak of checks like this as "laundering the data." Similarly, if we plan to take the square roots of input data and are dealing only with real numbers, we should check to see that the input data are positive. If we are calculating ages or heights of people, we should check that they do not exceed some reasonable upper limit. Many statistical programs have given extraordinary results because of a single keypunch error.

2. *Make sure that input data do not exceed program limits.* If we are reading data into an array, we should make sure that they do not exceed array dimensions. If our program gives valid results only for data within some range, we should check to make sure the data are in that range. If they are not, we should have the program print error statements and probably stop execution.

3. *End input with an end-of-file marker, not by count.* We have given examples of both ways of stopping to input data. An end-of-file mark is preferable because computers count better than people do. If input is to be ended by some predetermined count, some person must determine what that count is. If, instead, the computer reads input until it finds a sentinel or end-of-file mark, it can count the input data as it reads them.

4. *Echo and examine input data on output.* If input data are "echoed" (printed) on output, we may spot some mistakes that previous checks did not catch. Clear identification of the data should accompany the output. We should print names explicitly rather than giving numeric codes that we may have written within the program. Of course, we must avoid swamping the reader with masses of data.

12.7.4 *Common Mistakes*

Knowing and checking for common mistakes can help us avoid them. The suggestions below cover common problems.

1. *Initialize all variables.* A frequent error is to write an expression such as

SUM = SUM + TERM

without first setting SUM to 0 or some other correct initial value. If SUM is not initialized, it will begin as garbage and will continue that way. This mistake occurs so often that you should automatically check for it in every program.

2. *Watch for off-by-one mistakes.* Programs are frequently written to take some action one time too often or one time too few. We call these mistakes "off-by-one" errors. Whenever we have a counter or whenever we wish to loop a particular number of times, we should check the logic closely. Will the action be executed the desired number of times? Or will it be done once too often or once too little?

3. *Branch the right way on equality.* In assembly language programs we noted that branches on equality might result in going through a loop thousands of times if we were not careful. Thus we tried to avoid branches on equality. The situation in high-level programming is somewhat different. We must be careful to branch the right way on equality so that our program is logically correct and sensible. For example, suppose we are writing a program to examine payments on a bill, calculate the balance due, and print the next payment due. If the balance due is greater than 0, we wish to request a payment. How do we handle a balance of 0? You may have heard stories of computer outputs demanding payments of $0.00 until a check for $0.00 is finally received. We can avoid that situation by directing the computer to print that the bill has been paid when the balance is 0.

4. *Check a few answers by hand.* One way to spot less obvious mistakes is to check a few values by hand. Good choices for checking are extreme values—the lowest and highest values the program should handle. Also be sure

to check values that will test every part of the program.

5. *Watch for special problems with integers and real numbers.* Integers are best suited for counting and for calculations that will never have fractional parts. Avoid division with integers; the fractional part is lost.

Conversely, floating-point numbers are intended for calculations. They are poor candidates for counting. Decimal floating-point numbers must be converted to binary within the computer. The conversions are rarely exact. Hence a simple decimal fraction, such as 0.1, may be represented only approximately within the computer. If we use floating-point numbers only for calculations, we can usually estimate and live with their lack of precision. However, we should not count with them when we want an exact count. Integers are exact; real numbers may be only approximate.

12.7.5   *Comments and Program Documentation*

We have seen how comments can clarify a program both for ourselves and for anyone else who reads it. Yet comments have their advantages and disadvantages too. Here are a few guidelines for comments that will enhance your programs.

1. *Comments should explain modules, not merely echo the code.* It is easy to document a program with comments like those below.

```
PROFIT: DO WHILE (COUNT < 100);   /* DO WHILE COUNT <100*/
        GET LIST (X);             /* GET X */
        IF X > 0 THEN GAIN =       *IF X POSITIVE, ADD X
        GAIN + X;                 TO GAIN */
        ELSE LOSS=LOSS - X        /* OTHERWISE LOSS = LOSS - X */
        COUNT = COUNT + 1;        /* INCREMENT COUNT BY 1 */
        END PROFIT;               /* END DO WHILE */
```

These comments echo the code; they say just what the instructions already say. Comments should give new information or explain modules. One comment will do for this module.

```
/* READ DATA AND UPDATE GAIN AND LOSS */
```

2. *Use descriptive variable names.* Throughout the book we have emphasized this point. We are, of course, limited by the language we choose. BASIC does not lend itself to colorful variable names; at best we can pick the first letter of a descriptive name rather than automatically picking A, B, or C. In other languages we should always select names that mean something to us.

3. *See that comments and code agree.* Comments help us only when they accurately describe the program and when both code and comments are correct. They can give us a false sense of security. Suppose we read

```
/* SEARCH FOR NEGATIVE NUMBERS */
IF X>= 0 THEN
NEG_NUMBER = NEG_NUMBER +1
```

The comment tells us that we are searching for negative numbers. The name NEG_NUMBER reinforces the comment. But the code directs us to increment NEG_NUMBER when X is *not* negative. Here, code and comments do not agree. We would have to know more about the program to know how to correct it. The trouble is, we are likely to believe the comments even when they disagree with the code. To avoid this problem, many good programmers cover up the comments while they check a program to find what the program really does.

4. *Format clearly.* Formatting a program thoughtfully can increase its clarity. We have seen examples of how indentation can help show structure and thus increase readability. But with indentation we must be careful to choose a clear format. Suppose we try to read the segment below.

```
IF A > B
   THEN X = 0;
   ELSE IF A = B
      THEN IF C > D
         THEN X = 1;
         ELSE X = 2;
      ELSE IF C < D
         THEN X = 3;
         ELSE IF C = D;
            THEN X = 4;
            ELSE X = 5;
```

Despite the neat indentation this is confusing. How can we pick out the conditions for which X will be set to 2? Some conditions involve A and B, others involve C and D, and they are all jumbled together. We can rewrite this segment neatly by picking out the conditions for each case. We also remove the IF-THEN-ELSE statement from the IF-THEN part of IF A = B.

```
IF      A > B           THEN X = 0;
ELSE IF A = B & C > D   THEN X = 1;
ELSE IF A = B           THEN X = 2;
ELSE IF         C < D   THEN X = 3;
ELSE IF         C = D   THEN X = 4;
ELSE                         X = 5;
```

The result is much more readable. We can quickly scan the lines until we see the conditions for which we are looking. We can easily check whether the program gives the correct result for any conditions.

5. *Don't overcomment.* Too many comments can make a program almost unreadable. Avoid placing comments between every line of code.

12.S *Summary*

High-level languages simplify programming. Ideally they are machine independent and hence allow programs written for one computer to be run on another.

With small computers, especially, this ideal has not yet been reached. Features of any high-level language may or may not be implemented on a given minicomputer or microcomputer.

BASIC is the simplest scientific programming language. It features simple English statements and needs little formatting. Each statement begins with a line number. Statements may be typed in any order. The BASIC system arranges them in numerical order for execution. Control statements include GO TO, GO SUB, IF, and FOR.

FORTRAN is the most common scientific programming language. It demands careful attention to formatting and variable types. It has arithmetic, input/output, control, specification, and subprogram statements. The chief control statements are arithmetic and logic IFs, DO, and GO TO.

PL/I is a powerful language, well suited for structured programming. Its control structures allow sequential, alternative, and repetitive execution as well as calling other procedures. Basic modules in PL/I are procedures. Major control statements are IF-THEN-ELSE, DO-WHILE, and CALL. Although GO TO statements are permitted in PL/I, they are usually not needed. Thus haphazard transfers of control can be avoided.

Pascal is a relatively new programming language, suited for structured programming and allowing great flexibility in defining data types. It has the same control structures as PL/I.

Key Terms

alternative execution	internal procedure
arithmetic statement	line number
assignment statement	machine dependent
attribute	machine independent
BASIC	main procedure
control statement	mixed mode
default	PL/I
default convention	precedence
entry name	range
extension	real variable
field width	repetitive execution
FORTRAN	sentinel
identifier	specification statement
input/output statement	subprogram statement
integer variable	variable dictionary

12.R *References*

Good references on BASIC include the classic books by Kemeny and Kurtz (1971) and Spencer (1975). McCracken (1972, 1974, 1978) has written several excellent FORTRAN texts. Shortt and Wilson (1976) describe PL/I and structured programming. Jensen and Wirth (1974) provide a definitive treatment of Pascal. Readable and witty books on good programming practices are Kernighan and Plauger (1974 and 1976). They are highly recommended; most of the advice presented here follows their suggestions. For nitty-gritty information on programming for a particular computer, its user's manuals are the best source.

12.P *Problems*

The problems described below can be programmed in any of the three languages described in this chapter. Little mathematics is needed for these programs.

12.1. Write a program to separate a four-digit number into its four digits and compute their sum. For example, 2378 should be separated into 2, 3, 7, and 8. The sum should be calculated as $2 + 3 + 7 + 8 = 20$.

12.2. Write a program to reverse the digits of a four-digit number.

12.3. Starting with the digits 0 and 1, we can construct a series by adding two numbers together to get the next term of the series. This series, called a Fibonacci series, is 0, 1, 1, 2, 3, 5, 8, 13, and so on. Write a program to calculate and print the first 100 terms of this series.

12.4. A prime number is an integer that cannot be divided by any integer except itself and 1. The first several prime numbers are 1, 2, 3, 5, 7, 11, 13, and 17. Write a program to calculate and print all prime numbers between 1 and 500.

12.5. Write a program that will read any message and reverse the order of words in it. For example, the input message EVERY GOOD BOY DOES FINE should become FINE DOES BOY GOOD EVERY.

12.6. Write a program that will read any message and reverse the order of letters in each word. For example, the input message TINKER TO EVERS TO CHANCE would be REKNIT OT SREVE OT ECNAHC.

12.7. Write a program that will read any message and eliminate all double letters. For example, the message MY FATHER KILLED A KANGAROO would become MY FATHER KILED A KANGARO.

12.8. A palindrome is a message whose letters read the same backwards as forwards. A MAN, A PLAN, A CANAL, PANAMA is a palindrome. (Punctuation and spaces can be ignored.) Write a program that will read a message and determine whether it is a palindrome.

13 Interfacing Small Computers

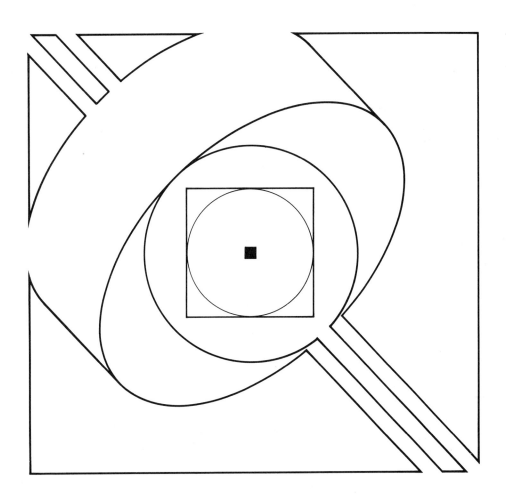

13.1 *Introduction*

By now we are proficient at programming small computers to solve a variety of problems. However, we do need an additional skill before we can design systems based on small computers, and that is the ability to interface CPU's with peripheral devices. This topic is quite complex. It is often the subject of a second course in small computers. In one chapter all we can hope to do is to overview the field of interfacing, to illustrate some of the major concepts, and to provide a few simple examples. As you gain additional experience with mini- and microcomputers, you will want to learn more about the rapidly changing area of interfacing.

Our discussion in this chapter will center on microcomputer interfacing. Minicomputer interfacing is less likely to be a problem because it is easier to find complete minicomputer systems that are well suited for most applications.

To show the range of interfacing problems we might first ask a few questions about any device we wish to interface to our CPU:

1. *At what speed can the device handle information transfers?* In the chapter on input/output we stated that the speed of information transfer of the device as compared with the speed of the CPU was an important factor in considering how we would program the transfer. In this chapter we will look at some of the hardware problems caused by differences in rates of transfer. Suppose we are dealing with a device, such as a Teletype, that is much slower than the CPU. We will need to hold or **latch** information sent to the device by the CPU until the device is ready for it. Similarly, information sent to an LED display should be latched so that the lights will continue to show the data transferred until new data are sent.

2. *Should operations of the device be synchronized with the CPU?* **Synchronous** transfers of information are those that are synchronized with the CPU. This implies that the external device and the CPU share the same clock. Actions of synchronous transfers can be scheduled; no signals are needed to show the beginning of a message or to acknowledge receipt. Although synchronous transfers are therefore very efficient, they can be used only with devices that are physically close together—within 10 meters or so. This limitation is directly related to the speed of electricity (or light). An electric signal can travel a maximum distance of 10 meters in approximately 33 nanoseconds (3.3×10^{-8} sec). While this time may seem almost instantaneous, it is an appreciable fraction of the basic cycle time of a small computer, which may be operating at 2 to 4 MHz, with corresponding cycle times of 500 to 250 nanoseconds, respectively. If the devices are spaced much farther apart, they will react to the clock at different times and hence not be synchronized.

Asynchronous transfers are those that can occur at any time without synchronization with the CPU. Because of the lack of synchronization, additional signals are needed to expedite message handling. For example, a **header** is needed to mark the start of a message. Usually, the sender and the receiver of the message must exchange signals before a transfer to show that both are ready and after a transfer to acknowledge receipt of the message. This procedure is called **handshaking.** Asynchronous systems are more complex but can more readily handle devices of varying speeds within one system.

3. *Is the transfer to proceed bit by bit or byte by byte?* **Serial** transfer occurs when one bit is transferred at a time. There is a hardware savings because few lines are needed to transfer the information. Many common devices, such as the Teletype, transfer information serially. Other devices, by contrast, transfer several bits of information on several lines at the same time, a technique known as **parallel** transfer. Most commonly, an 8-bit byte is the unit that is transferred in parallel, but larger or smaller units may also be found. Parallel transfers are faster than serial transfers and are better adapted to the CPU, which processes bytes, rather than bits of information. When information is transferred serially, we must arrange to hold several bits in a register until a complete byte has been received and is ready for CPU operations.

4. *Are the signals digital or analog?* We are familiar with digital representations of information because that has been the subject of the book thus far. Digital information is represented by discrete levels that can be designated 0 or 1 and combined to give any desired precision. Most information in the real world, however, is not sharply black or white and hence is not easily represented by 0's and 1's. Signals that can take on any value within some range, rather than being limited to certain discrete values, are called **analog** signals. Weights of individuals, musical intensity, altitude above sea level, and concentration of a chemical solution are examples of analog information. If we wish to measure and control analog signals with a small computer, we must first convert the analog signals to digital so that we can process the information in the CPU. After processing we may need to convert the digital outputs from the CPU back to analog. The interfacing problem, then, is to introduce certain devices that will convert analog signals to digital and others that will convert digital signals to analog.

5. *Should we observe some bus standard?* Interfacing small computers with peripheral devices would be very complex if each system designer were free to label signals, to assign bus use, and to arrange transfers in any way he or she chose. Agreeing on standard ways of handling information transfers simplifies system design.

6. *Does the CPU interface with many devices or just a few?* Semiconductor devices, such as microprocessors, can send electrical signals to only a few devices without overloading, much as a household circuit can accommodate only a few devices without overloading. If a system is to handle a large number of devices, it must have **bus drivers** to amplify the signals. In addition, if we intend to use only a few devices, we can address them quite simply; otherwise we may have to exercise some ingenuity in making address selections.

Interfacing is a rapidly changing subject. A few years ago interfacing was simply an adjunct of conventional logic design. Interconnections between a CPU and external devices were made with **gates**—electronic circuits that implemented the operations of AND, OR, and NOT or their equivalents. Now most interfacing is done with integrated circuit chips that contain the equivalent of dozens of gates combined into complex logic circuits. As the semiconductor industry continues to develop, it becomes possible to pack more and more logic functions onto a single integrated circuit. Not only does this reduce the number of chips needed for an interface but also it makes it possible for the microprocessor chip to accomplish more functions. Some of the most recent microprocessors have RAM or ROM on the CPU chip, reducing the need for separate memory chips.

Because of these improvements in semiconductor technology, tomorrow's interfaces will require fewer chips to accomplish the same functions. Alternatively, with the same number of chips a small computer system will be able to accomplish far more functions. As announcements of new integrated circuits are made weekly, we can be sure that we will constantly be learning about newer and better ways of interfacing. Thus in this chapter we will try not to concentrate on details of a rapidly changing technology. When we look at examples of current chips, our objective will be to observe their general operation—not to memorize pin numbers or timing data.

13.2 *Microcomputer Buses*

13.2.1 *Pin Allocations*

Several times during this book we have mentioned buses for various computer systems. Thus we are familiar with the idea of an address bus, a data bus, and a control bus for control and status information. Now, let's see what this means in terms of hardware by looking at a representative pin diagram, shown in Fig. 13.1. Most current 8-bit microcomputers are implemented on a chip with 40 or sometimes 42 pins. The number of pins is limited for economic reasons. The pins are ordinarily allocated as follows:

- 16 for an address bus to permit addressing 64K locations
- 8 for a bidirectional data bus
- 2 for power connections (the 8080 has 4)
- 2 for a clock or crystal to determine operating speed
- 12 for control lines

So long as the number of pins is limited to 40, major improvements in microcomputer design require either time sharing of lines or placing memory on the microcomputer chip. For example, a 16-bit microcomputer requires a 16-bit data bus. However, a 40-pin chip does not have 8 spare lines for increasing the

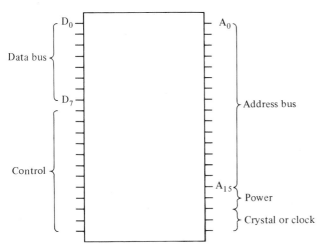

Fig. 13.1
Pin diagram of a hypothetical 40-pin, 8-bit microprocessor.

data bus width from 8 to 16 lines. The solution is to **multiplex** one of the buses—that is, to have it serve one purpose part of the time and another purpose the rest of the time. Addresses can be transferred on a bus for part of an instruction cycle, and data can be transferred during the rest of the cycle. To provide more control functions than the 8080, the 8085 multiplexes the 8 low-order address bits on the data bus. Multiplexing slows down microcomputer operation and requires additional logic to multiplex and demultiplex the buses. If, instead, sufficient memory can be included on the microcomputer chip, a 16-bit address bus may no longer be necessary. Additional lines then become available for data transfers.

The main difference between 8-bit microcomputers is their choices for control lines. Four functions must be provided:

• Control of memory transfers
• Control of input/output transfers
• Scheduling, such as for interrupt and DMA operations
• General supervision, such as resetting

The first two operations are similar. The microcomputer needs signals to instruct it to read from memory to the CPU or to write from the CPU to an external device. The other functions are more specialized and vary from one microcomputer to another.

13.2.2 *Bus Buffering*

Most microcomputers are not capable of driving (providing current) for more than a few devices. Yet the buses of a microcomputer must connect with every memory and input/output chip in the system. For a complex microcomputer system, the microcomputer's drive must be boosted by **buffers** or **drivers.** These come in three varieties:

- **Transmitters** drive signals from the CPU to the bus.
- **Receivers** amplify signals on the bus for the CPU.
- **Transceivers** boost signals in either direction.

A bus that has been enhanced by a driver is called a **buffered** bus. Figure 13.2 shows use of bus drivers. As semiconductor technology improves, we can expect to see buffering increasingly done in connection with other functions rather than by separate chips.

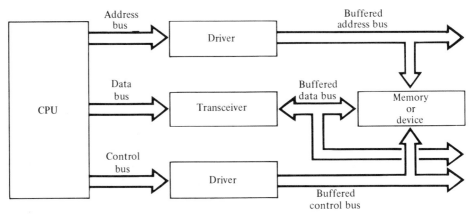

Fig. 13.2
Buffered buses.

13.3 *Addressing Schemes*

An 8-bit microcomputer system can address 65,536 locations. Most of these locations will be used for memory. If the microcomputer has memory-mapped input/output, some will be used for external devices. Memory will be divided into ROM for programs and fixed tables and RAM for data storage and scratchpad use. ROM and RAM typically come in units of 256 bytes. (Larger units, such as 1K or 4K bytes, are becoming increasingly available, but the principles of addressing remain the same.)

A memory chip that contains 256 bytes must be connected to 8 address lines to select any one of those 256 (or 2^8) locations. This requires 8 of our 16 address lines; we would ordinarily choose the 8 low-order lines, A_0–A_7. With the remaining 8 lines, we must be able to select the particular memory chip we wish to address. Each chip has one or more **chip-select** (CS) lines that enable it. We have two basic ways to do so. The first, called linear selection, is useful only for addressing a small number of chips. The second, called **fully decoded addressing,** can be used for as many chips as desired (up to the limit of 64K).

   Linear selection involves typing one address line to each chip-select input. Suppose that we tie address line A_{15} to the chip-select input of a ROM. Then whenever A_{15} is 1, that ROM will be selected. (Some chip-selects take inverted inputs—that is, they are activated by a 0—but the principle remains the same.) We then could tie A_{14} to another 256-byte ROM and tie A_{13} to a 256-byte RAM. We might tie lines A_9 and A_8 to a 1K ROM for address selection and use A_{10} to select that ROM. (Do you see how this works?) Lines A_{11} and A_{12} could be used for external devices in a memory-mapped system. Figure 13.3 shows linear selection for this system.

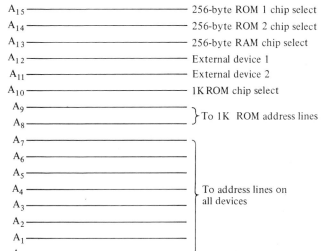

Fig. 13.3
Linear selection.

   The main advantage of linear selection is its simplicity. No logic is necessary for chip selection since each chip is selected by a dedicated address line. The main advantage is that few memory locations can be addressed. To illustrate, here is a list of the accessible memory locations for the preceding example. (We assume that we have connected the 8 low-order address lines to the external devices.)

Hex memory addresses	Device
0000–03FF	1K ROM
0800–08FF	External device 2
1000–10FF	External device 1
2000–20FF	256-byte RAM
4000–40FF	256-byte ROM 1
8000–80FF	256-byte ROM 2

We have no way of accessing any other addresses. Hence we have wasted a good deal of possible memory space—far more than we have used. In a small system this might not matter. However, if we need to access more memory, we must choose another scheme.

Fully decoded addressing can reach all 65,536 addresses by logically combining the high-order address bits for the chip-select inputs. Suppose, for example, that we wished to access memory locations 7000–70FF—territory not reachable by linear selection. These locations have in common the characteristic that A_{15} is 0; A_{14}, A_{13}, and A_{12} are 1; and A_{11}, A_{10}, A_9, and A_8 are all 0. We must logically combine these values of the high-order address lines in an AND operation, just as we would do in a software extract operation. This requires an 8-input AND gate; we would connect lines A_{14}, A_{13}, and A_{12} to three inputs and the complements of A_{15}, A_{11}, A_{10}, A_9, and A_8 to the other five inputs. This connection is shown in Fig. 13.4. A bar above an address line indicates that it is inverted.

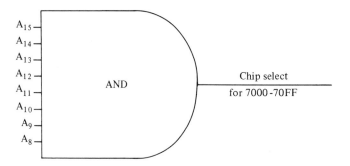

Fig. 13.4
Selection of locations 7000–7OFF.

Instead of using similar AND gates for selecting each device, we use **decoders,** which are the equivalent of several sets of AND gates. A typical example is a three-to-eight decoder. It can select any one of eight output lines, depending on the states of three address inputs. Each of the output lines can be connected to a chip-select input. Some devices have their own decoders on board; they provide several chip-select inputs and decode them internally.

13.4 *Examples of Simple Interfaces*

Let's consider a simple interface. Suppose we wish to connect seven switches through a microcomputer to a seven-segment display. The input side of the circuit to do so might look something like Fig. 13.5. Each switch is first connected to a **debouncing** device, which eliminates irregularities from the switching signal. As shown in Fig. 13.6, moving a switch creates a ragged signal, one that bounces between 0 and 1 before settling down. The bounce is due to mechanical jitter in the switch and usually lasts no more than 20 milliseconds. The switch debouncer converts this to a clean signal that moves

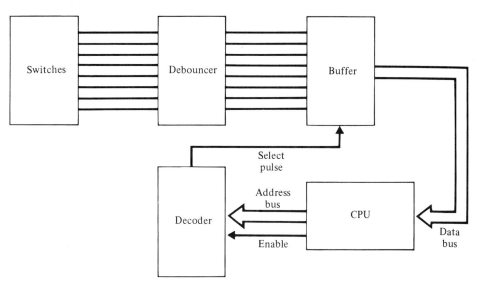

Fig. 13.5
Circuit to input byte from switches.

smoothly from 0 to 1. Debouncing can be done by hardware that filters and smooths the signal or by software that requires a signal to remain stable for 20 ms before further processing.

After the switch outputs have been debounced, they are passed through a buffer to the data bus. The CPU enables the buffer output by generating a select pulse for the buffer. Whether the CPU has memory-mapped or isolated input/output, the select pulse ordinarily results from some combination of the address lines plus an enable signal from the CPU. Alternatively, linear selection and an enable signal can be used, or a decoder can form the select pulse. When the

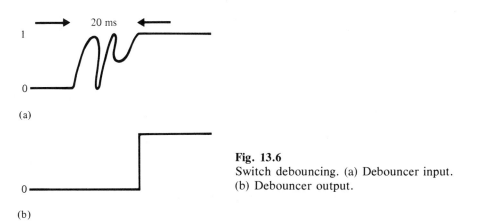

Fig. 13.6
Switch debouncing. (a) Debouncer input.
(b) Debouncer output.

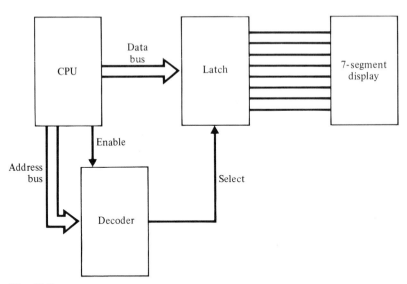

Fig. 13.7
Circuit to output byte to seven-segment display.

buffer is selected, its current value—the debounced and buffered switch settings—are read into the accumulator of the CPU.

The output of the circuit is shown in Fig. 13.7. An 8-bit latch is attached to the data bus; the latch, when selected, acquires and holds the value of the data bus. The output of the latch is connected to the seven-segment display. The latch is selected by a decoder in the same way as was the buffer for the switch inputs. The CPU can output the contents of the accumulator to the data bus and select the latch. The display will then show that value until the CPU sends a new value and again selects the latch.

The **seven-segment display** is shown in Fig. 13.8. Its seven segments are lettered "a" through "g." By lighting or not lighting each segment we can create all the hexadecimal characters as shown in Fig. 13.8(b). (Why do we not use capital B and D?) Some seven-segment displays have an eighth segment for a decimal point, which may be either right or left of the main display.

Now with the complete system we can enter any value on the switches and show it on the seven-segment display while the microcomputer controls the timing. For example, the CPU could introduce a delay of several seconds between setting the switches and displaying a character.

A variation of this problem is to display the hexadecimal value of the data bus on two seven-segment displays. A circuit for doing this is shown in Fig. 13.9. (From here on we will omit the device selection circuits, but we will understand that there must always be a way for the CPU to select an input or output device.) The contents of the data bus have been divided into four-bit nibbles—high-order bits D_7 to D_4 and low-order bits D_3 to D_0. Each nibble is

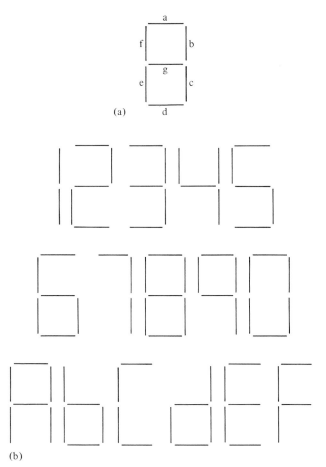

Fig. 13.8
Seven-segment display. (a) Display. (b) Characters.

sent to a hexadecimal-to-seven-segment decoder/driver. This single integrated circuit converts (decodes) the four-bit hexadecimal input to seven-line output, codes it for a seven-segment display, and buffers it to the level needed by the display. The output is directly connected to a seven-segment display.

Instead of using simple toggle switches for input, we may prefer to use a hexadecimal keyboard, such as the one shown in Fig. 13.10. Keyboards are usually organized into rows and columns; in this case, the keyboard is arranged with four rows and four columns. The depressing of a key can be sensed by scanning rows in succession with a 1 and looking for a 1 in a column. The coincidence of a 1 in a row scanned and a resulting 1 in a column shows the key that was depressed. To eliminate bounce, this value must stay constant for at least 20 ms. Additional software routines may protect against the case in which

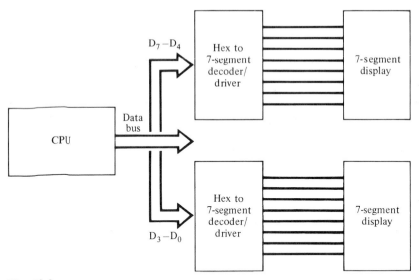

Fig. 13.9
Displaying hexadecimal data.

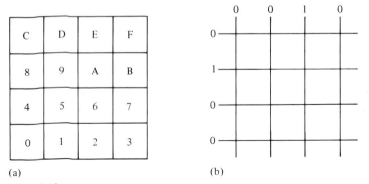

(a)   (b)

Fig. 13.10
Hexadecimal keyboard. (a) Keyboard configuration. (b) Sensing a coincidence when key A is depressed.

two or more keys are kept depressed at once; they may refuse to identify any key in such a case or may identify only the first key depressed or the last key depressed.

13.5 Programmable Parallel Interfaces

Parallel input/output transfers for microprocessors are often handled with **programmable parallel interface** chips, such as the one shown in Fig. 13.11. These chips can be programmed to handle transfers between the CPU and two to three 8-bit ports (or more four-bit ports.) They, too, are subject to the 40-pin

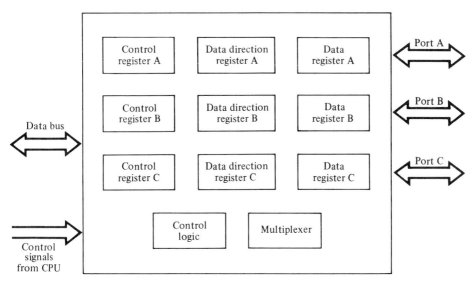

Fig. 13.11
Programmable parallel interface chip.

limit, so that no more than 32 lines can usually be allocated to data lines. The programmable parallel interface chip ordinarily has the following registers for each port.

- A **data register** to hold data being transferred; it can usually be latched for either input or output transfers.
- A **data direction register** that can be programmed bit by bit for input or output transfers; for example, all odd-numbered bits could be used as inputs and all even-numbered bits as outputs.
- A **control register** for control functions such as address decoding, handshaking, buffering, and port configurations.

In addition, the programmable parallel interface has control logic to control overall operations and a multiplexer to select the port to be connected to the data bus.

Most microcomputer manufacturers offer one or more programmable parallel interfaces. The Intel 8255 has four ports, two with eight bits and two with just four bits. It lacks data direction registers, but each port can be selected as either input or output. The Motorola 6820 has just two ports with full data direction selection.

13.6 *Serial Data Transmission*

Other integrated circuits are designed to handle serial or bit-by-bit data transmission. A number of common low- and medium-speed devices, ranging from

teletypewriters to terminals, transfer data serially and asynchronously. The chip that handles these transfers is called a **UART,** short for **universal asynchronous receiver transmitter.**

Before looking at the design of a UART, we will first consider the way in which a serial character is transferred. Each character has three or four parts:

- a **start bit**
- 5 to 8 **data bits**
- an optional **parity bit**
- 1, 1½, or 2 **stop bits**

The start and stop bits are needed to signal the beginning and end of a character. Any delay between characters when transmitting at less than the maximum data rate is filled with **idling bits,** which are the same as the stop bit. Figure 13.12 shows serial character transmission at maximum and less than maximum data rates for a character with a start bit, eight data bits, and two stop bits. Note that the transmission begins when the signal goes to 0. It ends with two consecutive 1's. If another character is not transmitted immediately, the signal stays at 1 until a new start bit pulls it to 0.

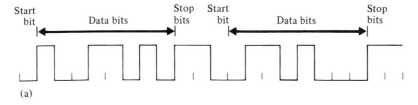

(a)

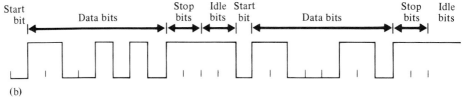

(b)

Fig. 13.12
Serial character transmission. (a) At maximum data rate. (b) At less than maximum data rate.

A UART is shown in Fig. 13.13. It has three parts:

- A **transmitter** converts parallel data to serial.
- a **receiver** converts serial data to parallel.
- A **control unit** handles all control functions.

The receiver must strip the start and stop bits from a character, check for parity if the format includes parity, and accumulate the data bits in a register for

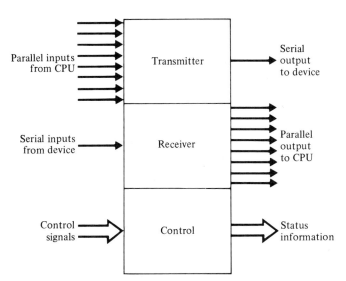

Fig. 13.13
UART for serial-to-parallel data conversion.

parallel output. The transmitter must do the reverse, namely, generate start, stop, and parity bits and send the character as a bit stream. The receiver and transmitter are separate so that the UART can receive data from one source and transmit data to another source at the same time. External clocks are provided for the receiver and transmitter.

The rate of data transmission is called the **baud rate.** If a character has 11 bits and if 10 characters are transmitted per second, the baud rate is

11 bits per character × 10 characters per second = 110 baud.

This differs from the **data rate**—the number of data bits per second. For our example of 8 data bits per character, the data rate is

8 data bits per character × 10 characters per second = 80 bits/sec

Most microcomputer manufacturers have UART's. The Intel 8251 USART is particularly interesting. The S in the name stands for synchronous. The USART can handle both asynchronous and synchronous data transmission and reception with the aid of a **mode register.** The first byte of a transmission sets the mode register for either synchronous or asynchronous transmission.

13.7 *D/A and A/D Conversion*

13.7.1 *Analog Signals*

Most signals in the real world are **analog** rather than digital. An analog signal can have any value in some range; that is, it can vary continuously. It is not

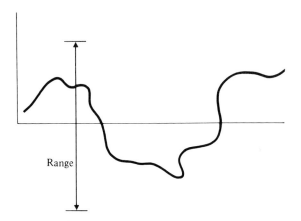

Fig. 13.14
Analog signal.

restricted to discrete values as are the digital signals we have discussed until
now. (See Fig. 13.14.) Temperature, motor speed, time, and pressure are
examples of analog signals that we might wish to analyze with a computer. To
process any one of these, we must convert it to an electric signal—either
current or voltage—with a **transducer.** Then we may convert the electric analog
signal to digital signals with an **analog/digital (A/D)** converter. After processing
the digital signals with a computer, we can convert the digital result to analog
with a **digital/analog (D/A)** converter. The electric analog signal can then be
converted via a transducer to another type of analog signal. Fig. 13.15 illustrates these processes.

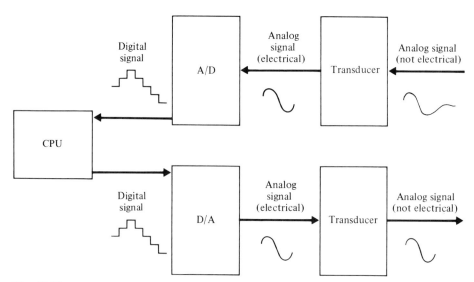

Fig. 13.15
System with transducers and converters.

Consider a sophisticated climate control system for regulating the environment of a room. Sensors measure the temperature, humidity, and other characteristics of several parts of the room. In a temperature sensor, a transducer converts the temperature to an analog electric signal. A/D converters then convert each analog signal into a digital signal for processing by a digital computer. The processing results in digital control signals that may be converted to analog signals by D/A converters. These analog electric signals may then be converted by transducers to other signals to control the system. For example, the processing may result in mechanical movements to open a valve to increase the flow of fuel to a furnace.

Thus D/A and A/D converters are common parts of control systems. Typically, the analog signal—whether at input or output—is carried by just one line. The digital signal usually requires n lines, where n is the number of bits. Sometimes the digital signal will be transmitted in sequence (serially) on a single line.

A **sample-and-hold** amplifier is often used with either an A/D or a D/A converter. As its name suggests, a sample-and-hold amplifier is intended to sample a signal at some instant of time and then hold that value. With an A/D converter, a sample-and-hold circuit can remove **glitches** (narrow pulses that occur when outputs change) in the output analog signal. Figure 13.16 shows A/D and D/A converters with sample-and-hold circuits.

Several important parameters characterize A/D and D/A converters. The digital signal has n bits, ranging from the most significant bit (MSB) on the left

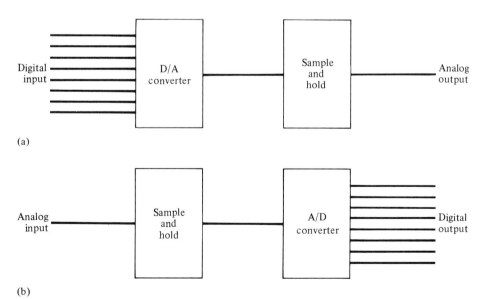

(a)

(b)

Fig. 13.16
D/A and A/D conversion. (a) Digital/analog conversion. (b) Analog/digital conversion.

to the least significant bit (LSB) on the right. For our purposes the most important parameters are the following.

- **Resolution**—The smallest change in an analog signal that can be produced by a D/A converter or distinguished by an A/D converter; the analog equivalent of the LSB.
- **Accuracy**—Precision of output relative to a standard.
- **Quantizing error**—uncertainty associated with converting an analog signal to digital, ideally no more than $\pm\frac{1}{2}$ LSB.
- **Linearity**—The maximum deviation from a straight line connecting the end points (0 and maximum output) of the transfer function, ideally less than $\pm\frac{1}{2}$ LSB.
- **Offset error**—Error by which the transfer function fails to pass through the origin.

Figure 13.17 shows some of these characteristics for an A/D converter.

13.7.2 *Digital Coding*

D/A and A/D converters can use several digital codes to relate analog and digital signals. Converters may have unipolar or bipolar analog values.

- A *unipolar* converter handles analog values between 0 and approximately full scale (FS), which is ordinarily a positive value, such as 5 volts.
- A *bipolar* converter handles analog signals ranging between negative full scale ($-$FS) and positive full scale ($+$FS), such as between -10 volts and $+10$ volts.

Table 13.1
Common unipolar codes

Analog voltage	Natural binary	Complementary binary	Gray code
7 v	111	000	100
6	110	001	101
5	101	010	111
4	100	011	110
3	011	100	010
2	010	101	011
1	001	110	001
0	000	111	000

Common unipolar codes are shown in Table 13.1 for a converter dealing with analog voltages ranging between 0 and 8 volts. The least significant bit (LSB) represents 1 volt. Full scale is thus eight volts, but the largest value that

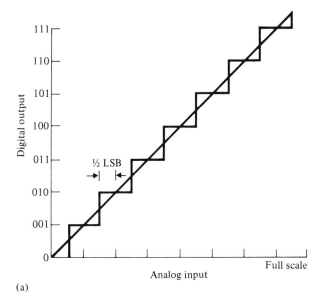

(a)

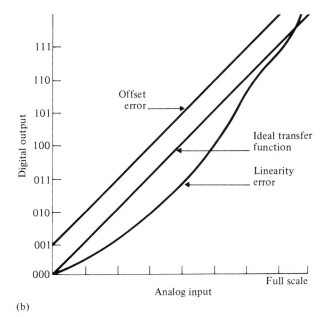

(b)

Fig. 13.17
Transfer function of an A/D converter. (a) Ideal, showing quantizing error. (b) Offset and linearity errors.

can be represented is 7 volts, equivalent to FS − 1 LSB. Unipolar codes include:

- **Natural binary**—0 is represented by all 0's; FS − 1 LSB is represented by all 1's.

- **Complementary binary** (also called reverse sense binary)—Each representation is the bit-by-bit logical complement of the natural binary code; 0 is represented by all 1's; FS − 1 LSB is represented by all 0's.

- **Gray code**—The representation of any two adjacent analog values differs in only one bit position.

Common bipolar codes are shown in Table 13.2 for analog voltages ranging between −4 and +4 volts. The usual binary codes for number representation can be used. All three use the MSB for the sign, with 0 positive and 1 for negative.

Table 13.2
Common bipolar codes

Analog voltage	Sign-and-magnitude	1's complement	2's complement	Offset binary	Complementary offset binary
+ 3 v	011	011	011	111	000
2	010	010	010	110	001
1	001	001	001	101	010
0	000	000	000	100	011
− 0	100	111	—	—	—
− 1	101	110	111	011	100
− 2	110	101	110	010	101
− 3	111	100	101	001	110
− 4			100	000	111

Sign-and-magnitude code uses the remaining bits to represent the binary equivalent of the level; these bits are symmetric about 0. It works well near 0 volts, since its transitions between small positive and small negative values are smooth because few bits change. However, the circuits for sign-and-magnitude conversion are relatively complex and expensive.

1's complement code is the same as sign-and-magnitude for positive levels; for negative levels, the representations are the complements of those for the corresponding positive levels. It also is relatively difficult and expensive to implement.

2's complement code has the same representations for positive levels as the preceding two codes; for negative levels, each representation is the complement of that for the corresponding positive level plus one. Note that sign-and-magnitude and 1's complement have representations for negative zero, which must be suppressed either by hardware or by software. They can represent values between $-FS + 1$ LSB to FS $- 1$ LSB. 2's complement can represent values between $-FS$ and FS $- 1$ LSB.

Offset binary can be considered a variation of 2's complement. It is a shifted binary code in which $-FS$ is represented by all 0's and 0 analog is represented by 1000 . . . 0; hence, it is a natural binary code. It is the easiest code to implement. Its main disadvantage is that a major transition (all bits changing) occurs at analog 0. This can cause glitches if the bits do not all change at the same time. Another possibility is **complementary offset binary,** in which each representation is the complement of that for offset binary. Hence, $-FS$ is represented by all 1's and $+FS$ by all 0's. BCD converters are also available.

13.7.3 *D/A Converters*

We will discuss D/A converters first because they are simpler than A/D converters. A D/A converter weights each bit of the input digital signal according to its position and sums the results. It accomplishes these actions by operating on the input current. Thus the basic output of a D/A converter is a current. If an output voltage is desired, a D/A converter with a special amplifier can convert the output current to voltage. However, the current-to-voltage conversion takes time, thus current output D/A converters are faster than voltage output D/A converters. The time required for the D/A output to arrive and stay within one bit of its stable value is called **settling time.** It may depend on the maximum number of bit changes between signals; the fastest settling time usually occurs when the input signal changes by only one bit from its previous value. The maximum settling time is an important measure for D/A converters and is shorter for those with current outputs.

13.7.4 *A/D Converters*

A basic component of A/D converters is an analog **comparator,** a device with two analog inputs and a binary output, as shown in Fig. 13.18. A comparator compares an arbitrary analog signal to a reference analog signal. As long as the unknown signal is less than the reference, the comparator output is 0. As soon as the unknown signal equals or exceeds the reference signal, the comparator output becomes 1. Of course, the output can be complemented or the two signals reversed if desired.

A/D converters use several methods. We will discuss four:

- Parallel A/D converters
- Successive approximation A/D converters
- Counter A/D converters
- Dual slope A/D converters

Parallel or simultaneous A/D converters are conceptually the simplest. The analog input signal is compared simultaneously to a large number of reference

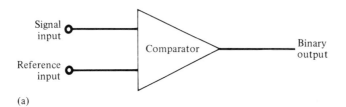

(a)

Comparator inputs	Comparator output
Signal < Reference	0
Signal ≥ Reference	1

(b)

Fig. 13.18
Analog comparator. (a) Comparator. (b) Table of operation.

signals with as many comparators. The comparator outputs are decoded through a simple logic decoding network. All the comparators with reference inputs less than or equal to the unknown input will output 1's; all the comparators with references greater than the unknown input will output 0's.

The main disadvantage of parallel A/D converters is the large number of comparators required. The example shown in Fig. 13.19(a) requires three comparators to yield a two-bit output. In general $2^n - 1$ comparators are required for an n-bit output; hence, 255 comparators are needed for 8 bits. Because comparators are expensive, parallel A/D converters are rarely used unless speed is extremely important. Because of their simple structure, they can operate at very high speeds; rates of 20 MHz (20 million conversions per second) are possible.

Successive approximation is the most widely used method of A/D conversion. It works by comparing the input voltage with a D/A converter output, one bit at a time. As shown in Fig. 13.19(b), a control circuit drives a D/A converter whose output is fed to a comparator. When the START signal occurs, the control circuit sends a MSB signal of 1 to the D/A converter, which sends a signal of ½FS to the comparator. If the input exceeds ½FS, the MSB is left on; otherwise it is reset to 0. In either case, the next bit is tried. The process continues with successive trials much like a binary search. After the comparison with the LSB is finished, the conversion is complete. The control circuit sends a STATUS signal to the output register to show that the binary output is available.

As an example of this method, suppose that the input voltage is 10.2 volts and that the A/D converter has a full-scale reading of 16 volts and an output of 4 bits. The first comparison compares the input signal of 10.2 volts with ½FS or 8 volts. Because the input signal is greater, the MSB is left on and the second bit is turned on, yielding ¾FS or 12 volts. The second comparison shows that the input signal is less than 12 volts, so the second bit is reset to 0. Now the third bit

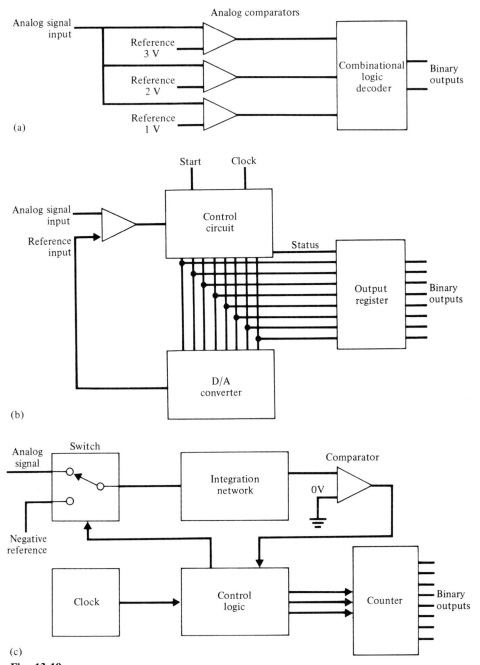

Fig. 13.19
A/D converters. (a) Parallel A/D converter. (b) Successive approximation A/D converter. (c) Dual slope A/D converter.

is turned on, resulting in a reference voltage of ⅝FS or 10 volts. The input signal exceeds this, so the third bit is left on. Finally the fourth bit is turned on, yielding 11/16 FS or 11 volts. The input signal is less than 11 volts, so the fourth bit is reset to 0. The resulting binary output of 1010 is held in the output register. The control circuit then turns the STATUS signal on, showing that the conversion is finished.

Successive approximation combines high resolution with good speed and accuracy. It has a fixed conversion time per bit, independent of the value of the analog input. Speeds as high as 100 nanoseconds per bit can be obtained, giving conversion rates of 1 MHz for 10 bits. Serial output data can be obtained if desired, MSB first.

Counter A/D conversion uses a circuit much like the successive approximation A/D converter; the counter A/D converter is not illustrated. The main difference is in the control circuit. The counter A/D converter has a counter that drives the D/A converter. As the counter successively generates 0000, 0001, 0010, . . . , the 4-bit D/A converter successively sends 0, 1/16FS, ⅛FS, 3/16 FS, . . . to the comparator. As soon as this reference input from the D/A converter equals or exceeds the unknown signal, the conversion stops. The control circuit sends the counter output to the output register and turns on a STATUS or END OF CONVERSION (EOC) signal to show that the binary output is available.

The main advantage of the counter A/D converter is its simple design and correspondingly low cost. It also offers good accuracy. However, it is very slow. Conversion time is proportional to input voltage and is longest for a full-scale input. In some applications where input voltages are known to change slowly, speed can be improved by using an **up-down counter,** one that can count either up or down from its previous value. In this case, the converter does not reset to 0. Instead, it compares the input signal with its last result and begins incrementing or decrementing from there. Thus the converter can track slowly varying inputs. It is then called a **servo A/D converter,** because it applies information about the previous signal to control the conversion.

Dual slope A/D converters operate indirectly, by converting voltage to time with an integrating network and then measuring the elapsed time with a counter. Figure 13.19(c) shows a typical circuit. A switch allows connecting either of two inputs—the unknown analog signal or a known negative reference—to the integrator. The output of the integrator is applied to the comparator. The other terminal of the comparator is grounded; that is, it is at 0 volts.

Conversion begins with the unknown input signal connected to the integrator. The comparator will turn on as soon as the integrator output exceeds a small **threshold** voltage. As soon as the output of the integrator becomes sufficiently positive to trigger the comparator, the output of the comparator starts the counter counting a predetermined number of clock pulses, T_1. When this number is reached, the input of the integrator is switched to the negative reference and the counter is reset to 0. The integrator then integrates the negative reference until it passes the comparator threshold. Then the counter is stopped, holding a number T_2. The unknown input voltage can be calculated as

$$\text{input voltage} = \frac{T_2}{T_1} \times \text{reference voltage}.$$

Two advantages are obtained from the double integration. First, conversion accuracy is independent of the clock frequency as long as the clock is reasonably fast and stable. Second, conversion accuracy is independent of the accuracy of the integrator; any variations are cancelled by the dual integration. Variations of the dual slope A/D converter use one or three integrations, but dual integration is the most common.

Other advantages of this method are relatively low cost, simplicity, and high linearity. Resolution is limited basically by the analog resolution of the comparator. The main disadvantage is its long conversion time, typically several milliseconds.

Analog multiplexers To cut costs, an A/D converter is often timeshared by several analog channels. An **analog multiplexer** connects the analog channels to a single A/D converter. Digital address inputs to the analog multiplexer determine which of the input channels is connected to the A/D converter at any time. The analog multiplexer has a settling time, similar to that of D/A converters. It is also characterized by a throughput rate, the highest rate at which the multiplexer can switch between channels at its specified accuracy. The throughput rate is determined by the settling time.

13.8   Bus Organizations

Buses can be organized as parallel or serial (bit-serial or bit-by-bit). Parallel buses excel at high-speed communication and are used for most device-to-device communication on mini- and microcomputer buses. Serial buses require fewer lines and are used primarily to connect terminals, such as Teletypes and CRTs, to computers.

13.8.1   Parallel Buses

Parallel buses transfer all bits of information across individual wires at one time. A parallel bus must include lines for data, addresses, and control. A typical 8-bit microcomputer parallel bus will have 8 data lines, 16 address lines, and 5–12 control lines. A 16-bit microcomputer or minicomputer line needs 16 data lines, 16–24 address lines, and many control lines. The PDP-11 Unibus, for example, has 56 lines including 16 data lines and 18 address lines. We will look briefly at several examples of parallel buses.

IEEE-488-1975 bus The IEEE-488-1975 bus is intended for connecting computers or programmable calculators with instruments such as voltmeters and signal generators. Hewlett-Packard did the original work on this bus, which is sometimes referred to as the GPIB or General Purpose Interface Bus. Hewlett-Packard holds a patent on the handshake method of acknowledging signals on this bus.

The bus can connect as many as 15 instruments attached to a cable of length up to 20 meters. There should be no more than 2 meters of cable per instrument for fewer than 10 instruments. So long as this length limit is met, the bus allows communication of 8-bit bytes of information at rates as high as 250,000 bytes per second.

Each instrument on the bus can perform one or more of the following roles.

- A **talker** can transmit data to other instruments.
- A **listener** can receive data from other instruments.
- A **controller** controls the talkers and listeners.

Each talker or listener can be enabled or disabled at any time by the controller, which manages all activity on the bus. Typically the controller—perhaps a computer or calculator—can also serve as a talker or listener.

The 488 bus has 16 lines, grouped as follows:

- 8 data lines
- 5 control lines
- 3 handshake lines

There are no address lines, so the data bus also serves for transferring addresses.

The handshaking function is the key to bus communications. Before looking at all three handshake lines, we will consider a simpler example of handshaking using only two lines. The basic idea of handshaking is simple. One device says, "Hello, how are you?" The second says, "Fine, and by the way I have something for you." The first replies, "Great, I'm ready." The second then says, "OK, here it is." The first responds, "Thanks, I've got it."

On a bus, handshaking can be done with two lines, called DAV (DAta Valid), handled by the talker, and NDAC (Not Data Accepted), handled by the listener. The initial N on NDAC simply means that it is active when 0 rather than when 1.

Let's assume that a talker is sending a series of data bytes to a listener. To understand handshaking we can examine the sequence, starting at any point. The following steps occur.

1. With DAV = 0, the talker has data byte D_0 on the data bus.

2. As soon as the talker sees NDAC = 1, it makes DAV = 1 to show the listener that the data byte is valid. The talker must keep the data on the line until it sees DNAC = 0.

3. The listener accepts the data and then makes NDAC = 0 to show acceptance. The listener must keep NDAC = 0 until it sees DAV = 0.

4. The talker acknowledges DNAC = 0 by making DAV = 0. It then gets ready for the next transfer by placing data byte D_1 on the data bus. The talker must wait for NDAC = 1 before making DAV = 1.

5. When the listener sees DAV = 0, it realizes that the talker knows that the data byte has been accepted. Hence the listener makes NDAC = 1 in preparation for the next transfer.

Table 13.3
Handshaking for consecutive data bytes

Data	Talker DAV (DAta Valid)	Listener NDAC (Not Data ACepted)	Step
D_0	0	1	1
D_0	1	1	2
D_0	1	0	3
D_1	0	0	4
D_1	0	1	1
D_1	1	1	2
D_1	1	0	3
D_2	0	0	4

Table 13.3 shows these steps for transferring two consecutive data bytes.

When several listeners are all to receive data from the bus, each one makes its DNAC line 0 to show acceptance of data. The individual NDAC lines are connected together in such a way that the collective NDAC line will become 0 only when all listeners have accepted data. The talker acknowledges the collective NDAC signal by making DAV = 0, recognizing that all listeners have accepted data and showing that data on the bus are being changed. Each listener acknowledges DAV = 0 by setting its NDAC line to 1.

The third bus line—NRFD (Not Ready for Data)—helps coordinate transfers.

As each listener accepts data, it makes NRFD = 1 at the same time that it sets NDAC = 0. As each listener sees DAV = 0, it sets NRFD = 0 while making NDAC = 1. The collective NRFD signal becomes 1 as soon as the first listener has acknowledged DAV = 1. The collective NRFD signal becomes 0 when the last listener has acknowledged DAV = 0. (The actual implementation has different logic assignments, a complication that we will ignore.)

Now that we understand the handshaking procedure, we can consider the control lines that the controller uses. They are as follows.

- ATN (attention) distinguishes between uses of the bus to carry addresses or commands.
- IFC (interface clear) forces all instruments to an idle state.
- REN (remote enable) selects local or remote operation.

- SRQ (service request) allows an instrument to request service with an interrupt.
- EOI (end or identify) labels the last byte of the talker's message or, together with ATN, allows polling of instruments for identification.

When ATN = 1, the first seven bits of the data bus specify commands; the eighth can be used as a parity check. By general agreement (although not by the standard), certain meanings are assigned to these commands. Examples are:

- **Unlisten**—All instruments previously established as listeners are dismissed from listening.
- **Untalk**—The previous talker is dismissed as a talker.
- **Clear**—All instruments are forced to a clear state.

Use of the bus can become quite complicated. We will illustrate it with a typical sequence of commands, in which the controller acts first as a talker and then as a listener.

1. Controller initializes the interface with IFC.
2. Controller initializes all instruments by the clear command with handshaking.
3. Controller issues the listen address for one instrument with ATN and handshaking and becomes a talker.
4. Controller sends data bytes to the device with handshaking.
5. Controller gives unlisten command to the device with handshaking.
6. Controller issues talk address of the device with ATN and handshaking and becomes a listener.
7. Controller sets ATN to data mode and receives data, ending with an EOI signal.

S100 bus The S100 bus is a popular bus for 8-bit microcomputers, designed by MITS for their Altair 8080-based microcomputers. It provides for 100 signals, hence the name S100. It has several idiosyncracies, many resulting from the features of the 8080, such as a four-phase clock, that are not common on microcomputers. The data bus consists of two 8-bit unidirectional lines instead of a single 8-bit bidirectional line. However, two sets of data lines are frequently wired together as a bidirectional bus. The distribution of power is complex; each of the two 50-pin modules comprising the bus has its own regulator for dc voltages. The bus includes:

- 8 data lines for input to the CPU
- 8 data lines for output from the CPU
- 16 address lines
- 3 power supply lines

- 8 vectored interrupt lines
- 39 control lines
- Other lines reserved for future use

PDP-11 Unibus The PDP-11 Unibus carried 56 signals for transferring 16-bit words with 18-bit addresses. As previously discussed, all PDP-11 bus transfers are synchronous and depend on interlocking control signals (handshaking). All communications are positively acknowledged by the receivers of the communications. The bus is conceptually divided into three parts:

- A 41-line data transfer section
- A 12-line priority arbitration section
- A 3-line initialization section

The signals are summarized in Table 13.4. In all data transfers one device is a **bus master** and another a **slave.** The master controls the transfer in much the same way as a controller on the 488 bus. Master sync and slave sync signals provide handshaking.

Table 13.4
Unibus lines

Section	Name	Mnemonic	Function	No. of Lines
Data transfer	Address	A 17:007	Device or memory address	18
	Data	D 15:00	Data transfer	16
	Control	C0, C1	Type of transfer	2
	Master sync	MSYN	Timing control	1
	Slave sync	SSYN	Timing control	1
	Parity	PA, PB	Parity Check	2
	Interrupt	INTR	Interrupt	1
Priority arbitration	Bus request	BR4, BR5 BR6, BR7	Request bus use	4
	Bus grant	BG4, BG5 BG6, BG7	Grant bus use	4
	Non-processor Grant	NPR	Request bus use	1
	Grant selection	SACK	Acknowledge grant	1
	Acknowledge Bus busy	BBSY	Bus busy	1
Initialization	Initialize	INIT	System reset	1
	AC low	AC LO	Power monitoring	1
	DC low	DC LO	Power monitoring	1

13.8.2 *Serial Buses*

Serial buses may be synchronous or asynchronous. Synchronous bus transfers are usually reserved for data rates of more than 10,000 bits per second. Asynchronous bus transfers are commonly used for data rates up to 20,000 bits per second. Some bus standards can be used for either synchronous or asynchronous transfers.

Some timing information is needed for both asynchronous and synchronous transfers. Earlier in the chapter we examined the format for serial characters for UARTs and noted that each character began with a start bit and ended with one or more stop bits. Other asynchronous formats also contain at least two extra bits per character for start and stop, resulting in data rates substantially less than baud rates. Even in synchronous transfers some bits are wasted, although less so than in asynchronous transfers. If data were sent continuously without synchronization bits, the receiver might lose synchronization and scramble all data bits thereafter. To avoid this problem, synchronizing characters are sent every 100 bytes or so.

Synchronous communications employ **protocols** that govern the format of messages. A typical synchronous message begins with synchronization characters, proceeds with blocks of data interspersed with synchronization characters, and ends with a check sum and an end of record character. When the message is received, the check sum is recalculated; if it does not agree with the transmitted check sum, the receiver asks for retransmission of the block.

SYNC	DATA	SYNC	DATA	SYNC	DATA	CHECKSUM	END

RS232C Bus The RS232C bus standard of the Electronics Industry Association (EIA) contains electrical and physical specifications for bit-serial transfers. It is intended for transfers at rates of up to 19,200 baud and is primarily used for connecting terminals to systems. At low baud rates the connection is often made through voice-grade telephone lines—that is, ordinary telephone lines that were not designed for data communication. A **modem** (short for modulator-demodulator) connects the terminal to the phone line. When the terminal sends data, the modem converts 1's into tones at one frequency and 0's into tones at a second frequency; this process is called **modulation.** When the terminal receives data, the modem converts the tones into 1's and 0's **(demodulation).**

The RS232C bus provides 25 lines for data and control of two channels—a primary high-speed channel and a secondary lower-speed channel that is rarely used. Each channel has two lines—one for sending data and one for receiving data. Thus the bus provides **full duplex** operation—simultaneous transmission and reception. (A channel that allows only sending or only receiving at one time has half duplex operation. A channel that allows transmission in only one direction is **simplex.**) Eleven standard data rates, ranging from 50 baud to

19,200 baud, can be used; typical operations are at 110 or 300 baud for teletypewriters and 1200 and above for CRT terminals.

Control signals include the necessary control and status information for the modem and bus, such as "transmit data," "receive data," "clear to send," "clear to receive," and signals for timing and data rate selection.

Current loop The simplest standard for serial communication is a **current loop,** often used by teletypewriters. As the name suggests, this is a simple loop (constructed from a pair of wires) through which a current flows. A switch at the transmitter can open the loop to designate a logic 0 or close the loop for a logic 1. When the loop is open, no current flows; when the loop is closed, a current of 20 milliamperes flows.

13.S *Summary*

A good interfacing design requires thinking about speed of device operation, synchronous or asynchronous transfer, serial or parallel transfer, digital or analog signals, bus standards, and the number of devices to be interfaced. In some cases, the device will determine the choices that can be made; in other cases, the designer can decide them.

The number of pins available on a microprocessor is limited for economic reasons. Most 8-bit microprocessors have 8 pins for data, 16 for addresses, 2 each for power and clock, and 12 for control functions. The control lines must provide for memory and input/output transfers, scheduling, and general supervision. If more flexibility is needed, one of the buses can be multiplexed so that it serves different purposes at different times. If a bus must drive more than just a few devices, drivers must be used to boost signal strength.

Two addressing schemes are commonly used for memory-mapped input/output. Linear selection involves dedicating address lines to separate chip-select inputs; it is useful for addressing only a few chips. Fully decoded addressing requires logic circuitry for the chip-select inputs and can be used for as many chips as desired.

Parallel input/output transfers for microprocessors are often handled by programmable parallel interface chips. They contain two or more data registers, data direction registers (which usually can be programmed bit by bit), and control registers.

Serial data transmission is usually handled by a universal asynchronous receiver transmitter (UART). Each character is formatted with a start bit, one or more stop bits, and optionally, a parity bit in addition to the data bits. The transmitter of the UART does the formatting; the receiver later strips the extra bits and converts serial data to parallel. The rate of data transmission, called the baud rate, includes the rate for transmitting the added bits; it is higher than the data rate, which includes only the rate of the basic data bits.

Analog signals must be converted to digital with an A/D converter before digital processing; the digital signals are reconverted to analog by a D/A converter. A sample-and-hold amplifier, associated with the analog signal, is used to remove glitches. Coding schemes for the digital data can be unipolar, representing values between 0 and full scale, or bipolar, representing values between positive and negative full scale readings. D/A converters are relatively simple devices that weigh each bit of the input signal proportional to its position. A/D converters are based on comparators—devices that compare unknown analog signals with reference signals. A/D converters include parallel, successive approximation, counter, and dual slope.

Buses can be organized in parallel or in serial fashion. Parallel buses are best suited to high-speed communication and represent the main bus organization used on small computers. Serial buses require fewer lines and are primarily intended for connecting terminals to CPU's. The IEEE-488 bus for parallel 8-bit communications can connect with as many as 15 instruments. It provides for handshaking among talkers, listeners, and controllers. The PDP-11 Unibus has 56 signal lines, including 16 for data and 18 for address.

Serial buses may be synchronous or asynchronous. Synchronous communications employ protocols that govern the format of messages and provide for synchronization characters, check sums, and end-of-record characters. For transmission at any distance a modem (short for modulator-demodulator) is used; it converts 1's into tones at one frequency and 0's into tones at another frequency. Transmission can be full duplex—simultaneous transmission and reception; half duplex—transmission or reception on the same channel; or simplex—send only or receive only. The RS232 bus provides a high-speed channel and a low-speed channel for full duplex operation at rates up to 19,200 baud. The current loop is a simpler system used mostly by teletypewriters.

Key Terms

accuracy	complementary offset
analog	binary
analog/digital (A/D)	controller
asynchronous	control register
baud rate	counter A/D conversion
bipolar converter	current loop
buffer	data register
bus	data direction register
bus driver	debouncer
bus master	decoder
chip select	demodulator
clear	digital/analog (D/A)
comparator	dual slope
complementary binary	full duplex

fully decoded
addressing
gate
glitch
gray code
half duplex
handshaking
header
idling bit
latch
linearity ·
linear selection
listener
modem
mode register
modulation
multiplex
multiplexer
natural binary
offset binary
offset error
parallel
parallel A/D conversion
parity bit
programmable parallel
interface
protocol

quantizing error
receiver
resolution
sample-and-hold
amplifier
serial
servo A/D converter
settling time
seven-segment display
simplex
slave
start bit
stop bit
successive
approximation
synchronous
talker
threshold
transceiver
transducer
transmitter
UART
unipolar converter
unlisten
untalk
up-down converter

13.R   *References*

Information on interfacing is most often found in manuals and in trade magazines. Two good books are Peatman (1977) and Lesea and Zaks (1977).

13.Q   *Questions*

13.1. Characterize synchronous transfers.

13.2. Characterize asynchronous transfers.

13.3. What are the relative advantages and disadvantages of synchronous and asynchronous transfers?

13.4. Compare serial and parallel transfers.

13.5. List some of the questions you should answer about your system before designing an interface.

13.6. Compare analog and digital information.

13.7. How has semiconductor technology affected the way interfacing is done?

13.8. How are pins allocated on a microprocessor?

13.9. What are the advantages and disadvantages of multiplexing buses?

13.10. What are the four control functions of a microprocessor?

13.11. Explain the two methods of implementing memory-mapped input/output.

13.12. Discuss switch debouncing.

13.13. How does a seven-segment display operate?

13.14. Describe a programmable parallel interface.

13.15. What bits must be added to the data byte of a character before serial transfer?

13.16. Explain the operation of a UART.

13.17. What is the purpose of a sample-and-hold amplifier?

13.18. What are some important parameters that characterize A/D and D/A converters?

13.19. Discuss some common unipolar and bipolar codes.

13.20. Discuss four methods of A/D conversion.

13.21. Describe the operation of handshaking.

13.22. Distinguish between full duplex, half-duplex, and simplex operation.

References

Abrams, M.D., and P.G. Stein (1973). *Computer Hardware and Software*. Reading, Mass.: Addison-Wesley.

Aho, A.V., J.E. Hopcroft, and J.D. Ullman (1974). *The Design and Analysis of Computer Algorithms*. Reading, Mass.: Addison-Wesley.

Barna, A., and D.I. Porat (1976). *Introduction to Microcomputers and Microprocessors*. New York: Wiley-Interscience.

Barron, D.W. (1972). *Assemblers and Loaders*. New York: Elsevier.

Bell, C.G., J.C. Mudge, and J.E. McNamara (1978). *Computer Engineering*. Bedford, Mass.: Digital Press.

Bohl, M. (1971). *Flowcharting Techniques*. Chicago: Science Research Associates.

Booth, T.L. (1971). *Digital Networks and Computer Systems*. New York: Wiley.

Booth, T.L., and Y.T. Chien (1974). *Computing: Fundamentals and Applications*. New York: Wiley.

Bowles, K.L. (1977). *Microcomputer Problem Solving Using PASCAL*. New York: Springer-Verlag.

Bycer, B.B. (1975). *Flowcharting: Programming, Software Design & Computer Problem Solving*. New York: Wiley.

Conway, R., and D. Gries (1976). *Primer on Structured Programming*. Cambridge, Mass.: Winthrop.

Cooper, J.W. (1977). *The Minicomputer in the Laboratory*. New York: Wiley-Interscience.

Cooper, L., and M. Smith (1973). *Standard FORTRAN: A Problem-Solving Approach*. Boston: Houghton Mifflin.

Eckhouse, R.H. (1975). *Minicomputer Systems*. Englewood Cliffs, N.J.: Prentice-Hall.

Eckhouse, R.H., and L.R. Morris (1979). *Minicomputer Systems*. 2nd ed. Englewood Cliffs, N.J.: Prentice-Hall.

Elson, M. (1975). *Data Structures*. Chicago: Science Research Associates.

Finkel, J. (1975). *Computer/Aided Experimentation: Interfacing to Microcomputers.* New York: Wiley-Interscience.

Flores, I. (1973). *Peripheral Devices.* Englewood Cliffs, N.J.: Prentice-Hall.

Gear, C.W. (1974). *Computer Organization and Programming.* New York: McGraw-Hill.

Gruenberger, F., and D. Babcock (1973). *Computing with Minicomputers.* New York: Wiley-Interscience.

Hamacher, V.C., Z.G. Vranesic, and S.G. Zaky (1978). *Computer Organization.* New York: McGraw-Hill.

Hayes, J.P. (1978). *Computer Architecture and Organization.* New York: McGraw-Hill.

Hilburn, J.L., and P.M. Julich (1976). *Microcomputers/Microprocessors.* Englewood Cliffs, N.J.: Prentice-Hall.

Hill, F.J., and G.R. Peterson (1978). *Digital Systems: Hardware Organization and Design.* New York: Wiley.

Jensen, K., and N. Wirth (1974). *Pascal: User Manual and Report.* New York: Springer-Verlag.

Kemeny, J.G., and T.E. Kurtz (1971). *BASIC Programming.* New York: Wiley.

Kernighan, B.W., and P.J. Plauger (1970). *Software Tools.* Reading, Mass.: Addison-Wesley.

Kernighan, B.W., and P.J. Plauger (1974). *The Elements of Programming Style.* New York: McGraw-Hill.

Klingman, E.G. (1977). *Microprocessor Systems Design.* Englewood Cliffs, N.J.: Prentice-Hall.

Korn, G.A. (1973). *Minicomputers for Engineers and Scientists.* New York: McGraw-Hill.

Korn, G.A. (1977). *Microprocessors & Small Digital Computer Systems for Engineers and Scientists.* New York: McGraw-Hill.

Lesea, A., and R. Zaks (1977). *Microprocessor Interfacing Techniques.* Berkeley, Calif.: Sybex.

Leventhal, L. (1978a). *6800 Assembly Language Programming.* Berkeley, Calif.: Osborne & Associates.

Leventhal, L. (1978b). *8080A/8085 Assembly Language Programming.* Berkeley, Calif.: Osborne & Associates.

Lewis, T.G., and M.Z. Smith (1976). *Applying Data Structures.* Boston: Houghton Mifflin.

McCluskey, E.J. (1965). *Introduction to the Theory of Switching Circuits.* New York: McGraw-Hill.

McCracken, D.D. (1972). *A Guide to FORTRAN IV Programming.* New York: Wiley.

McCracken, D.D. (1974). *A Simplified Guide to FORTRAN Programming.* New York: Wiley.

McCracken, D.D. (1978). *A Guide to PL/M Programming for Microcomputer Applications.* Reading, Mass.: Addison-Wesley.

McIntire, T.C. (1978). *Software Interpreters for Microcomputers.* New York: Wiley.

Osborne, A. (1976). *8080 Programming for Logic Design*. Berkeley, Calif.: Osborne & Associates.

Osborne, A. (1978). *An Introduction to Microcomputers*. Berkeley, Calif.: Osborne & Associates.

Peatman, J.B. (1977). *Microcomputer-based Design*. New York: McGraw-Hill.

Ruston, H. (1978). *Programming with PL/I*. New York: McGraw-Hill.

Schriber, T.J. (1969). *Fundamentals of Flowcharting*. New York: Wiley.

Shortt, J., and T.C. Wilson (1976). *Problem Solving and the Computer*. Reading, Mass.: Addison-Wesley.

Soucek, B. (1972). *Minicomputers in Data Processing and Simulation*. New York: Wiley-Interscience.

Soucek, B. (1976). *Microprocessors and Microcomputers*. New York: Wiley-Interscience.

Southern, R.W. (1972). *PDP-11 Programming Fundamentals*. Ottawa: Algonquin.

Spencer, D.D. (1975). *A Guide to BASIC Programming*. 2nd ed. Reading, Mass.: Addison-Wesley.

Stone, H.S. (1972). *Introduction to Computer Organization and Data Structures*. New York: McGraw-Hill.

Stone, H.S., ed. (1975). *Introduction to Computer Architecture*. Chicago: Science Research Associates.

Stone, H.S., and D.P. Siewiorek (1975). *Introduction to Computer Organization and Data Structures*. New York: McGraw-Hill.

Weitzman, C. (1974). *Minicomputer systems*. Englewood Cliffs, N.J.: Prentice-Hall.

Weller, W.J. (1975). *Assembly Level Programming for Small Computers*. Lexington, Mass.: Lexington Books.

Wester, J.G., and W.D. Simpson (1976). *Software Design for Microprocessors*. Dallas: Texas Instruments.

Zaks, R. (1977). *Microprocessors*. Berkeley, Calif.: Sybex.

Index